D1372674

Major World Regions

GGS 101

ISBN 9781118943823

Copyright © 2014 John Wiley & Sons, Inc. All rights reserved. No part of this publication may be reproduced, stored in a retrieval system or transmitted in any form or by any means, electronic, mechanical, photocopying, recording, scanning or otherwise, except as permitted under Sections 107 or 108 of the 1976 United States Copyright Act, without either the prior written permission of the Publisher, or authorization through payment of the appropriate per-copy fee to the Copyright Clearance Center, Inc. 222 Rosewood Drive, Danvers, MA 01923, Web site: www.copyright.com. Requests to the Publisher for permission should be addressed to the Permissions Department, John Wiley & Sons, Inc., 111 River Street, Hoboken, NJ 07030-5774, (201)748-6011, fax (201)748-6008, Web site: http://www.wiley.com/go/permissions.

Printed in the United States of America 10 9 8 7 6 5 4 3 2 1

List of Titles

Geography: Realms, Regions, and Concepts, 16th edition
by H. J. De Blij, Peter O. Muller, and Jan Nijman
Copyright © 2014, ISBN: 978-1-118-67395-9

Table of Contents

WORLD REGIONAL
GEOGRAPHY: Global Perspectives

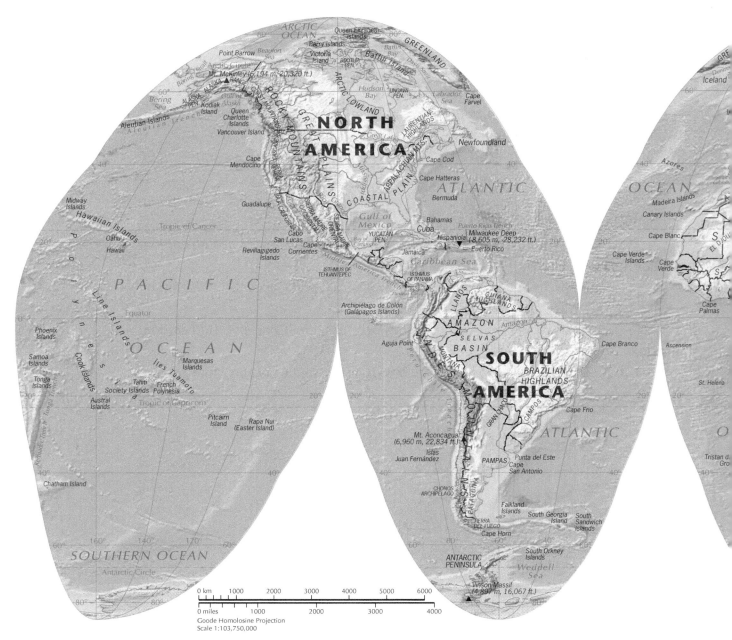

FIGURE G-1

© H. J. de Blij, P. O. Muller, and John Wiley & Sons, Inc.

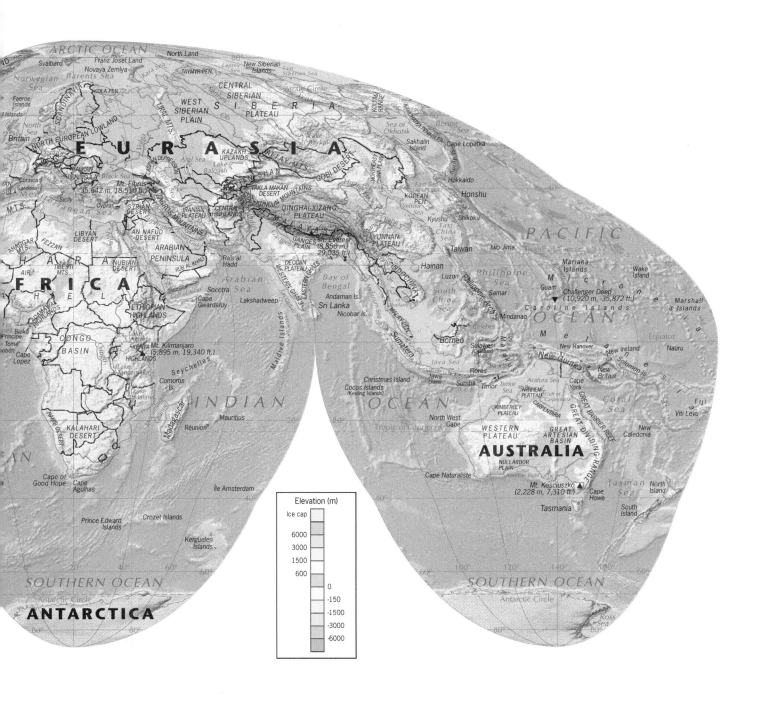

ARCTIC OCEAN

Svalbard
Franz Josef Land
Novaya Zemlya
North Land
New Siberian Islands
Faeroe Islands
Norwegian Sea
Barents Sea
Kara Sea
TAYMYR PEN.
Laptev Sea
East Siberian Sea
KOLA PEN.
SCANDINAVIA
CENTRAL SIBERIAN PLATEAU
Arctic Circle
North Sea
I Islands
Britain
NORTH EUROPEAN LOWLAND
WEST SIBERIAN PLAIN
S I B E R I A
KOLYMA RANGE
KAMCHATKA PENINSULA
Bering Sea
E U R A S I A
URAL MTS.
Ob
KAZAKH UPLANDS
ALTAY MTS.
NORTHEAST CHINA PLAIN
Sea of Okhotsk
Cape Lopatka
Corsica
BALKAN PENINSULA
Black Sea
CASPIAN DEPRESSION
Aral Sea
Lake Balqash
TIAN SHAN
GOBI DESERT
Huang
Sakhalin Island
Kurile Islands
IAN SULA
Sardinia
Sicily
Mt. Elbrus (5,642 m, 18,510 ft.)
Caspian Sea
TAKLA MAKAN DESERT
KOREAN PEN.
Sea of Japan
Hokkaido
MTS.
Iranian Sea
Mediterranean Sea
Cyprus
SYRIAN DESERT
ZAGROS MOUNTAINS
IRANIAN PLATEAU
CENTRAL HIGHLANDS
KUNLUN MOUNTAINS
QINGHAI-XIZANG PLATEAU
YUNNAN PLATEAU
Yellow Sea
Honshu
Kyushu
Shikoku
East China Sea
Taiwan
PACIFIC
AHAGGAR MTS.
FEZZAN
LIBYAN DESERT
AN NAFUD DESERT
ARABIAN PENINSULA
Gulf
HIMALAYAS
Mt. Everest (8,850 m, 29,035 ft.)
GANGES PLAIN
Ganges
Iwo Jima
Tropic of Cancer
Mariana Islands
Wake Island
AIR
TIBESTI MTS.
NUBIAN DESERT
RUB AL KHALI
Ras al Hadd
DECCAN PLATEAU
WESTERN GHATS
EASTERN GHATS
Bay of Bengal
Hainan
Luzon
Philippine Sea
Guam
Challenger Deep (-10,920 m, -35,872 ft.)
Marshall Islands
A F R I C A
SAHEL
Arabian Sea
Cape Gwardafuy
Socotra
Lakshadweep
Andaman Is.
Sri Lanka
Nicobar Is.
South China Sea
Samar
Mindanao
Caroline Islands
Micronesia
Bioko
Principe
Tomé
obon
ABYSSINIAN HIGHLANDS
ETHIOPIAN HIGHLANDS
Lake Victoria
Kenya
Mt. Kilimanjaro (5,895 m, 19,340 ft.)
Maldive Islands
Borneo
Celebes
Sulawesi (Celebes)
Melanesia
New Hanover
New Ireland
Solomon Is.
Nauru
Equator
Cape Lopez
CONGO BASIN
HIGHLANDS
Lake Tanganyika
Seychelles
Java Sea
Jawa (Java)
Flores
New Guinea
New Britain
Lake Malawi
Comoros Is.
I N D I A N
Christmas Island
Cocos Islands (Keeling Islands)
Sumba
Timor
Timor Sea
Arafura Sea
ARNHEM PLATEAU
Gulf of Carpentaria
Cape York
Coral Sea
Fiji
Viti Levu
Madagascar
Mozambique Channel
Mauritius
O C E A N
North West Cape
KIMBERLEY PLATEAU
CARPENTARIA
GREAT BARRIER REEF
KALAHARI DESERT
NAMIB DESERT
Réunion
Tropic of Capricorn
WESTERN PLATEAU
GREAT ARTESIAN BASIN
GREAT DIVIDING RANGE
New Caledonia
Cape of Good Hope
Cape Agulhas
Île Amsterdam
AUSTRALIA
NULLARBOR PLAIN
Tasman Sea
North Island
Prince Edward Islands
Crozet Islands
Cape Naturaliste
Great Australian Bight
Mt. Kosciuszko (2,228 m, 7,310 ft.)
Cape Howe
South Island
Kerguelen Islands
Tasmania

Elevation (m)

Ice cap
6000
3000
1500
600
0
-150
-1500
-3000
-6000

SOUTHERN OCEAN

Antarctic Circle

SOUTHERN OCEAN

Antarctic Circle

Ross Sea

ANTARCTICA

Camel traders in Pushkar, a small town in India's Rajasthan State, relaxing at the end of a November day in 2011. Pushkar features the biggest annual camel fair on Earth, with tens of thousands of camels (and horses) changing hands during the five-day event.

© Jan Nijman

IN THIS CHAPTER

- The power of maps
- The spatial order of the world
- Global climate change
- Dangerous places
- Globalization and its discontents
- The power of place

CONCEPTS, IDEAS, AND TERMS

A view of Florence, one of Europe's most iconic, historical cities and birthplace of the Renaissance. The famous Duomo (cathedral) lies at center stage.

© Jan Nijman

What are your expectations as you open this book? You have signed up for a course that will take you around the world to try to understand how it functions today. You will discover how interesting and unexpectedly challenging the discipline of geography is. We hope that this course, and this book, will open new vistas, bring new perspectives, and help you navigate our increasingly complex and often daunting world.

You could not have chosen a better time to be studying geography. The world is changing on many fronts, and so is the United States. Still the most formidable of all countries, the United States remains a great power capable of influencing nations and peoples, lives and livelihoods from pole to pole. That power confers on Americans the responsibility to learn as much as they can about those nations and livelihoods, so that the decisions of their government representatives are well-informed. But in this respect, the United States is no superpower. Geographic literacy is a measure of international comprehension and awareness, and Americans' geographic literacy ranks low among countries of consequence. That is not a good thing, neither for the United States nor for the rest of the world, because such geographic fogginess tends to afflict not only voters but also the representatives they elect, from the school board to Congress.

A WORLD ON MAPS

Just a casual glance at the pages that follow reveals a difference between this and other textbooks: there are almost as many maps as there are pages. Geography is more closely identified with maps than any other discipline, and we urge you to give as much (or more!) attention to the maps in this book as you do to the text. It is often said that a picture is worth a thousand words, and the same or more applies to maps. When we write "see Figure XX," we really mean it . . . and we hope that you will get into the habit. We humans are territorial creatures, and the boundaries that fence off our 200 or so countries reflect our divisive ways. Other, less visible borders—between religions, languages, rich, and poor—partition our planet as well. When political and cultural boundaries are at odds, there is nothing like a map to summarize the circumstances. Just look, for example, at the map of the African Transition Zone in Chapter 6B: this area's turbulence and challenges are steeped in geography.

Maps in Our Minds

All of us carry in our minds maps of what psychologists call our activity space: the apartment building or house we live in, the streets nearby, the way to school or workplace, the general layout of our hometown or city. You will know what lane to use when you turn into a shopping mall, or where to park at the movie theater. You can probably draw from memory a pretty good map of your hometown. These mental maps [1] allow you to navigate your activity space with efficiency, predictability, and safety. When you arrived as a first-year student on a college or university campus, a new mental map will have started forming. At first you needed a GPS, online, or hardcopy map to find your way around, but soon you dispensed with that because your mental map was sufficient. And it will continue to improve as your activity space expands.

If a well-formed mental map is useful for decisions in daily life, then an adequate mental map is surely indispensable when it comes to decision making in the wider world. You can give yourself an interesting test. Choose some part of the world, beyond North America, in which you have an interest or about which you have a strong opinion—for example, Israel, Iran, Pakistan, North Korea, or China. On a blank piece of paper, draw a map that reflects your impression of the regional layout there: the country, its neighbors, its internal divisions, major cities, seas (if any), and so forth. That is your mental map of the place. Put it away for future reference, and try it again at the end of this course. You will have proof of your improved mental-map inventory.

The Map Revolution

The maps in this book show larger and smaller parts of the world in various contexts. Some depict political configurations; others display ethnic, cultural, economic, or environmental features. ***Cartography*** (the making of maps) has undergone a dramatic technological revolution—a revolution that continues. Earth-orbiting satellites equipped with remote sensing technology (special on-board sensors and imaging instruments) transmit remotely sensed information to computers on the surface, recording the expansion of deserts, the shrinking of glaciers, the depletion of forests, the growth of cities, and myriad other geographic phenomena. Earthbound computers possess ever-expanding capabilities not only to organize this information but also to display it graphically. This allows geographers to develop a ***geographic information system (GIS)***, bringing information to a monitor's screen that would have taken months to assemble just a few decades ago.

There has also been a map revolution in the astounding proliferation of navigation systems in cars and on mobile phones. Smartphones allow the use of maps on the go, and many of us, in the developed world at least, have become dependent on them to traverse cities, to get to a store or restaurant, even to move around shopping malls. Google, the biggest company in this market, used to aim at cataloguing all of the world's information, but today it is also aiming to map the world in almost unimaginable detail. And the competition is now joined by Nokia and Apple. Whereas the maps on our smartphones allow us to move around more efficiently, the maps in this book are aimed at better *understanding* the world and its constituent parts.

Satellites—even spy satellites—cannot record everything that occurs on the Earth's surface. Sometimes the borders between ethnic groups or cultural sectors can be discerned by satellites—for example, in changing types of houses or religious shrines—but this kind of information tends to require on-the-ground verification through field research and reporting. No satellite view of Iraq could show you the distribution of Sunni and Shia Muslim adherents. Many of the boundaries you see on the maps in this book cannot be observed from space because long stretches are not even marked on the ground. So the maps you are about to "read" have their continued uses: they summarize complex situations and allow us to begin forming durable mental maps of the areas they represent.

There is one other point we should make that is especially important when it comes to world maps: never forget that the world is a sphere, and to project it onto a two-dimensional flat surface must necessarily entail some very significant distortions. Try peeling an orange and flat-tening the entire peel on a surface—you will have to tear it up and try to stretch it in places to get the job done. Take a look at Figure G-1 and note how the Atlantic Ocean and other segments of the planetary surface are interrupted. You can produce a map like this in many different ways, but you will always end up distorting things. When studying world maps, there is nothing like having a globe at hand to remind you of our three-dimensional reality.

GEOGRAPHY'S PERSPECTIVE

Geography is sometimes described as the most interdisciplinary of disciplines. That is a testimonial to geography's historic linkages to many other fields, ranging from geology to economics and from sociology to political science. And, as has been the case so often in the past, geography is in the lead on this point. Today, interdisciplinary studies and research are more prevalent than ever. The old barriers between disciplines are breaking down.

This is not to suggest that college and university departments are no longer relevant; they are just not as exclusive as they used to be. These days, you can learn some useful geography in economics departments and some good economics in geography departments. But each discipline still has its own particular way of looking at the world.

A Spatial Perspective

Most disciplines focus on one key theme: economics is about money; political science is about power; psychology

---

From the Field Notes . . .

"On the descent into Tibet's Lhasa Gongga Airport, I had a great view of the Yarlung Zangbo Valley, its braided stream channels gently flowing toward the distant east. The Yarlung Zangbo is the highest major river on Earth, running from the Tibetan Plateau into northeastern India where it joins the mighty Brahmaputra River that continues on to Bangladesh where it empties into the Indian Ocean. It was mid-October and the water levels were low. The landing strip of the airport can be seen in the center-right of the photo, on the south bank. The airport is quite far from Lhasa, the Tibetan capital, located about 62 kilometers (40 mi) to its southwest. Despite major road and tunnel construction, it is still more than an hour's drive. The airport had to be built away from the city and in this widest part of the valley because it allows the easiest landings and takeoffs in this especially rugged terrain. It lies at 3700 meters above sea level (12,100 ft), one of the highest airports in the world."

www.conceptcaching.com

© Jan Nijman

is about the mind; biology is about life. Geography, then, is about space on the Earth's surface. More specifically, geographers are interested in the organization of **terrestrial space**. Social space (cities, buildings, political boundaries, etc.) as well as natural space (climates, terrain, water bodies, etc.) are not randomly configured. Instead, there generally prevails a particular order, regularity, even predictability about the ways in which space is organized. Sometimes it is the deliberate work of human beings and sometimes it is the work of nature, but very often there are particular patterns. Geographers consider these spatial patterns and processes as not only interesting but also crucial to how we live and how we organize our societies. The spatial perspective [2] has defined geography from its beginning.

Environment and Society

There is another glue that binds geography and has done so for a very long time: an interest in the relationships between human societies and the natural (physical) environment. Geography lies at the intersection of the social and natural sciences and integrates perspectives from both, being the only discipline to do so explicitly. This perspective comes into play frequently: environmental change is in the news on a daily basis in the form of worldwide climate change, but this current surge of global warming is only the latest phase of endless atmospheric and ecological fluctuation. Geographers are involved in understanding current environmental issues not only by considering climate change in the context of the past, but also by looking carefully at the implications of global climate change for human societies.

More generally, think of this relationship between humans and their environment as a two-way street. On one hand, human beings have always had a transformative effect on their natural surroundings, from the burning of forests to the creation of settlements. On the other hand, humans have always been heavily dependent on the natural environment, their individual and collective behaviors very much a product of it. There are so many examples that it is hard to know where to begin or when to end: we eat what nature provides and traditional diets vary regionally; rivers allow us to navigate and connect with other peoples—or they serve as natural boundaries like the Rio Grande; wars are fought over access to water or seaports; landlocked countries seem to have different cultures from those of islands; and so on.

At times we are faced with the interrelationship between humans and their environment. For example, humans modify the environment through escalating carbon dioxide emissions (the so-called greenhouse effect) and are subsequently confronted with the need to adjust to rising sea levels. We will always be part of nature, no matter how far technology advances.

Spatial Patterns

Geographers, therefore, need to be conversant with the location and distribution of salient features on the Earth's surface. This includes the natural (physical) world, simpli-fied in Figure G-1, as well as the human world, and our inquiry will view these in temporal (historical) as well as spatial perspective. We take a penetrating look at the overall geographic framework of the contemporary world, the still-changing outcome of thousands of years of human achievement and failure, movement and stagnation, stability and revolution, interaction and isolation. The spatial structure of cities, the layout of farms and fields, the networks of transportation, the configurations of rivers, the patterns of climate—all these form part of our investigation. As you will find, geography employs a comprehensive spatial vocabulary with meaningful terms such as area, distance, direction, clustering, proximity, accessibility, and many others we will encounter in the pages ahead. For geographers, some of these terms have more specific definitions than is generally assumed. There is a difference, for example, between *area* (surface) and *region*, between *boundary* and *frontier*, and between *place* and *location*. The vocabulary of geography holds some surprises, and what at first may seem to be simple ideas turn out to be complex concepts.

Scale and Scope

One prominent item in this vocabulary is the term scale [3]. Whenever a map is created, it represents all or part of the Earth's surface at a certain level of detail. Obviously, Figure G-1 displays a very low level of detail; it is little more than a general impression of the distribution of land and water as well as lower and higher elevations on our planet's surface. A limited number of prominent features such as the Himalayas and the Sahara are named, but not the Pyrenees Mountains or the Nile Delta. At the bottom of the map you can see that one inch at this scale must represent about 1650 miles of the real world, leaving the cartographer little scope to insert information.

A map such as Figure G-1 is called a *small-scale* map because the ratio between map distance and real-world distance, expressed as a fraction, is very small at 1:103,750,000. Increase that fraction (i.e., zoom in), and you can represent less territory—but also enhance the amount of detail the map can represent. In Figure G-2, note how the fraction increases from the smallest (1:103,000,000) to the largest (1:1,000,000). Montreal, Canada is just a dot on Map A but an urban area on Map D. Does this mean that world maps like Figure G-1 are less useful than larger-scale maps? It all depends on the purpose of the map. In this chapter, we often use world maps to show global distributions as we set the stage for the more detailed discussions to follow. In later chapters, the scale tends to become larger as we focus on smaller areas, even on individual countries and cities. But whenever you read a map, be aware of the scale because it is a guide to its utility.

The importance of the scale concept is not confined to maps. Scale plays a fundamental role in geographic research and in the ways we think about geographic problems: scale in terms of *level of analysis*. This is sometimes

EFFECT OF SCALE

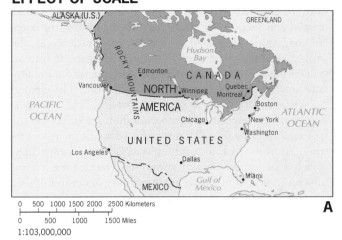

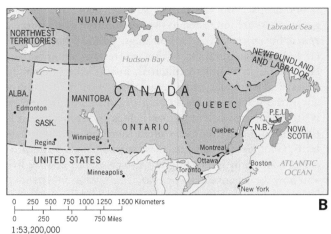

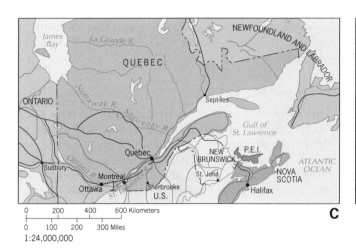

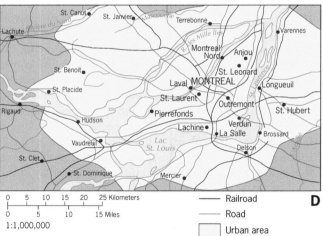

FIGURE G-2

© H. J. de Blij, P. O. Muller, and John Wiley & Sons, Inc.

referred to as *operational scale*, the scale at which social or natural processes operate or play out. For instance, if you want to investigate the geographic concentration of wealth in the United States, you can do so at a range of scales: within a neighborhood, a city, a county, a State,* or at the national level. You choose the scale that is the most appropriate for your purpose, but it is not always that straightforward. Suppose you had to study patterns of ethnic segregation: what do you think would be the most relevant scale(s)?

In this book, our main purpose is to understand the geography of the world at large and how it works, and so, inevitably, we must deal with large spatial entities. Our focus is on the world's realms and on the main regions

---

*Throughout this book we will capitalize State when this term refers to an administrative subdivision of a country: for example, the U.S. State of Ohio or the Australian State of New South Wales. Since this term is also synonymous with country (e.g., the state of Brazil), we use the lower case when referring to such a national state.

within those realms, and in most cases we will have to forego analyses at a finer scale. For our purposes, it is the big picture that matters most.

WORLD GEOGRAPHIC REALMS

Ours is a globalized, interconnected world, a world of international trade and travel, migration and movement, tourism and television, financial flows and Internet traffic. It is a world that, in some contexts, has taken on the properties of a "global village"—but that village still has its neighborhoods. Their names are Europe, South America, Southeast Asia, and others familiar to us all. Like the neighborhoods of a city or town, these global neighborhoods may not have sharply defined borders, but their persistence, after tens of thousands of years of human dispersal, is beyond doubt. Geographers call such global neighborhoods geographic realms [4]. Each of these realms possesses a particular combination of environmental, cultural, and organizational properties.

These characteristic qualities are imprinted on the landscape, giving each realm its own traditional attributes and social settings. As we come to understand the human and environmental makeup of these geographic realms, we learn not only where they are located but also why they are located where they are (a key question in geography), how they are constituted, and what their future is likely to be in our fast-changing world. Figure G-3, therefore, forms the overall framework for our investigation in this book.

Criteria for Geographic Realms

The existence and identification of world geographic realms depends on a combination of factors. Our world offers a highly complex and variable environment of large and small continents, enormous oceans and countless waterways, innumerable islands, diverse habitats and cultures, and intricate political geographies. What constitutes a realm depends on the circumstances, but we can still identify three main sets of criteria:

- *Physical and Human* Geographic realms are based on sets of spatial criteria. They are the largest units into which the inhabited world can be divided. The criteria on which such a broad regionalization is based include both physical (that is, natural) and human (or social) yardsticks. On the one hand, South America is a geographic realm because physically it is a continent and culturally it is comprised of comparable societies. The realm called South Asia, on the other hand, lies on a Eurasian landmass shared by several other geographic realms; high mountains, wide deserts, and dense forests combine with a distinctive social fabric to create this well-defined realm centered on India.

- *Functional* Geographic realms are the result of the interaction of human societies and natural environments, a *functional* interaction revealed by farms, mines, fishing ports, transport routes, dams, bridges, villages, and countless other features that mark the landscape. According to this criterion, Antarctica is a continent but not a geographic realm.

- *Historical* Geographic realms must represent the most comprehensive and encompassing definition of the great clusters of humankind in the world today. China lies at the heart of such a cluster, as does India. Africa constitutes a geographic realm from the southern margin of the Sahara (an Arabic word for desert) to the Cape of Good Hope and from its Atlantic to its Indian Ocean shores.

Figure G-3 displays the 12 world geographic realms based on these criteria. As we will show in greater detail later, waters, deserts, and mountains as well as cultural and political shifts mark the borders of these realms. We shall discuss the positioning of these boundaries as we examine each realm.

Delineating Realms: Boundaries and Transition Zones

Oceans and seas are the most common natural boundaries of the world's realms, such as the South Atlantic to Subsaharan Africa's west or the North Atlantic to North America's east. But where two geographic realms meet, transition zones [5], not sharp boundaries, often mark their contacts.

We need only remind ourselves of the border zone between the geographic realm in which most of us live, North America, and the adjacent realm of Middle America. The line in Figure G-3 coincides with the boundary between Mexico and the United States, crosses the Gulf of Mexico, and then separates Florida from Cuba and the Bahamas. But Hispanic influences are strong in North America north of this boundary, and the U.S. economic influence is strong south of it. The line, therefore, represents an ever-changing zone of regional interaction. Again, there are many ties between South Florida and the Bahamas, but the Bahamas resemble a Caribbean more than a North American society. Miami has so many Cuban and Cuban-American inhabitants that it is sometimes referred to as the second-largest Cuban city after Havana.

In Africa, the transition zone from Subsaharan to North Africa is so wide and well defined that we have put it on the world map; elsewhere, transition zones tend to be narrower and less easily represented. In the first half of this second decade of the twenty-first century, such countries as Belarus (between Europe and Russia) and Kazakhstan (between Russia and Muslim Southwest Asia) lie in inter-realm transition zones. Remember, over much (though not all) of their length, borders between realms are zones of regional change.

Transition zones are fascinating spaces: it is almost as if they rebel against a clear ordering of the world's geography. They remind us that the world is a restless and contested place with shifting boundaries and changing geographic fortunes. They challenge the geographer's mapping skills, and, above all, they underscore just how complex the study of geography is. As you will see, transition zones are often places of tension and/or conflict.

Geographic Realms: Dynamic Entities

Had we drawn Figure G-3 before Columbus made his voyages from 1492 (and assuming we had the relevant geographical knowledge), the map would have looked different: indigenous states and peoples would have determined the boundaries in the Americas; Australia and New Guinea would have constituted a single realm, and New Zealand would have been part of the Pacific Realm. The colonization, Europeanization, and Westernization of the world changed that map dramatically. Since World War II, the world map has been redrawn as a result of decolonization and the rise and then demise of the Cold War. That Cold War division between western and eastern Europe has now given way to far-reaching European integration across that geographic realm. Realms and regions are dynamic entities, and geography is always subject to change.

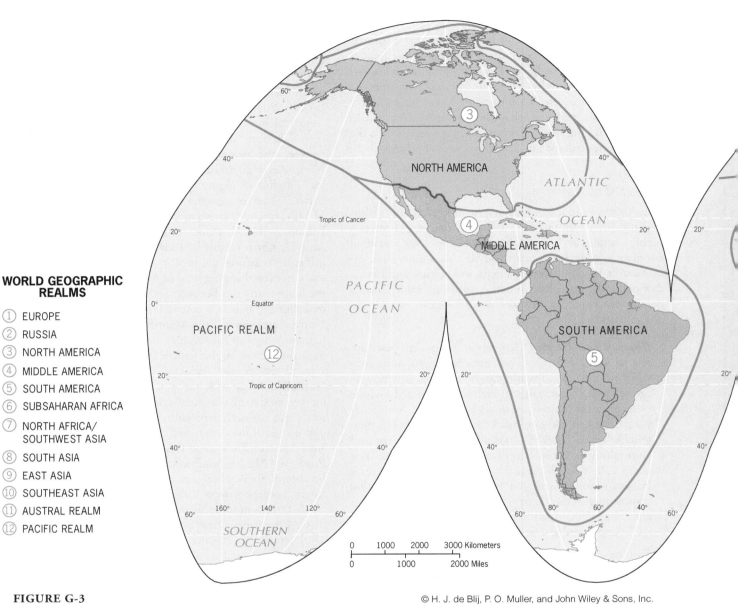

WORLD GEOGRAPHIC REALMS

① EUROPE
② RUSSIA
③ NORTH AMERICA
④ MIDDLE AMERICA
⑤ SOUTH AMERICA
⑥ SUBSAHARAN AFRICA
⑦ NORTH AFRICA/ SOUTHWEST ASIA
⑧ SOUTH ASIA
⑨ EAST ASIA
⑩ SOUTHEAST ASIA
⑪ AUSTRAL REALM
⑫ PACIFIC REALM

FIGURE G-3

© H. J. de Blij, P. O. Muller, and John Wiley & Sons, Inc.

Two Varieties of Realms

The world's geographic realms can be divided into two categories. The first are *monocentric* realms that are dominated by a single major political entity, in terms of territory and/or population. North America (United States), Middle America (Mexico), East Asia (China), South Asia (India), Russia, and the Austral Realm (Australia) are all monocentric realms. They are, in their entirety, heavily influenced by the presence of that one country. It is as if the realm is organized around them.

The second type of realm is *polycentric* in nature. In these, the appearance, functioning, and organization of the realm are dispersed among a number of more or less equally influential regions or countries. Europe, North Africa/Southwest Asia, Subsaharan Africa, and the Pacific Realm all fall into this category. Polycentric realms can be more volatile in some ways, their development determined by the sum of many different parts.

Two of the world's realms are a bit more difficult to categorize. Southeast Asia is a dynamic realm that contains almost a dozen countries, some of them regarded as emerging economies. Arguably, Indonesia is becoming the most influential power, but it may be premature to label this a monocentric realm. The other realm that seems to fall in-between is South America. Here it is Brazil that has the biggest population and increasingly the largest and most influential economy. South America, more emphatically than Southeast Asia, seems to be moving toward a monocentric reorganization of its realm.

Of course, some of the dominant powers in the monocentric realms influence events beyond their realm and demonstrate a truly global reach. The United States has dominated world events in an unprecedented manner since the

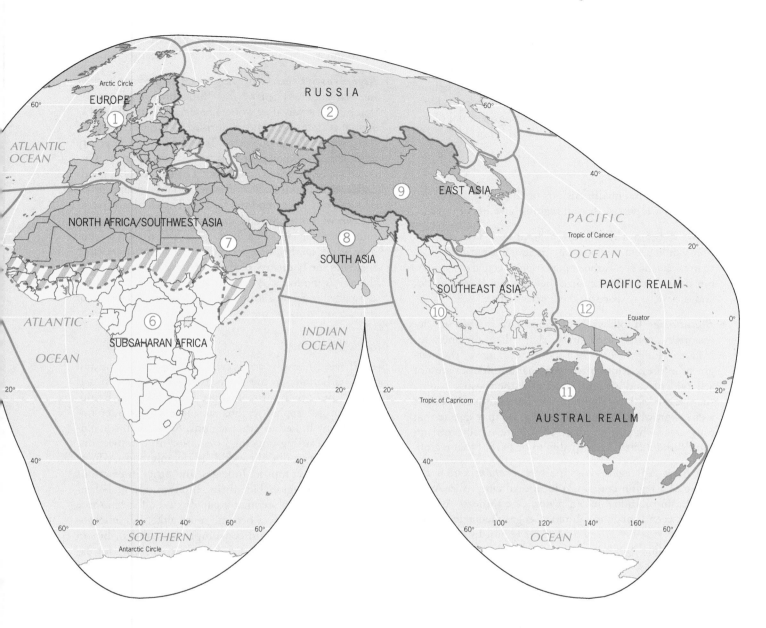

Second World War, but more recently it has had to make way for newly emergent powers. Nowadays, the rise of China is a hot topic of debate. We will see, for example, that China's role in South America has grown rapidly while that of the United States has waned. Our discussion of the various realms will give due consideration to the influence of global trends and outside powers.

REGIONS WITHIN REALMS

The compartmentalization of the world into geographic realms establishes a broad global framework, but for our purposes a more refined level of spatial classification is needed. This brings us to an important organizing concept in geography: the **regional concept** [6]. To establish regions within geographic realms, we need more specific criteria.

Let us use the North American realm to demonstrate the regional idea. When we refer to a part of the United States or Canada (e.g., the South, the Midwest, or the Prairie Provinces), we employ a regional concept—not scientifically but as part of everyday communication. We reveal our perception of local or distant space as well as our mental image of the region we are describing.

But what exactly is the Midwest? How would you draw this region on the North American map? Regions are easy to imagine and describe, but they can be difficult to outline on a map. One way to define the Midwest is to use the borders of States: certain States are part of this region, others are not. You could use agriculture as the principal criterion: the Midwest is where corn and/or soybeans occupy a certain percentage of the farmland. Look ahead to Figure 3B-6, where you will notice that a different name for this region is used—the Heartland—because of the differing (agricultural) criteria that define it. Each method results in a different delimitation; a Midwest based on States is different from a Midwest based on farm production or on industrial activity. Therein lies an important principle: regions are devices that allow us to make spatial generalizations, and they are based on artificial criteria to help us construct them. If you were studying the geography behind politics, then a Midwest region defined by State boundaries would make sense. If you were studying agricultural distributions, you would need a different definition.

Criteria for Regions

Given these different dimensions of the same region, we can identify properties that all regions have in common:

- **Area** To begin with, all regions have *area*. This observation would seem obvious, but there is more to this idea than meets the eye. Regions may be intellectual constructs, but they are not abstractions: they exist in the real world, and they occupy space on the Earth's surface.

- **Boundaries** It follows that regions have *boundaries*. Occasionally, nature itself draws sharp dividing lines, for instance along the crest of a mountain range or the margin of a forest. More often, regional boundaries are not self-evident, and we must determine them using criteria that we establish for that purpose. For example, to define a citrus-growing agricultural region, we may decide that only areas where more than 50 percent of all farmland stands under citrus trees qualify to be part of that region.

- **Location** All regions also possess *location*. Often the name of a region contains a locational clue, as in Amazon Basin or Indochina (a region of Southeast Asia lying between India and China). Geographers refer to the absolute location [7] of a place or region by providing the latitudinal and longitudinal extent of the region with respect to the Earth's grid coordinates. A more useful measure is a region's relative location [8], that is, its location with reference to other regions. Again, the names of certain regions reveal aspects of their relative locations, as in *Mainland* Southeast Asia and *Equatorial* Africa.

- **Homogeneity** Many regions are marked by a certain *homogeneity* or sameness. Homogeneity may lie in a region's human (cultural) properties, its physical (natural) characteristics, or both. Siberia, a vast region of northeastern Russia, is marked by a sparse human population that resides in widely scattered, small settlements of similar form, frigid climates, extensive areas of permafrost (permanently frozen subsoil), and cold-adapted vegetation. This dominant uniformity makes it one of Russia's natural and cultural regions, extending from the Ural Mountains in the west to the Pacific Ocean in the east. When regions display a measurable and often visible internal homogeneity, they are called formal regions [9]. But not all formal regions are visibly uniform. For instance, a region may be delimited by the area in which, say, 90 percent or more of the people speak a particular language. This cannot be seen in the landscape, but the region is a reality, and we can use that criterion to draw its boundaries accurately. It, too, is a formal region.

- **Regions as Systems** Other regions are marked not by their internal sameness but by their functional integration—that is, by the way they work. These regions are defined as spatial systems [10] and are formed by the areal extent of the activities that define them. Take the case of a large city with its surrounding zone of suburbs, urban-fringe countryside, satellite towns, and farms. The city supplies goods and services to this encircling zone, and it buys farm products and other commodities from it. The city is the heart, the *core* of this region, and we call the surrounding zone of interaction the city's hinterland [11]. But the city's influence wanes on the outer periphery of that hinterland, and there lies the boundary of the functional region of which the city is the focus. A functional region [12], therefore, is usually forged by a structured, urban-centered system of interaction. It has a core and a periphery.

Interconnections

Even if we can easily demarcate a particular region and even if its boundaries are sharp, that does not mean it is isolated from other parts of the realm or even the world. All human-geographic regions are more or less interconnected, being linked to other regions. As we shall see, globalization is causing ongoing integration and connections among regions around the world. Trade, migration, education, television, computer linkages, and other interactions sometimes blur regional identities. Interestingly, globalization tends to have a seemingly paradoxical effect: in some ways, regions and places become more alike, more homogeneous (think of certain consumption patterns), but in other respects the contrasts can become stronger (for example, a reassertion of ethnic or religious identities).

THE PHYSICAL SETTING

This book focuses on the geographic realms and regions produced by human activity over thousands of years. But we must not overlook the natural environments in which all this activity took place because we can still recognize the role of those environments in how people make their living. Certain areas of the world, for example, presented opportunities for plant and animal domestication that other areas did not. The people who happened to live in those favored areas learned to grow wheat, rice, or root crops and to domesticate oxen, goats, or llamas. We can still discern those early patterns of opportunity on the map in the twenty-first century. From such opportunities came adaptation and invention, and thereby arose villages, towns, cities, and states. But people living in other kinds of environments found it much harder to achieve this organization. The Americas, for instance, had no large animals that could be domesticated except llamas. This meant that societies created agricultural systems that did not involve ploughing as there were no draught animals. When Europeans introduced cows, horses,

From the Field Notes . . .

© H.J. de Blij

AP/Wide World Photos

"Flying over Iceland's volcanic topography (left photo) is to see our world in the making: this is some of the youngest rock on the planet, and even at rest you can sense its impermanence. Here nature shows us what mostly goes on deep below the surface along the mid-oceanic ridges, where tectonic plates pull apart and lava pours out of fissures and vents. When that happens on dry land, the results can be catastrophic. In the 1780s, an Icelandic volcano named Laki, in a series of eruptions, killed tens of thousands and caused a global ecological crisis. In 2010, the eruption of this far smaller volcano, Eyjafjallajökull (right photo), disrupted air travel for weeks across much of the Northern Hemisphere."

www.conceptcaching.com

and other livestock, this change completely revolutionized the environments and cultural systems of the Western Hemisphere. The modern map carries many such imprints of the past.

Natural (Physical) Landscapes

The landmasses of Planet Earth present a jumble of natural landscapes [13] ranging from rugged mountain chains to smooth coastal plains (Fig. G-1). Certain continents are readily linked with a dominant physical feature—for instance, North America and its Rocky Mountains, South America with its Andes and Amazon Basin, Europe with its Alps, Asia with its Himalaya Mountains and numerous river basins, and Africa with its Sahara and Congo Basin. Physical features have long influenced human activity and movement. Mountain ranges form barriers to movement but have also channeled the spread of agricultural and technological innovations. Large deserts similarly form barriers as do rivers, although rivers also permit accessibility and connectivity between people. River basins in Asia still contain several of the planet's largest population concentrations: the advantages of fertile soils and ample water supplies that first enabled clustered human settlement now sustain hundreds of millions in crowded South and East Asia.

As we study each of the world's geographic realms, we will find that physical landscapes continue to play significant roles in this modern world. That is one reason why the study of world regional geography is so important: it puts the human map in environmental as well as regional perspective.

Geology and Natural Hazards

Our planet may be 4.5 billion years old, but it is far from placid. As you read this chapter, Earth tremors are shaking the still-thin crust on which we live, volcanoes are erupting, storms are raging. Even the continents themselves are moving measurably, pulling apart in some areas, colliding in others. Hundreds of thousands of human lives are lost to natural calamities of this sort in almost every decade (over 350,000 in the 2010–2012 period alone), and such events have at times altered the course of history.

About a century ago a geographer named Alfred Wegener, a German scientist, used spatial analysis to explain something that is obvious even from a small-scale map like Figure G-1: the apparent jigsaw-like fit of the landmasses, especially across the South Atlantic Ocean. He concluded that the landmasses on the map are actually pieces of a supercontinent that existed hundreds of millions of years ago (he called it ***Pangaea***) that drifted away when, for some reason, that supercontinent broke up. His hypothesis of continental drift [14] set the stage for scientists in other disciplines to search for a mechanism that might make this possible, and much of the answer to that search proved to lie in the crust beneath the ocean surface. Today we know that

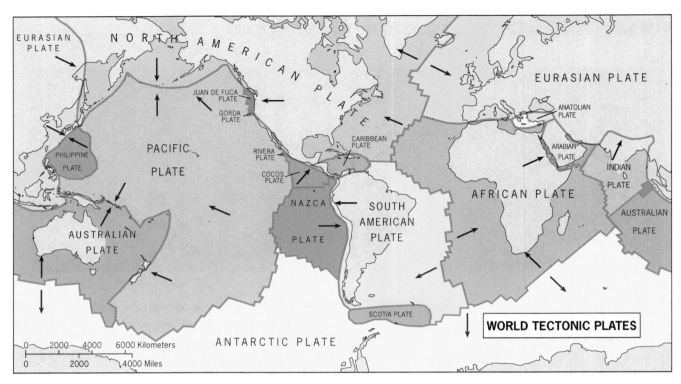

FIGURE G-4

© H. J. de Blij, P. O. Muller, and John Wiley & Sons, Inc.

the continents are "rafts" of relatively light rock that rest on slabs of heavier rock known as tectonic plates [15] (Fig. G-4) whose movement is propelled by giant circulation cells in the red-hot magma below (when this molten magma reaches the surface through volcanic vents, it is called lava).

Inevitably, moving tectonic plates collide. When they do, earthquakes and volcanic eruptions result, and the phy-sical landscape is thrown into spectacular relief. Com-pare Figures G-4 and G-5, and you can see the outlines of the tectonic plates in the distribution of these hazards to human life. The 2010 earthquake adjacent to Port-au-Prince, Haiti measured 7.0 on the Richter scale. Although a shallow quake, its epicenter was located in a very densely populated area. Nearly 300,000 people died, a similar

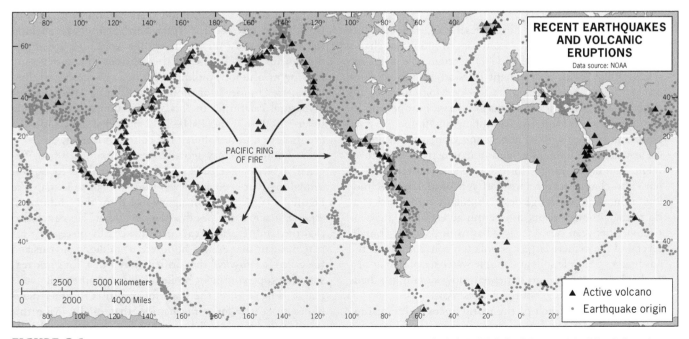

FIGURE G-5

© H. J. de Blij, P. O. Muller, and John Wiley & Sons, Inc.

number were injured, and 1.3 million were made homeless and destitute. The Earth's largest ocean is almost completely encircled by active volcanoes and earthquake epicenters. Appropriately, this is called the Pacific Ring of Fire [16].

It is useful to compare Figure G-5 to Figure G-3 to see which of the world's geographic realms are most susceptible to the hazards inherent in crustal instability. Russia, Europe, Africa, and Australia are relatively safe; in other realms the risks are far greater in one sector than in others (western as opposed to eastern North and South America, for instance). As we shall discover, for certain parts of the world the activity mapped in Figure G-5 presents a clear and present danger. Some of the world's largest cities (e.g., Tokyo, Mexico City) lie in zones that are highly vulnerable to sudden disaster—as indeed occurred with Japan's huge 2011 earthquake and tsunamis not very far north of Tokyo.

Climate

The prevailing climate [17] constitutes a key factor in the geography of realms and regions (in fact, some regions are essentially defined by climate). But climates change: those dominating in certain regions today may not have prevailed there several thousand years ago. Thus any map of climate, including the maps in this chapter, is but a still-picture of our always-changing world.

Climatic conditions have swung back and forth for as long as the Earth has had an atmosphere. Periodically, an ice age [18] lasting tens of millions of years chills the planet and causes massive ecological change. One such ice age occurred while Pangaea was still in one piece, between 250 and 300 million years ago. Another started about 35 million years ago, and we are still experiencing it. The current epoch of this ice age, on average the coldest yet, is called the *Pleistocene* and has been going on for nearly 2 million years.

In our time of global warming this may come as a surprise, but we should remember that an ice age is not a period of unbroken, bitter cold. Rather, an ice age consists of surges of cold, during which glaciers expand and living space shrinks, separated by warmer phases when the ice recedes and life spreads poleward again. The cold phases are called glaciations [19], and they tend to last longest, although milder spells create some temporary relief. The truly warm phases, when the ice recedes poleward and mountain glaciers melt away, are known as interglacials [20]. We are living in one of these interglacials today. It even has a geologic name: the *Holocene*.

Imagine this: just 18,000 years ago, great icesheets had spread all the way south to the Ohio River Valley, covering most of the Midwest; this was the zenith of a glaciation that had lasted about 100,000 years, the *Wisconsinan Glaciation* (Fig. G-6). The Antarctic Icesheet was bigger

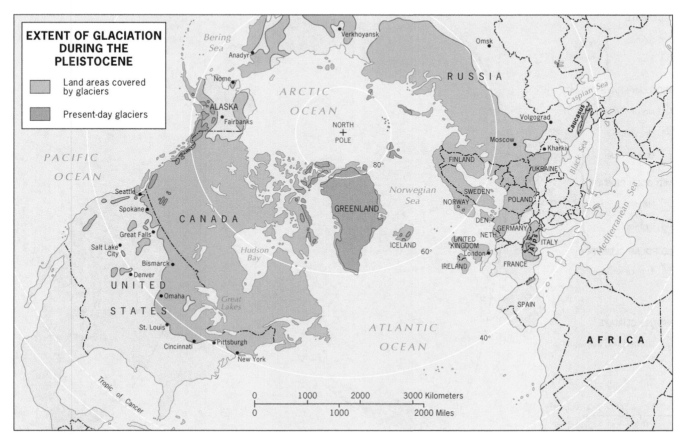

FIGURE G-6

© H. J. de Blij, P. O. Muller, and John Wiley & Sons, Inc.

than ever, and even in the tropics, great mountain glaciers pushed down valleys and onto plateaus. But then Holocene warming began, the continental and mountain glaciers receded, and ecological zones that had been squeezed between the advancing icesheets now spread north and south. In Europe particularly, where humans had arrived from Africa via Southwest Asia during one of the milder phases of the Wisconsinan Glaciation, living space expanded and human numbers grew.

Global Climate Change

Today we are living in an era of global climate change [21], particularly natural global warming that has been accelerated by anthropogenic (human-source) causes. Since the Industrial Revolution, we have been emitting gases that have enhanced nature's **greenhouse effect** whereby the sun's radiation becomes trapped in the Earth's atmosphere. This is leading to a series of climate changes, especially the overall warming of the globe. One important international organization of experts, the Intergovernmental Panel on Climate Change (IPCC), predicts an increase of 2–3°C (3.6–5.4°F) overall for the globe, but with significant regional variability (e.g., more at higher latitudes, less at lower latitudes). Precipitation patterns are predicted to become more variable, particularly in regions where they are already seasonal.

This change in temperature may seem small but is expected to have significant impacts on global climate patterns, agricultural zones, and the quality of human lives. The full ramifications are not known, but scenarios

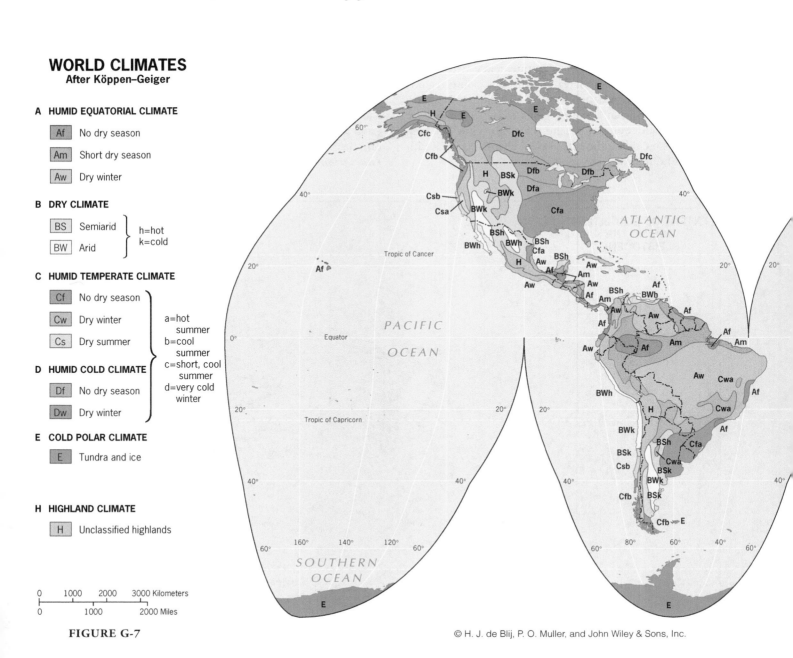

WORLD CLIMATES
After Köppen–Geiger

A HUMID EQUATORIAL CLIMATE

Af	No dry season
Am	Short dry season
Aw	Dry winter

B DRY CLIMATE

| BS | Semiarid |
| BW | Arid |

h=hot
k=cold

C HUMID TEMPERATE CLIMATE

Cf	No dry season
Cw	Dry winter
Cs	Dry summer

a=hot summer
b=cool summer
c=short, cool summer
d=very cold winter

D HUMID COLD CLIMATE

| Df | No dry season |
| Dw | Dry winter |

E COLD POLAR CLIMATE

| E | Tundra and ice |

H HIGHLAND CLIMATE

| H | Unclassified highlands |

0 1000 2000 3000 Kilometers
0 1000 2000 Miles

FIGURE G-7

© H. J. de Blij, P. O. Muller, and John Wiley & Sons, Inc.

are being modeled so that societies can confront the changes that are coming. Leaders of some countries are more skeptical than others, and some have already made greater adjustments than others. One of the most significant consequences of global climate change is that the icecap atop the Arctic Ocean is melting faster than even recent models predicted, with environmental and geopolitical implications. We pick up this issue in Chapters 2A and 12.

Climate Regions

We have just learned how variable climate can be, but in a human lifetime we see little evidence of this variability. We talk about the *weather* (the immediate state of the atmosphere) in a certain place at a given time, but as a technical term *climate* defines the aggregate, total record of weather conditions at a place or in a region over the entire period during which records have been kept.

Figure G-7 may appear very complicated, but this map is useful even at a glance. Devised long ago by Wladimir Köppen and subsequently modified by Rudolf Geiger, it represents climatic regions through a combination of colors and letter symbols. In the legend, note that the *A* climates (rose, orange, and peach) are equatorial and tropical; the *B* climates (tan, yellow) are dry; the *C* climates (shades of green) are temperate, that is, moderate and neither hot nor cold; the *D* climates (purple) are cold; the *E* climates (blue) are frigid; and the similar *H* climates (gray) prevail in highlands like the Tibetan Plateau and the upper reaches of the Andes.

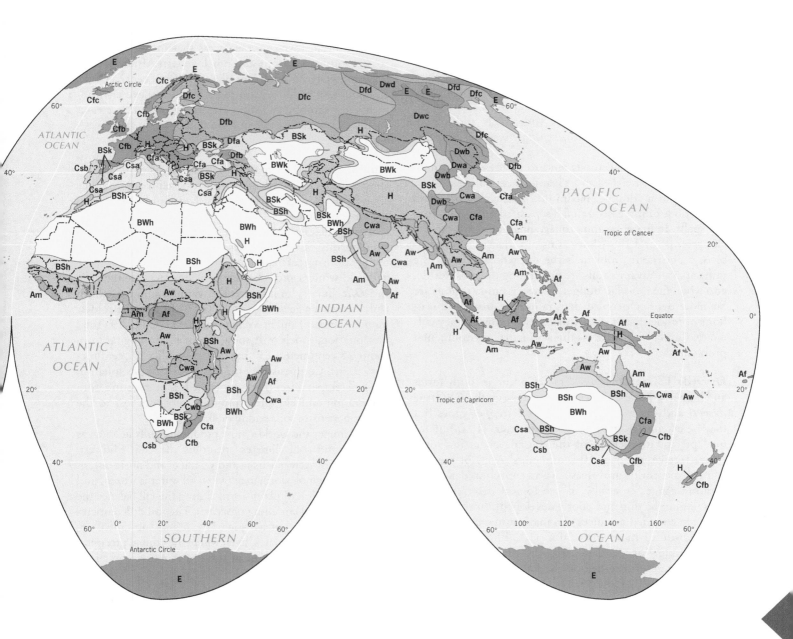

Figure G-7 merits your attention because familiarity with it will help you understand much of what follows in this book. The map has practical utility as well. Although it depicts climatic regions, daily weather in each color-coded region is relatively standard. If, for example, you are familiar with the weather in the large area mapped as *Cfa* in the southeastern United States, you will feel at home in Uruguay (South America), Kwazulu-Natal (South Africa), New South Wales (Australia), and Fujian Province (China). Let us look at the world's climatic regions in some detail.

Humid Equatorial (A) Climates The humid equatorial, or tropical, climates are characterized by high temperatures all year and by heavy precipitation. In the *Af* subtype, the rainfall arrives in substantial amounts every month; but in the *Am* areas, the arrival of the annual wet *monsoon* (the Arabic word for "season" [see Chapter 8A]) marks a sudden enormous increase in precipitation. The *Af* subtype is named after the vegetation that develops there—the tropical rainforest. The *Am* subtype, prevailing in part of peninsular India, in a coastal area of West Africa, and in sections of Southeast Asia, is appropriately referred to as the monsoon climate. A third tropical climate, the *savanna (Aw)*, has a wider daily and annual temperature range and a more strongly seasonal distribution of rainfall.

Savanna rainfall totals tend to be lower than those in the rainforest zone, and savanna seasonality is often expressed in a "double maximum." Each year produces two periods of increased rainfall separated by pronounced dry spells. In many savanna zones, inhabitants refer to the "long rains" and the "short rains" to identify those seasons; a persistent problem is the unpredictability of the rain's arrival. Savanna soils are not among the most fertile, and when the rains fail hunger looms. Savanna regions are far more densely peopled than rainforest areas, and millions of residents of the savanna subsist on what they cultivate. Rainfall variability is their principal environmental problem.

Dry (B) Climates Dry climates occur in both lower and higher latitudes. The difference between the *BW* (true *desert*) and the moister *BS* (semiarid *steppe*) varies but may be taken to lie at about 25 centimeters (10 in) of annual precipitation. Parts of the central Sahara in North Africa receive less than 10 centimeters (4 in) of rainfall. Most of the world's arid areas have an enormous daily temperature range, especially in subtropical deserts (whose soils tend to be thin and poorly developed). In the Sahara, there are recorded instances of a maximum daytime shade temperature of more than 50°C (122°F) followed by a nighttime low of less than 10°C (50°F). But the highest temperature ever recorded on the Earth's surface is not in the Sahara: in 2013, the 56.7°C (134°F) measured in California's Death Valley a century earlier was officially recognized as the hottest.

Humid Temperate (C) Climates As the map shows, almost all these mid-latitude climate areas lie just beyond the Tropics of Cancer and Capricorn (23.5° North and South latitude, respectively). This is the prevailing climate in the southeastern United States from Kentucky to central Florida, on North America's west coast, in most of Europe and the Mediterranean, in southern Brazil and northern Argentina, in coastal South Africa, in eastern Australia, and in eastern China and southern Japan. None of these areas suffers climatic extremes or severity, but the winters can be cold, especially away from water bodies that moderate temperatures. These areas lie midway between the winterless equatorial climates and the summerless polar zones. Fertile and productive soils have developed under this regime, as we will note in our discussion of the North American and European realms.

The humid temperate climates range from moist, as along the densely forested coasts of Oregon, Washington, and British Columbia, to relatively dry, as in the so-called Mediterranean (dry-summer) areas that include not only coastal southern Europe and northwestern Africa but also the southwestern tips of Australia and Africa, central Chile, and Southern California. In these Mediterranean environments, the scrubby, moisture-preserving vegetation creates a natural landscape different from that of richly green western Europe.

Humid Cold (D) Climates The humid cold (or "snow") climates may be called the continental climates, for they seem to develop in the interior of large landmasses, as in the heart of Eurasia or North America. No equivalent land areas at similar latitudes exist in the Southern Hemisphere; consequently, no *D* climates occur there. Great annual temperature ranges mark these humid continental climates, and cold winters and relatively cool summers are the rule. In a *Dfa* climate, for instance, the warmest summer month (July) may average as high as 21°C (70°F), but the coldest month (January) might average only −11°C (12°F). Total precipitation, much of it snow, is not high, ranging from about 75 centimeters (30 in) to a steppe-like 25 centimeters (10 in). Compensating for this paucity of precipitation are cool temperatures that inhibit the loss of moisture from evaporation and evapotranspiration (moisture loss to the atmosphere from soils and plants).

Some of the world's most productive soils lie in areas under humid cold climates, including the U.S. Midwest, parts of southwestern Russia and Ukraine, and northeastern China. The winter dormancy (when all water is frozen) and the accumulation of plant debris during the fall balance the soil-forming and enriching processes. The soil differentiates into well-defined, nutrient-rich layers, and substantial organic humus accumulates. Even where the annual precipitation is light, this environment sustains extensive coniferous forests.

Cold Polar (E) and Highland (H) Climates Cold polar (*E*) climates are differentiated into true icecap conditions, where permanent ice and snow keep vegetation from gaining a foothold, and the tundra, which may have average temperatures above freezing up to four months of the year. Like rainforest, savanna, and steppe, the term *tundra* is vegetative as well as climatic, and the boundary between the **D** and **E** climates in Figure G-7 corresponds closely to that between the northern coniferous forests and the tundra.

Finally, the **H** climates—the unclassified highlands mapped in gray (Fig. G-7)—resemble the **E** climates. High elevations and the complex topography of major mountain systems often produce near-Arctic climates above the tree line, even in the lowest latitudes such as the equatorial section of the high Andes of South America.

Let us not forget an important qualification concerning Figure G-7: this is a still-picture of a changing scene, a single frame from an ongoing film. Climate continues to change, and only a few decades from now climatologists are likely to be modifying the climate maps to reflect new data. Who knows: we may even have to redraw those familiar coastlines. Environmental change is a never-ending challenge.

You will find larger-scale maps of climate in several of the regional chapters that follow, but it is useful to refer back to this Köppen-Geiger map whenever the historical or economic geography of a region or country is under discussion. The world climatic map reflects agricultural opportunities and limitations as well as climatic regimes, and as such helps explain some enduring patterns of human distribution on our planet. We turn next to this crucial topic.

REALMS OF POPULATION

Earlier we noted that population numbers by themselves do not define geographic realms or regions. Population distributions, and the functioning society that gives them common ground, are more significant criteria. That is why we can identify one geographic realm (the Austral) with less than 30 million people and another (South Asia) with more than 1.7 billion inhabitants. Neither population numbers nor territorial size alone can delimit a geographic realm. Nevertheless, the map of world population distribution shows some major clusters that are part of some specific realms (Fig. G-8).

Before we examine these clusters in some detail, remember that the world's human population now rounds off at 7.2 billion (see Appendix B for a detailed breakdown)—confined to the landmasses that constitute less than 30 percent of our planet's surface, much of which is arid desert, inhospitable mountain terrain, or frigid tundra. (Remember too that Fig. G-8 is another still-picture of an ever-changing scene: the rapid growth of humankind continues.) After thousands of years of slow growth, world population during the nineteenth and twentieth centuries grew at an increasing rate. That rate has recently been slowing down, even imploding in some parts of the world. But consider this: it took about 17 centuries following the birth of Christ for the world to add 250 million people to its numbers; now we are adding 250 million about every three years. While the *rate* of population growth has come down in some parts of the world, in absolute terms the global population continues to grow apace and is expected to reach 9.6 billion by 2050.

This raises the important question as to whether there are limits to the Earth's carrying capacity—will there be enough food to go around? That question has become more and more pressing over the past decade due to rapidly rising food prices resulting from increased demand in China and India, a dietary shift from grains to meat and vegetables, and the use of agricultural resources for the production of biofuels. The actual increase of population is only part of the problem; our growing appetite for certain

From the Field Notes . . .

"One early January morning in northern Vietnam, just outside the city of Ninh Binh, a girl came by on her bicycle, pulling an ox on a long rope. When I asked, through an interpreter, where she was taking the ox she replied that she had to take it to her uncle who still worked his land. The girl's own family was moving on to more urban lifestyles, with jobs in manufacturing or services. Vietnam has been changing and modernizing in recent years. Some sectors of the economy are growing vigorously and urbanization has proceeded apace. Sometimes people move to the cities, and sometimes the city comes to them (see the high-rise of the encroaching city in the left background). To the girl, it all seemed for the better. 'I like the city,' she said. She did not have much eye for the ox, but she proudly pointed to her new bicycle. To her, the future looked good."

© Jan Nijman　**www.conceptcaching.com**

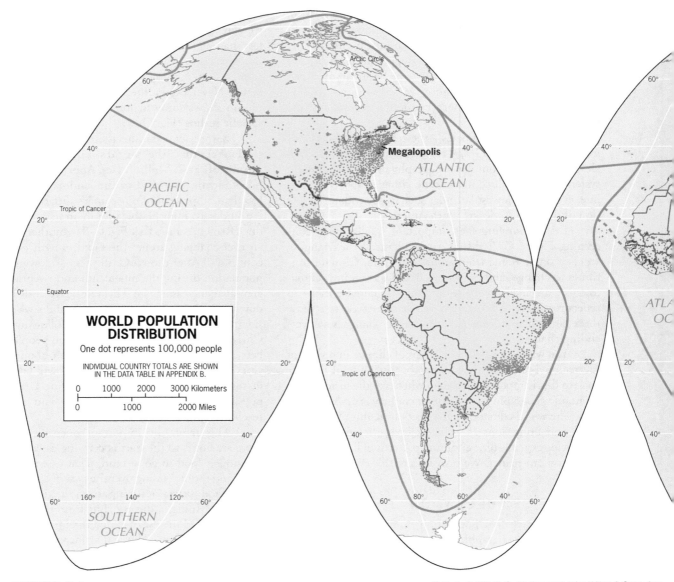

FIGURE G-8

© H. J. de Blij, P. O. Muller, and John Wiley & Sons, Inc.

products is another. And we are not just talking about food—think drinking water, fossil fuels, and minerals as well. Thus it seems inconceivable that 10 billion people by mid-century could be consuming the way we do today in the developed world.

Major Population Clusters

One way to present an overview of the location of people on the planet is to create a map of population distribution [22] (Fig. G-8). As you can see in the map's legend, each dot represents 100,000 people, and the clustering of large numbers of them in certain areas as well as the near-emptiness of others is readily evident. There is a technical difference between population distribution and **population density**, which is another way of showing where people live. Density maps reveal the number of

persons per unit area, requiring a different cartographic technique.

- **South Asia** The *South Asia* population cluster lies centered on India and includes its populous neighbors, Pakistan and Bangladesh. This huge agglomeration of humanity focuses on the wide plain of the Ganges River (**A** in Fig. G-8). South Asia recently became the world's largest population cluster, overtaking East Asia in 2010. A larger percentage of the people remain farmers here, although pressure on the land is greater, whereas agriculture is less efficient than in East Asia.

- **East Asia** Now surpassed by South Asia, the second-ranked *East Asia* population cluster lies centered on China and includes the Pacific-facing Asian coastal zone from the Korean Peninsula to Vietnam. Not long ago, we

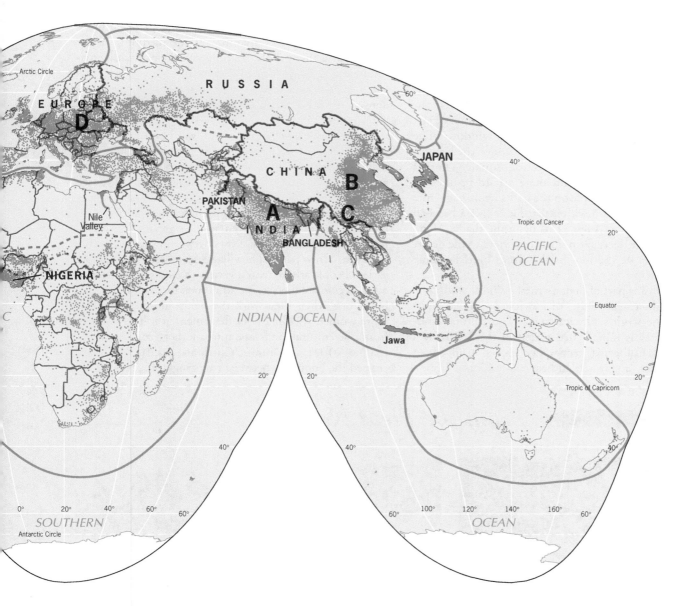

would have reported this as a dominantly rural, farming population, but rapid economic growth and associated urbanization have changed the picture. In China's interior river basins of the Huang (Yellow) and Chang/Yangzi (**B** and **C** on the map), and in the Sichuan Basin between these two letters, most of the people remain farmers. But the booming cities of coastal and increasingly interior China are attracting millions of new inhabitants, and in 2011 the Chinese urban population surpassed the 50-percent milestone.

• ***Europe*** The third-ranking population cluster, *Europe*, also lies on the Eurasian landmass but at the opposite end from China. The European cluster, including western Russia, counts more than 700 million inhabitants, which puts it in a class with the two larger Eurasian concentrations—but there the similarity ends. In Europe, the key to the linear, east-west orientation of the axis of population (**D** in Fig. G-8) is not a fertile river basin but a zone of raw materials for industry. Europe is among the world's most highly urbanized and industrialized realms, its human agglomeration sustained by factories and offices rather than paddies and pastures.

The three world population concentrations just discussed (South Asia, East Asia, and Europe) account for just about 4 billion of the world's 7.2 billion people. No other cluster comes close to these numbers. The next-ranking cluster, Eastern North America, is only about one-quarter the size of the smallest Eurasian concentrations. As in Europe, the population in this zone is concentrated in major metropolitan complexes; the rural areas are now relatively sparsely settled. Geographic realms and regions, therefore, display varying levels of urbanization [23], the percentage of the total population residing in cities and towns. Some regions are urbanizing far more rapidly than others, a phenomenon we will explain as we examine each realm.

REALMS OF CULTURE

Imagine yourself in a boat on the White Nile River, headed upstream (south) from Khartoum, Sudan. The desert sky is blue, the heat is searing. You pass by villages that look much the same: low, square, or rectangular dwellings, some recently whitewashed, others gray, with flat roofs, wooden doors, and small windows. The minaret of a modest mosque may rise above the houses, and you get a glimpse of a small central square. There is very little vegetation; here and there a hardy palm tree stands in a courtyard. People on the paths wear long white robes and headgear, also white, that looks like a baseball cap without the visor. A few goats lie in the shade. Along the river's edge lie dusty farm fields that yield to the desert in the distance. At the foot of the river's bluff lie some canoes.

All of this is part of Sudan's rural cultural landscape [24], the distinctive attributes of a society imprinted on its portion of the world's physical stage. The cultural landscape concept was initially articulated in the 1920s by a University of California geographer named Carl Sauer, who stated that "a cultural landscape is fashioned from a natural landscape by a culture group" and that "culture is the agent; the natural environment the medium." What this means is that people, starting with their physical environment and using their culture as their agency, fashion a landscape that is layered with forms such as buildings, gardens, and roads, and also modes of dress, aromas of food, and sounds of music.

Continue your journey southward on the Nile, and you will soon witness a remarkable transition. Quite suddenly, the square, solid-walled, flat-roofed houses of Sudan give way to the round, wattle-and-thatch, conical-roofed dwellings of South Sudan. You may note that clouds have appeared in the sky: it rains more here, and flat roofs will not do. The desert has given way to green. Vegetation, natural as well as planted, grows between houses, flanking even the narrow paths. The villages seem less orderly, more varied. People ashore wear a variety of clothes, the women often in colorful dresses, the adult men in shirts and slacks, but shorts when they work the fields, although you see more women wielding hoes than men. You have traveled from one cultural landscape into another, from Arabized, Islamic Africa to animist/Christian Africa. You have crossed the boundary between two geographic realms.

From the Field Notes . . .

© H.J. de Blij

© H.J. de Blij

"The Atlantic-coast city of Bergen, Norway displayed the Norse cultural landscape more comprehensively, it seemed, than any other Norwegian city, even Oslo. The high-relief site of Bergen creates great vistas, but also long shadows; windows are large to let in maximum light. Red-tiled roofs are pitched steeply to enhance runoff and inhibit snow accumulation; streets are narrow and houses clustered, conserving warmth . . . The coastal village of Mengkabong on the Borneo coast of the South China Sea represents a cultural landscape seen all along the island's shores, a stilt village of the Bajau, a fishing people. Houses and canoes are built of wood as they have been for centuries. But we could see some evidence of modernization: windows filling wall openings, water piped in from a nearby well."

www.conceptcaching.com

Mustafa Ozer/AFP/Getty Images, Inc.

The *hajj* is the yearly pilgrimage of Muslims to the holy city of Mecca in Saudi Arabia. The pilgrimage is referred to as the fifth "pillar" of Islam, the obligation of every able-bodied Muslim to worship Allah in this holiest of sites at least once in their lifetime. This is the Grand Mosque of Mecca on November 17, 2010, as more than two million Muslim pilgrims launched into the final rituals of this largest religious pilgrimage in the world.

No geographic realm, not even the Austral Realm, has just one single cultural landscape, but cultural landscapes help define realms as well as regions. The cultural landscape of the high-rise North American city with its sprawling suburbs differs from that of urban South America; the organized terraced paddies of Southeast Asia are unlike anything to be found in the rural cultural landscape of neighboring Australia. Variations of cultural landscapes within geographic realms, such as between highly urbanized and dominantly rural (and more traditional) areas, help us define the world's regions.

The Geography of Language

Language is the essence of culture. People tend to feel passionately about their mother tongue, especially when they believe it is threatened in some way. In the United States today, the English Only movement reflects many people's fears that the primacy of English as the national language is under threat as a result of immigration. As we will see in later chapters, some governments try to suppress the languages (and thus the cultures) of minorities in mistaken attempts to enforce national unity, provoking violent reactions.

In fact, languages emerge, thrive, and die out over time, and linguists estimate that the number of lost languages is in the tens of thousands—a process that continues. One year from the day you read this, about 25 more languages will have become extinct, leaving no trace. Just in North America, more than 100 native languages were lost during the past half-century. Some major ones of the past, such as Sumerian and Etruscan, have left fragments in later languages. Others, like Sanskrit and Latin, live on in their modern successors. At present, about 6800 languages remain, half of them classified by linguists as endangered; some of the "hot spots" are the Amazon, Siberia, northern Australia, and the Andes. By the end of this century, the bulk of the world's population will be speaking just a few hundred languages, which means that many millions will no longer be able to speak their ancestral mother tongues.

Scholars have tried for many years to unravel the historic roots and branches of the "language tree," and their debates continue. Geographers trying to map the outcome of this research keep having to modify the pattern, so you should take Figure G-9 as a work in progress, not the final product. At minimum, there are some 15 so-called *language families*, groups of languages with a shared but usually distant origin. The most widely distributed language family, the Indo-European (shown in yellow on the map), includes English, French, Spanish, Russian, Persian, and Hindi. This encompasses the languages of European colonizers that were carried and implanted worldwide, English most of all. Today, English serves as the national or official language of many countries and outposts, and remains the *lingua franca* (common second language) of government, commerce, and higher education in many multicultural societies (see Fig. G-9 inset map). In the postcolonial era, English became the chief medium of still another wave of ascendancy now in progress: globalization.

But even English may eventually go the way of Latin, morphing into versions you will hear (and learn to use) as you travel, forms of English that may, generations from now, be the successors that Italian and Spanish are to Latin. In Hong Kong, Chinese and English are producing a local "Chinglish" you may hear in the first taxi you enter. In Lagos, Nigeria, where most of the people

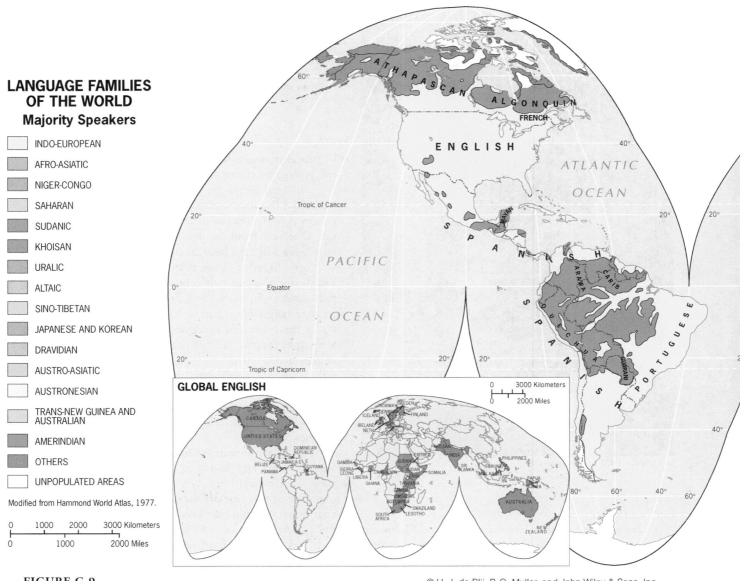

FIGURE G-9

© H. J. de Blij, P. O. Muller, and John Wiley & Sons, Inc.

are culturally and ethnically Yoruba, a language called "Yorlish" is emerging. No map can keep up with the constant evolution of language.

Landscapes of Religion

Religion played a crucial part in the emergence of ancient civilizations and has shaped the course of world history. Hinduism, for example, was one of the earliest religions that helped shape an entire realm (South Asia). Later, Buddhism, Christianity, and Islam emerged as major belief systems, often splitting up into various branches stretching across realms and regions. Figure G-10 shows the current distribution of world religions. Our world has become a more complicated place in recent times, and its patterns of religion are increasingly diffuse and dynamic. But today,

still, we find that geographic realms are often dominated by a single religion or family of religions: Christianity in Europe and the Americas, Islam in North Africa/Southwest Asia, Hinduism in South Asia, and Buddhism in mainland Southeast Asia. But the boundaries tend not to be very sharp and usually take the form of transition zones (e.g., between North and Middle America, or between North and Subsaharan Africa).

A WORLD OF STATES

Ours is a world of about 200 countries or states [25]. The political territorial organization of the world within a system of states hinges on the notion of sovereignty [26]. It is a concept from international law which means that the government of a state rules supreme within its borders.

Normally, states recognize each other's sovereignty, but this becomes a matter of contention at times of conflict and war.

In the tens of thousands of years of human history, the modern state is a relatively recent invention, and so is the international system of which it forms the cornerstone. The modern state emerged from other kinds of politico-territorial organization that have existed since the beginnings of complex civilizations. In the study of ancient history, scholars sometimes use the term polity or proto-state to indicate the difference. Ever since farm surpluses enabled the growth of large and prosperous towns, this was accompanied by the more sophisticated and centralized exercise of power and political organization. From these origins, the earliest states took shape.

Although ancient states such as the Greek city-states and the Roman Empire exhibited several qualities of modern states, it was not until the seventeenth century that European rulers and governments began to negotiate treaties that defined the state in international law. That is why the modern state is often described as based on the European state model [27], with definitions of nationality and sovereignty. Often, the model assumed that state and nation were ideally conterminous, so that a **nation-state** would enclose an ethnically and culturally homogeneous people within a national boundary. That was never truly the case (even France, the "model of models," had its minorities), and today the ideal state is defined as a clearly and legally defined territory inhabited by a citizenry governed from a capital city by a representative government. As we shall discover in Chapters 1A and 1B, not even in Europe itself are all governments truly representative, but the European state model has, for better or worse, been adopted throughout the world.

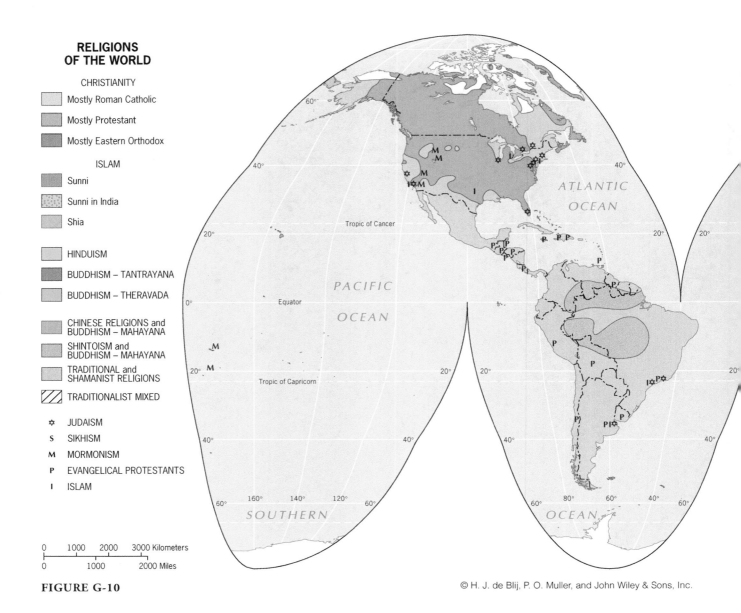

RELIGIONS OF THE WORLD

CHRISTIANITY
- Mostly Roman Catholic
- Mostly Protestant
- Mostly Eastern Orthodox

ISLAM
- Sunni
- Sunni in India
- Shia

- HINDUISM
- BUDDHISM – TANTRAYANA
- BUDDHISM – THERAVADA
- CHINESE RELIGIONS and BUDDHISM – MAHAYANA
- SHINTOISM and BUDDHISM – MAHAYANA
- TRADITIONAL and SHAMANIST RELIGIONS
- TRADITIONALIST MIXED

- ✡ JUDAISM
- S SIKHISM
- M MORMONISM
- P EVANGELICAL PROTESTANTS
- I ISLAM

0 1000 2000 3000 Kilometers
0 1000 2000 Miles

FIGURE G-10

© H. J. de Blij, P. O. Muller, and John Wiley & Sons, Inc.

So the modern state is a historical phenomenon, and there are also signs that it may not last forever. The state system today is challenged "from below" by ethnic minorities and regional secessionist movements (e.g., Tibetans in China; Scotland in the United Kingdom). And it is also challenged "from above" through increasingly powerful international organizations such as the European Union. Its member-states voluntarily transfer some of their power to "Brussels" (the EU's headquarters city) mainly because they think it will be to their economic advantage.

Even though many states find themselves negotiating these challenges through the decentralization of authority to regional governments or through the transfer of part of their authority to international bodies, it is important to keep in mind that they do so, almost always, with the capacity to retain their powers and to seize control at their discretion. For all our efforts to cooperate diplomatically

(the United Nations), economically (the European Union), strategically (the North Atlantic Treaty Organization), and in other ways, it is the state and its government—not regions or realms—that holds the power and the authority to make decisions in the global arena. Decidedly, this is still a world of states.

Subdivisions of the State

Meanwhile, we are all too well aware that states contain subdivisions. Even the smallest states are partitioned in this manner. As all Americans—as well as Mexicans, Brazilians, and Australians—know, some larger states call their subdivisions *States*: the State of Virginia, the State of Chihuahua, the State of Bahia, the State of Victoria. (As pointed out earlier, a state denotes a sovereign country whereas a [capitalized] State signifies a subdivision.) The subdivisions of other states have alternate names: provinces (Canada),

Adapted from E. H. Fouberg et al., *Human Geography*, 9e, based on several data sources.

regions (France), Autonomous Communities (Spain), Federal Districts (Russia), Divisions (Myanmar). And some of these subnational political units are becoming increasingly assertive, occasionally making their own decisions about their economic or social policies whether the central (state) government likes it or not. When that happens—in Quebec, in Catalonia, in Arizona—we should pay even closer attention to the map.

Our analysis of the world's regional geography requires data, and it is crucial to know the origin of these data. Unfortunately, we do not have a uniformly sized grid that we can superimpose over the globe: we must depend on the world's 190-plus countries to report vital information (think of this information as "state-istics"). Fortunately, all large and populous countries tend to also provide information on each of their subdivisions when they conduct their census. So at least some data are available at a finer scale.

Geopolitics and the State

As we shall observe in the pages that follow, states vary not only in terms of their dimensions, relative location, domestic resource base, productive capacity, and other physical and cultural properties, but also in terms of their influence in world affairs. Napoleon once remarked that "the politics of the state lies in its geography." There is no doubt that geography is vital to state affairs and to the relations among states within realms and regions. But the actual influence of geography is far from simple and difficult to measure. There can be many different aspects to a country's geography, and sometimes they are hard to separate from cultural or economic factors.

Take size, for example. Big countries tend to be more powerful than small countries, but this is hardly a perfect relationship, and economic prowess also counts for a great deal. Some relatively small countries carry a lot

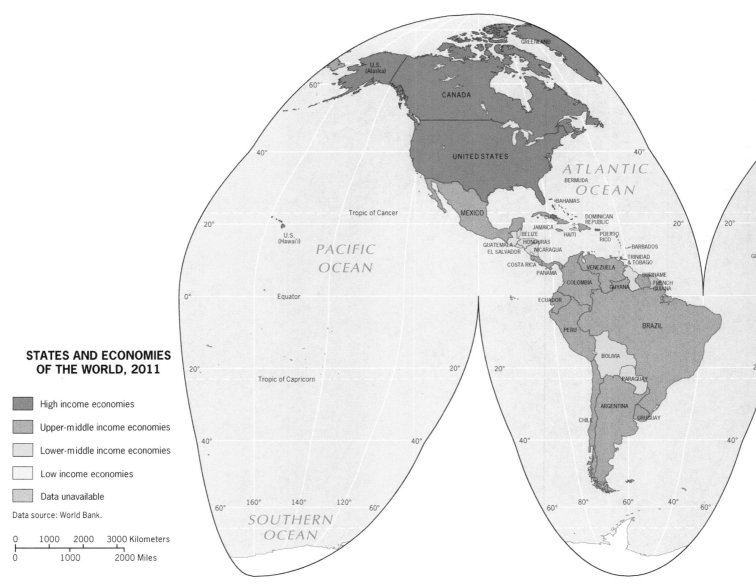

STATES AND ECONOMIES OF THE WORLD, 2011

High income economies

Upper-middle income economies

Lower-middle income economies

Low income economies

Data unavailable

Data source: World Bank.

0   1000   2000   3000 Kilometers

0   1000   2000 Miles

FIGURE G-11

© H. J. de Blij, P. O. Muller, and John Wiley & Sons, Inc.

of weight in international affairs, while other larger and more populous ones are much less influential. Think of Switzerland and its importance in the world of banking and finance; think of Israel and global geopolitics; think of Kuwait and oil.

When gauging the role of geography in international affairs we must also remember that while physical geography may be "permanent" in certain ways, the meaning ascribed to those geographic features can change over time. Think of the impact of transport and communications technology on relative distance, for example. And it is important that we consider the role of geography in historical context as well. For instance, the origins of the European Union must be understood in the context of World War II, particularly the role of Germany during and after the war.

States, Realms, and Regions

As Figures G-3 and G-11 suggest, geographic realms are mostly assemblages of states, and the borders between realms frequently coincide with the boundaries between countries—for example, between North America and Middle America along the U.S.-Mexico border. But a realm boundary can also cut across a state, as does the one between Subsaharan Africa and the Muslim-dominated realm of North Africa/Southwest Asia. Here the boundary takes on the properties of a wide transition zone, yet it still divides states such as Nigeria, Chad, and Ethiopia. The transformation of the margins of the former Soviet Union is creating similar cross-country transitions. Recently-independent states such as Belarus (between Europe and Russia) and Kazakhstan (between Russia and

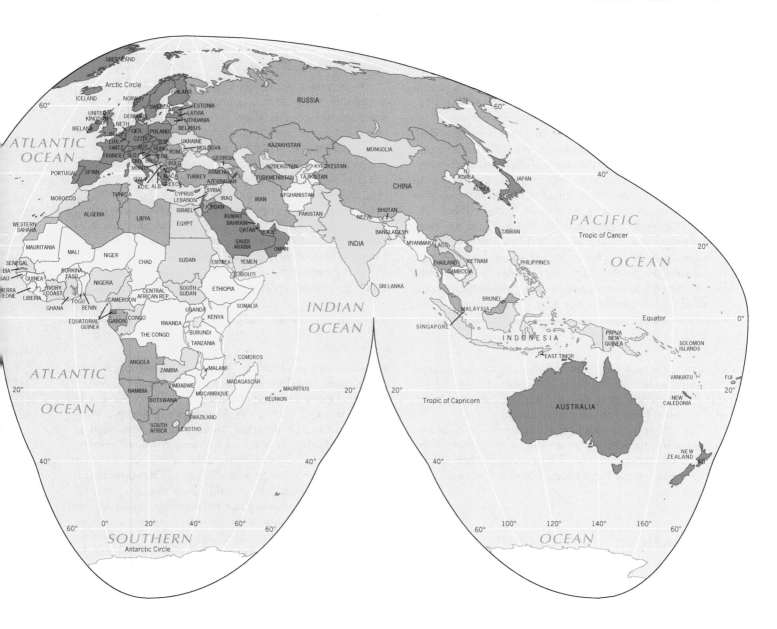

Muslim Southwest Asia) lie in transition zones of regional change.

Most often, however, geographic realms consist of groups of states whose boundaries also mark the limits of the realms. Look at Southeast Asia, for instance. Its northern border coincides with the political boundary that separates China (a realm practically unto itself) from Vietnam, Laos, and Myanmar (Burma). The boundary between Myanmar and Bangladesh (which is part of the South Asian realm) defines its western border. Here, the state boundary framework helps delimit geographic realms.

The global boundary framework is even more useful in delimiting regions within geographic realms. We shall discuss such divisions every time we introduce a Regions of the Realm (B) chapter, but an example is appropriate here. In the Middle American realm, we recognize four regions. Two of these lie on the mainland: Mexico, the giant of the realm, and Central America, which is constituted by the seven comparatively small states located between Mexico and the Panama-Colombia border (which also marks the boundary with the South American realm).

Political Geography

To our earlier criteria of physical geography, population distribution, and cultural geography, we now add ***political geography*** as a shaper of world-scale geographic regions. In doing so, we should be aware that the global boundary framework continues to change. Sometimes, new boundaries are created, as between Serbia and Kosovo when Kosovo declared its independence in 2008, or between (now-shrunken) Sudan and South Sudan in 2011. Occasionally, boundaries are eliminated, as was the case between former West and East Germany in 1990. And then,

The Gini Coefficient

ECONOMIC GEOGRAPHERS STUDY regional disparities and their causes, including variations of income. But it can be difficult to determine who is earning how much across sizeable populations. Enter Corrado Gini, an Italian statistician, who made pioneering contributions—including a mathematical formula to measure the degree of dispersion of a phenomenon through a population, including economic gains. His name is forever linked to an index that reveals what proportion of a population is sharing in the wealth, and who is not.

This index ranges from 0 (no differences at all; everyone earns the same amount) to 100 (one earner takes all). A country in which a few tycoons control all the wealth and everyone else labors for a pittance will have a "GC" leaning well toward 100; but a country with a more equitable spread of income will be much closer to 0.

As important as the actual number is the way the GC is changing. When China was under strict communist rule and before its modern economic boom began, its GC was low (nobody, of course, actually measured it). By 1993, however, it was reported to be 41; the newest figure—47 for the year 2012—shows that it now exceeds the United States (38 in 2012) in terms of inequality, with China's incomes increasingly concentrated in the country's wealthier Pacific Rim. India's GC, probably underestimated at around 40, may be rising even faster than China's. But Brazil, long exhibiting one of the world's highest GC's, has lately decreased to just above 50, partly as a result of social programs we discuss in Chapter 5B. The GC for some states is unavailable, even as an estimate. Certain governments prefer not to let the Gini out of the bottle.

---

of course, the meaning of boundaries can change because the countries involved agree on new political relationships; this is especially clear in the case of the European Union. But the overall state system has endured.

In Chapter 12, we will discuss a recent development in boundary-making: the extension of boundaries onto and into the oceans and seas. This process has been dividing up the last of the Earth's open frontiers, with uncertain consequences.

GEOGRAPHIES OF DEVELOPMENT

Finally, as we prepare for our study of world regional geography, it is all too clear that realms, regions, and states do not enjoy the same level of prosperity. The field of *economic geography* focuses on spatial aspects of the ways people make their living, and deals with patterns of production, distribution, and consumption of goods and services. As with all else in this world, these patterns reveal much variation. Individual states report the nature and value of their imports and exports, farm and factory output, and many other economic data to the United Nations and other international agencies. From such information, economic geographers can measure the comparative well-being of the world's countries (see the box titled "The Gini Coefficient"). The concept of development [28] is used to gauge a state's economic, social, and institutional growth.

Statistics: A Caution

The concept of development, as measured by data that reflect totals and averages for entire national populations, entails some pitfalls of which we should be aware from the start. When a state's economy is growing as a whole, and even when it is "booming" by comparison to other states, this does not automatically mean that every citizen is better off and the income of every worker is rising. Averages have a way of concealing regional variability and local stagnation. In very large states such as India and China, it is useful to assess regional, provincial, and even local economic data to discover to what extent the whole country is sharing in "development." In the case of India, we should know that the State of Maharashtra (containing the burgeoning city of Mumbai) is far ahead of most others when it comes to its share of the national economy. In China, the coastal provinces of the Pacific Rim far outstrip those of the interior. In Spain, the people of the Autonomous Community of Catalonia (focused on the city of Barcelona) delight in telling you that theirs is the most productive entity in the country. Hence, national (state-level) statistics can conceal as much as they reveal.

Development in Spatial Perspective

Various schemes to group the world's states into economic-geographic categories have come and gone, and others will probably arise in the future. For our purposes, the classification scheme used by the World Bank (one of the agencies that monitor economic conditions across the globe) is the most effective. It sorts countries into four categories based on the success of their economies: (1) high-income, (2) upper-middle-income, (3) lower-middle-income, and (4) low-income. These categories, when mapped, display interesting regional clustering (see Fig. G-11). Compare this map to our global framework (Fig. G-3), and you can see the role of economic geography in the layout of the world's geographic realms. Also evident are regional contrasts within realms—for instance, between Brazil and its western neighbors, between South Africa and most of

From the Field Notes . . .

"Thanks to a Brazilian intermediary I was allowed to enter and spend a day in two of Rio de Janeiro's hillslope *favelas*, an eight-hour walk through one into the other. Here live millions of the city's poor, in areas often ruled by drug lords and their gangs, with minimal or no public services, amid squalor and stench, in discomfort and danger. And yet life in the older *favelas* has become more comfortable as shacks are replaced by more permanent structures, electricity is sometimes available, water supply, however haphazard, is improved, and an informal economy brings goods and services to the residents. I stood in the doorway of a resident's single-room dwelling for this overview of an urban landscape in transition: satellite-television disks symbolize the change going on here. The often blue cisterns catch rainwater; walls are made of rough brick and roofs of corrugated iron or asbestos sheeting. No roads or automobile access, so people walk to the nearest road at the bottom of the hill. Locals told me of their hope that they will some day have legal

rights to the space they occupy. The Brazilian government at times expresses support for these claims, but it is complicated. As the photo shows, people live quite literally on top of one another, and mapping the chaos will not be simple (but will be made possible with geographic information systems). This would allow the government to tax residents, but it would also allow residents to obtain loans based on the value of their *favela* properties, and bring millions of Brazilians into the formal economy. The hardships I saw on this excursion were often dreadful, but you could sense the hope for, and anticipation of, a better future."

© H.J. de Blij　**www.conceptcaching.com**

the rest of Subsaharan Africa, and between west and east in Europe.

Economic geography is not the entire story, but along with factors of physical geography (such as climate), cultural geography (including resistance or receptivity to change and innovation), and political geography (history of colonialism, growth of democracy), it plays a powerful role in shaping our variable world.

A Core-Periphery World: Increasing Complexity

It has been obvious for a very long time that human success on the Earth's surface has focused on certain areas and bypassed others. The earliest cities and states of the Fertile Crescent, the empires of the Incas and the Aztecs, the dominance of ancient Rome, and many other hubs of activity tell the story of development and decay, of growth and collapse. In their heyday, such centers of authority, innovation, production, and expansion were the earliest core areas [29], places of dominance whose inhabitants exerted their power over their surroundings near and far. Such core areas grew rich and, in many cases, endured for long periods because their occupants skillfully exploited those surroundings—controlling and taxing the local population, forcing workers to farm the land and mine the resources at their command. This created a periphery [30] that sustained the core for as long as the system endured, so that core-periphery interactions, one-sided though they were, created wealth for the former and enforced stability in the latter.

In modern times, the world can be said to revolve, economically speaking, around a global core and periphery— the world economy, after all, has become a single integrated spatial system. In the nineteenth century, this core more or less coincided with western Europe, controlling as it did vast areas of the world through its empires. In the twentieth century, the core expanded first to North America and then grew to include Japan, Australia, and New Zealand. Since the 1960s, Hong Kong, Singapore, Taiwan, South Korea, and some of the (oil-) rich Gulf States have become part of the core as well. And as the twenty-first century opened, the newest entrant stepped forward: Pacific-fronting China. The global core, therefore,

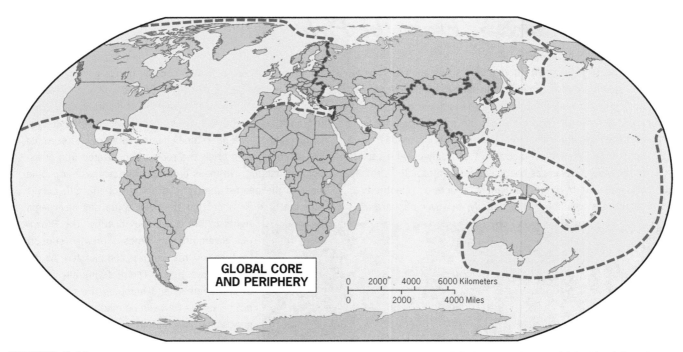

FIGURE G-12

© H. J. de Blij, P. O. Muller, J. Nijman, and John Wiley & Sons, Inc.

continues to evolve. As an economic-geographic phenomenon, it is mapped in Figure G-12 above. But keep in mind that here the core is defined purely in economic terms: if we were to include such other criteria as representative Western-style government, for example, China would not qualify.

It is also important to realize that core-periphery relationships are not limited to the global scale. Countries themselves can and do exhibit such patterns as well. China again is a case in point: its coastal provinces form the core, while the interior and westernmost reaches of the country are part of China's periphery. Uneven development, therefore, exists at a range of scales, from the urban to the global. Most functional regions, in essence, are **spatial networks** comprising nodes of variable centrality and importance, and this usually translates into different levels of economic development. Except for a few special cases, all countries contain core areas. These national cores are often anchored by the country's capital and/or largest city: Paris (France), Tokyo (Japan), Buenos Aires (Argentina), and Bangkok (Thailand) are just a few notable examples. Larger countries may have more than one core area, such as Australia with its eastern and western coast cores and intervening periphery.

The world continues to exhibit major differences in productivity and well-being. One of the most intriguing economic-spatial outcomes of globalization is that a growing number of countries have accelerated their development—but this growth is often confined to specific city-regions whereas the rest of the country remains quite poor.

GLOBALIZATION

Globalization [31] is essentially a geographical process in which spatial relations—economic, cultural, political— shift to ever broader scales (now driven in no small part by recent rapid advances in communication and transport technologies). What this means is that what happens in one place has repercussions in places ever more distant, thereby integrating the entire world into an ever "smaller" global village. Globalization comes into our homes via television, computers, and smartphones: news today has never traveled faster, and sometimes even government leaders turn to the Internet on their personal electronic devices to get the latest reports on international events.

Globalization is not something entirely new. The second half of the nineteenth century, for instance, also witnessed major advances in the intensification of global interdependence. It was particularly affected by new technologies such as the steamship, the railway, and the telegraph, which subsequently were followed by the first motor vehicles and airplanes. With today's newest technologies, the world is becoming ever more interconnected. Thus geography and our knowledge of the world's realms and regions become increasingly important—because what happens elsewhere will have consequences wherever you are.

Global Challenges, Shared Interests

Globalization plays out in various spheres, from the environmental to the cultural to the economic. Today's most

From the Field Notes . . .

© Jan Nijman

"Singapore is an outstanding example of a city propelled into prominence by forces of globalization. Located strategically on one of the world's busiest shipping lanes (the Strait of Malacca) and with a good harbor, this city-state was bound to benefit from expanding world trade. It now boasts the busiest transshipment port in the world and the city has also become a shopping magnet for elites all across the Southeast Asian realm. During a visit to Singapore in the summer of 2012, I had spotted a newly built, futuristic-looking skyscraper across the bay from downtown and thought it would be worth a visit. It turned out to be the huge Marina Bay Sands Hotel (developed by the Sands Corporation of Las Vegas) that opened for business in 2010. The rooftop features a spectacular pool with a view of the city and its port down below. Like most 'world-cities', Singapore is a hub of both production and consumption."

www.conceptcaching.com

pressing environmental issue, no doubt, is global warming, a threat to the world at large. It is clear that we must confront this problem together, but it is far from easy to agree on strategies. Some countries are bigger polluters than others, some have more resources than others, and some are more developed than others. How to divide the burdens? At the Durban (South Africa) Conference on Climate Change in 2011, for the first time governments from around the world committed themselves to preparing a comprehensive global agreement to reduce greenhouse gas emissions. The good news was that the deal included developed and developing countries, as well as the participation of the United States, which had been reluctant to get involved in previous international efforts. The bad news is that the process will be an excruciatingly slow one: the target date for completing the agreement is 2015, and the actual reductions of emissions would not commence until 2020. On top of that, it remains to be seen if the agreement will be legally binding.

Culturally, too, the world is coming closer together, and this is most apparent in global migration flows. Such migration used to be uncommon because most people were rooted in their home environment, where they lived out their entire lives. When residential relocation did occur, it used to be one-way, with people migrating from one place to another and then staying put. But in the current globalization era, migration flows have intensified, in part because people now possess far greater knowledge about opportunities elsewhere. Moreover, it is now much easier to travel back and forth, which allows migrants to maintain close ties with their original home countries. Not surprisingly, as the number of highly mobile *transnational migrants* has increased, they have become instrumental in the spreading of cultures around the world. Examples include Algerians in Paris, Haitians in Montreal, Cubans in Miami, Mexicans in Los Angeles, Indians in Singapore, and Indonesians in Sydney.

But it is also important to keep in mind that people's mobility is often constrained, because some parts of this highly uneven world are so much better off than others. High-income countries are a magnet for migrants, but all too often they cannot get access. Millions of workers aspire to leave the periphery, which contains the world's poorest regions, to seek a better life somewhere in the core. Trying to get there, many of them die

© Scott Houston/© Corbis

The "Occupy Wall Street" demonstration in New York City on October 11, 2011. The protests that began here, in the form of deliberate illegal squatting and resistance to removal by the police, soon spread to cities across the United States and around the world. Under the banner of "We are the 99%," these demonstrators insist that the vast majority of people do not benefit from global finance and that the politicians are on the side of big business. In New York and elsewhere, these protests relied on a hard core of thousands of determined demonstrators and, while short-lived, made headlines around the world.

every year in the waters of the Mediterranean, the Caribbean, and the Atlantic. Others risk their lives at the barriers that encircle the global core as if it were a gated community—from the "security fence" between Mexico and the United States to the walls that guard Israel's safety to the razor wire that encircles Spain's outposts on North Africa's shore.

When the world economy entered a deep, extended downturn in 2008, unemployment skyrocketed and opportunities for migrants declined accordingly. In Europe, undocumented migration plunged 33 percent from 2008 to 2009 alone, and along the U.S.-Mexican border the number of interceptions fell by 23 percent during the same 12-month period. As the global economy recovers, immigration rates are expected to increase concomitantly.

Winners and Losers

If a geographic concept can arouse strong passions, globalization is it. To most economists, politicians, and businesspeople, this is the best of all possible worlds—the march of international capitalism, open markets, and free trade. In theory, globalization breaks down barriers to foreign trade, stimulates commerce, brings jobs to remote places, and promotes social, cultural, political, and other kinds of exchanges. High-tech workers in India are employed by computer firms based in California. Japanese cars are assembled in Thailand. American footwear is made in China. Fast-food restaurant chains spread standards of service and hygiene as well as familiar (and standardized) menus from Tokyo to Tel Aviv to Tijuana. If wages and standards of employment are lower in peripheral countries than in the global core, production will shift there and the gap will shrink. Everybody wins. Economic geographers can prove that global economic integration allows the overall economies of poorer countries to grow faster: compare their international trade to their national income, and

you will find that the *gross national income (GNI)** of those that engage in more foreign trade (and thus are more "globalized") rises, while the GNI of those with less actually declines.

But there is another, more complicated issue. Although many countries, even lesser-developed ones that were able to latch onto globalization, have witnessed accelerated economic growth and rising per capita incomes, inequality within these countries has frequently increased just as fast. In other words, uneven development within countries has become more pronounced. As noted earlier, this is particularly obvious in China, the fastest-growing economy in the world over the past two decades: much of this growth took place in its Pacific coastal zone, not in the interior of the country, and income differentials became ever wider. And the same is true in India and most other *emerging markets*. This is why a regional approach is so important to understanding what is going on in the world economy.

Globalization in the economic sphere is proceeding under the auspices of the World Trade Organization (WTO), of which the United States is the leading architect. To join, countries must agree to open their economies to foreign trade and investment. The WTO has 159 member-states (Russia being among the latest to join in 2012), all expecting benefits from their participation. But the leading global-core countries themselves do not always oblige when it comes to creating a "level playing field." The case of the Philippines is often cited: Filipino farmers found themselves competing against North American and European agricultural producers who receive subsidies to support production as well as the export of their products—and losing out. Meanwhile, low-priced, subsidized U.S. corn appeared on Filipino markets. As a result, the Philippine economy lost several hundred thousand farm jobs, wages went down, and WTO membership had the effect of severely damaging its agricultural sector. Not

---

*Gross national income (GNI) is the total income earned from all goods and services produced by the citizens of a country, within or outside of its borders, during a calendar year. *Per capita GNI* is a widely used indicator of the variation of spendable income around the globe and is reported for each country in the farthest-right column of the Data Table in Appendix B.

surprisingly, the notion of globalization is not popular among rural Filipinos.

Opposition to globalization is not confined to the periphery: in the United States and western Europe, WTO meetings have often been plagued by protests and demonstrations by those who believe that the global economy is "rigged" to benefit the few while most lose out. The global financial crisis that began in 2008 created a more specific, concrete target of such criticism: in 2011, the so-called "Occupy Wall Street" demonstrators in New York City triggered a global protest movement against corporate greed and corruption of the financial sector. Their slogan, "We are the 99%" (see photo), underscored their claim that the great majority of people in the world do not benefit from the workings of the global economy.

The Future

As with all significant transformations, the overall consequences of globalization are uncertain. Critics maintain that one of its most insidious outcomes is a steadily widening gap between rich and poor, a polarization of wealth that is likely to destabilize the world. Proponents argue that, as with the Industrial Revolution, it will take time for the benefits to spread—but that globalization's ultimate effects will be advantageous to all. Indeed, the world is functionally shrinking, and we will find evidence for that throughout this book. But the "global village" still retains its distinctive neighborhoods, and globalization has not erased their particular properties—in some cases even sharpening the contrasts. In the chapters that follow, we use the vehicle of geography to identify and investigate them.

REALMS AND REGIONS: THE STRUCTURE OF THIS BOOK

At the beginning of this chapter, we introduced a map of the great geographic realms of the world (Fig. G-3). We then addressed the task of dividing these realms into regions, and we used criteria ranging from physical geography to economic geography. The result is Figure G-14. On this map, note that we display not only the world geographic realms but also the regions into which they subdivide. The numbers in the legend reveal the order in which the realms and regions are discussed, starting with Europe (1) and ending with the Pacific Realm (12).

Before we launch our survey, here is a brief summary of the 12 geographic realms and their regional components:

Europe (1)

Territorially small, politically still fragmented but economically united, Europe has had a very turbulent history and has been disproportionately influential in global affairs.

The regionalization of this realm is today best approached within a core/periphery framework. Generally speaking, Europe's core lies in its west, with a wide periphery curving across the realm's southern, eastern, and far northern domains.

Russia (2)

Territorially enormous and politically unified, Russia was the dominant force in the former Soviet Union that disintegrated in 1991. Undergoing a difficult transition from dictatorship to democracy and from communism to capitalism, Russia is geographically complex and continues to change. We define five regions: the Russian Core in the west, the Southeastern Frontier, Siberia, the Far East, and Transcaucasia.

North America (3)

Another realm in the global core, North America consists of the United States and Canada. We identify nine regions: the North American Core, the Maritime Northeast, French Canada, the South, the Southwest, the Pacific Hinge, the Western Frontier, the Continental Interior, and the Northern Frontier. Five of these regions extend across the U.S.-Canada border.

Middle America (4)

Nowhere in the world is the contrast between the global core and periphery as sharply demarcated as it is between North and Middle America. This small, fragmented realm divides into four regions: Mexico, Central America, and the Caribbean Basin's Greater and Lesser Antilles.

South America (5)

The continent of South America also defines a geographic realm in which Iberian (Spanish and Portuguese) influences dominate the cultural geography but indigenous imprints survive. We recognize four regions: the Caribbean North, composed of Caribbean-facing states; the Andean West, with its strong aboriginal influences; the Southern Cone; and Brazil, the realm's giant.

Subsaharan Africa (6)

Between the African Transition Zone in the north and South Africa's southernmost Cape lies Subsaharan Africa. The realm consists of five regions: Southern Africa, East Africa, Equatorial Africa, West Africa, and the African Transition Zone itself.

North Africa/Southwest Asia (7)

This vast geographic realm has several names, extending as it does from North Africa into Southwest and, indeed, Central Asia. It is a very complex and volatile realm, and much of

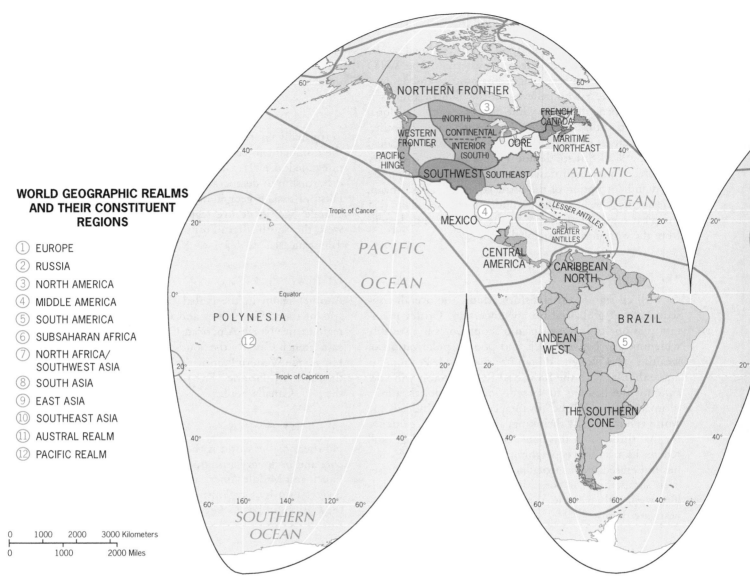

WORLD GEOGRAPHIC REALMS AND THEIR CONSTITUENT REGIONS

① EUROPE
② RUSSIA
③ NORTH AMERICA
④ MIDDLE AMERICA
⑤ SOUTH AMERICA
⑥ SUBSAHARAN AFRICA
⑦ NORTH AFRICA/ SOUTHWEST ASIA
⑧ SOUTH ASIA
⑨ EAST ASIA
⑩ SOUTHEAST ASIA
⑪ AUSTRAL REALM
⑫ PACIFIC REALM

FIGURE G-13

© H. J. de Blij, P. O. Muller, and John Wiley & Sons, Inc.

this is related to its particular regional geographies. There are six regions: Egypt and the Lower Nile Basin, the Maghreb in North Africa, the Middle East, the Arabian Peninsula, and toward the east, the Empire States and Turkestan.

South Asia (8)

Physically, South Asia is one of the most clearly defined geographic realms, but has a complex cultural geography. It consists of five regions: India at the center, Pakistan to the west, Bangladesh to the east, the Mountainous North, and the Southern Islands that include Sri Lanka and the Maldives.

East Asia (9)

The vast East Asian geographic realm extends from the deserts of Central Asia to the tropical coasts of the South

China Sea and from Japan to the Himalayan border with India. We identify seven regions: China's Coastal Core, Interior, and Western Periphery; Mongolia; the Korean Peninsula; Japan; and Taiwan.

Southeast Asia (10)

Southeast Asia is a varied and intriguing mosaic of natural landscapes, cultures, and economies. Influenced by India, China, Europe, and the United States, it includes dozens of religions and hundreds of languages plus economies reflecting both the global core and periphery. Physically, Southeast Asia consists of a broad peninsular mainland and an offshore arc consisting of thousands of islands. The two regions (Mainland and Insular) are based on this distinction.

Austral Realm (11)

Australia and its neighbor New Zealand form the Austral geographic realm by virtue of continental dimensions, insular separation, and predominantly Western cultural heritage. The regions of this realm are defined by physical as well as cultural geography: in Australia, a highly urbanized, two-part core and a vast, desert-dominated interior; and in New Zealand, two main islands that exhibit considerable geographic contrast.

Pacific Realm (12)

The enormous Pacific Ocean, larger than all the landmasses combined, contains tens of thousands of islands large and small. Dominant cultural criteria warrant three regions: Melanesia, Micronesia, and Polynesia.

As this introductory chapter demonstrates, our world regional survey is no mere description of places and areas. We have combined the study of realms and regions with a look at geography's ideas and concepts—the notions, generalizations, and basic theories that make the discipline what it is. We continue this method in the chapters ahead so that we will become better acquainted with the world and with geography. By now you are aware that geography is a wideranging, multifaceted discipline. It is often described as a social science, but that is only half the story: in fact, geography straddles the divide between the social and the physical (natural) sciences. Many of the ideas and concepts you will encounter have to do with the multiple interactions between human societies and natural environments.

Regional geography allows us to view the world in an all-encompassing way. As we have seen, regional geography borrows information from many sources to create

THE RELATIONSHIP BETWEEN REGIONAL AND SYSTEMATIC GEOGRAPHY

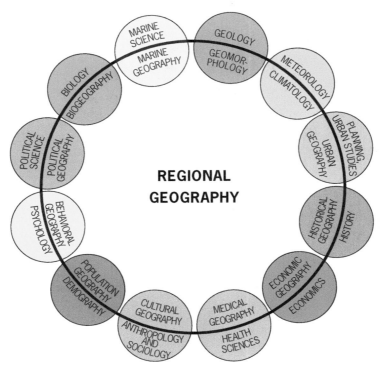

FIGURE G-14   © H. J. de Blij, P. O. Muller, and John Wiley & Sons, Inc.

an overall image of our divided world. Those sources are not random. They represent topical or ***systematic geography***. Research in the systematic fields of geography makes our world-scale generalizations possible. As Figure G-14 shows, these systematic fields relate closely to those of other disciplines. Cultural geography, for example, is allied with anthropology; it is the spatial perspective that distinguishes cultural geography. Economic geography focuses on the spatial dimensions of economic activity; political geography concentrates on the spatial imprints of political

What Do Geographers Do?

A SYSTEMATIC SPATIAL perspective and an interest in regional study are the unifying themes and enthusiasms of geography. Geography's practitioners include physical geographers, whose principal interests are the study of geomorphology (land surfaces), research on climate and weather, vegetation and soils, and the management of water and other natural resources. There also are geographers whose research and teaching concentrate on the ecological interrelationships between the physical and human worlds. They study the impact of humankind on our globe's natural environments and the influences of the environment (including such artificial contents as air and water pollution) on human individuals and societies.

Other geographers are regional specialists, who often focus their work for governments, planning agencies, and multinational corporations on a particular region of the world. Still other geographers—who now constitute the largest group of practitioners—are devoted to topical or systematic subfields such as urban geography, economic geography, and cultural geography (see Fig. G-14). They perform numerous tasks associated with the identification and resolution (through policy-making and planning) of spatial problems in their specialized areas. And, increasingly, there are geographers who combine their fascination for spatial questions with cutting-edge technical expertise.

Geographic information systems (GIS), digital mapping, remote sensing, geospatial data analysis, and geovisualization are among the myriad specializations listed by the 10,000-plus professional geographers of North America. On the book's website, you will find much information on the discipline, how one trains to become a geographer, and the many exciting (and rapidly expanding) career options that are open to the young professional.

behavior. Other systematic fields include historical, medical, behavioral, environmental, and urban geography. We will also draw on information from biogeography, marine geography, population geography, geomorphology, and climatology (as we did earlier in this chapter).

These systematic fields of geography are so named because their approach is global, not regional. Take the geographic study of cities, urban geography. Urbanization is a worldwide process, and urban geographers can identify certain human activities that all cities in the world exhibit in one form or another. But cities also display regional properties. The typical Japanese city is quite distinct from, say, the African city. Regional geography, therefore, borrows from the systematic field of urban geography, but it injects this regional perspective.

In the following chapters we call upon these systematic fields to give us a better understanding of the world's realms and regions. As a result, you will gain insights into the discipline of geography as well as the regions we investigate. As you will see, geography is vital to interpreting, comprehending, and coping with our rapidly transforming world (see box titled "What Do Geographers Do?" and the book's website for a detailed discussion of career opportunities).

POINTS TO PONDER

- Within the next few years or so China is expected to surpass the United States as the biggest national economy in the world.
- The global human population recently surpassed 7 billion and is predicted to reach 9.6 billion by 2050. Will there be enough food and water to go around?
- In this second decade of the twenty-first century, almost 1 billion people must survive on less than one U.S. dollar a day.
- Global warming is expected to cause a significant rise in sea level by the end of the twenty-first century, though estimates vary widely.
- The number of smartphones in use, worldwide, passed the 1 billion mark in 2012; the majority of these devices have map navigation applications.
- Globalization may cause the world to "shrink," but marked differences remain among geographic realms and regions.

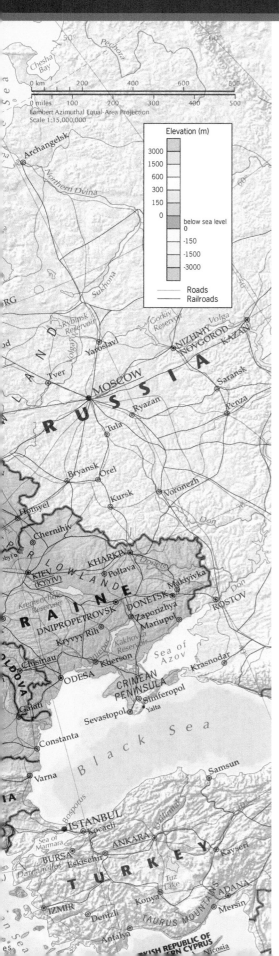

IN THIS CHAPTER

- A history of dominance in the modern world
- Has the EU reached its limits?
- The perennial question of Europe's eastern boundary
- Is Islam embedding itself in western Europe?
- Aging Europe
- The geography of the Euro crisis

CONCEPTS, IDEAS, AND TERMS

FIGURE 1A-1 © H. J. de Blij, P. O. Muller, and John Wiley & Sons, Inc.

Over the past five centuries, Europe and Europeans have influenced and changed the rest of the world more than any other realm or people has done. For good or bad, much of the world would look very different today if it had not been for Europe. The realm's empires spanned the globe and transformed societies far and near. European colonialism propelled an early wave of globalization. Millions of Europeans migrated from their homelands to the Old World as well as the New, changing (and sometimes nearly obliterating) traditional communities and creating new societies from Australia to North America. Colonial power and economic incentive combined to impel the movement of millions of imperial subjects from their ancestral homes to distant lands: Africans to the Americas, Indians to Africa, Chinese to Southeast Asia, Malays to South Africa's Cape, Native Americans from east to west. In agriculture, industry, politics, and other spheres, Europe generated revolutions—and then exported those revolutions across the world, thereby consolidating the European advantage.

But throughout much of that 500-year period of European hegemony, Europe also was a cauldron of conflict. Religious, territorial, and political disputes precipitated bitter wars that even spilled over into the colonies. And during the twentieth century, Europe twice plunged the world into war. The terrible, unprecedented toll of World War I (1914–1918) was not enough to stave off World War II (1939–1945), which again drew in the United States and ended with the first-ever use of nuclear weapons in Japan. In the aftermath of that war, Europe's weakened powers lost most of their colonial possessions and a new rivalry emerged: an ideological Cold War between the communist Soviet Union and the capitalist United States. This Cold War lowered an Iron Curtain across the heart of Europe, leaving most of the east under Soviet control and most of the west in the American camp. Western Europe proved resilient, overcoming the destruction of war and the loss of colonial power to regain economic strength. Meanwhile, the Soviet communist experiment failed at home and abroad, and in 1990 the last vestiges of the Iron Curtain were lifted. Since then, a massive effort has been underway to reintegrate and reunify Europe from the Atlantic coast to the Russian border, the key geographic story of this chapter.

DEFINING THE REALM

GEOGRAPHICAL FEATURES

As Figure 1A-1 shows, Europe is a realm of peninsulas and islands on the western margin of the world's largest landmass, Eurasia. It is a realm containing 600 million people and 40 countries, but it is territorially quite small. Yet despite its modest proportions it has had—and continues to have—a major impact on world affairs. For many centuries Europe has been a hearth of achievement, innovation, invention, and domination.

Europe's Eastern Boundary

The European realm is bounded on the west, north, and south by Atlantic, Arctic, and Mediterranean waters, respectively. But where is Europe's eastern limit? Each episode in the historical geography of eastern Europe has left its particular legacy in the cultural landscape.

Twenty centuries ago, the Roman Empire ruled much of it (Romania is a cartographic reminder of

A view of Place de la Concorde, on the right (north) bank of the River Seine in Paris. This square was the main execution site of aristocrats and royalty during the French Revolution. Note the central 3300-year-old obelisk, which once stood at the entrance of Egypt's Luxor Temple, that was 'gifted' to France in 1829.

© Jan Nijman

major geographic qualities of
EUROPE

1. The European geographic realm lies on the western flank of the Eurasian landmass.

2. Though territorially small, Europe is heavily populated and fragmented into 40 states.

3. European natural environments are highly varied, and Europe's resource base is rich and diverse.

4. Europe's geographic diversity, cultural as well as physical, created strong local identities, specializations, and opportunities for trade and commerce.

5. The European Union (EU) is a historic and unique effort to achieve multinational economic integration and, to a lesser degree, political coordination.

6. Europe's relatively prosperous population is highly urbanized and rapidly aging.

7. Local demands for greater autonomy as well as cultural challenges posed by immigration are straining the European social fabric.

8. Despite Europe's momentous unification efforts, east-west contrasts still mark the realm's regional geography.

9. The ongoing "euro crisis" poses a threat to the EU and suggests that the single currency was introduced too soon for some members. It is possible that certain countries will either choose or be forced to exit the Union.

that period); for most of the second half of the twentieth century, the Soviet Empire controlled nearly all of it. In the intervening two millennia, Christian Orthodox church doctrines spread from the southeast, and Roman Catholicism advanced from the northwest. Turkish (Ottoman) Muslims invaded and created an empire that reached the environs of Vienna. By the time the Austro-Hungarian Empire ousted the Turks, millions of eastern Europeans had been converted to Islam. Albania and Kosovo today remain predominantly Muslim countries. Meanwhile, it is often said that western Europe's civilization had its cradle in ancient Greece, but that lies farther still to the southeast, beyond the former Yugoslavia.

Eastern Europe's tumultuous history, itself an expression of the absence of clear natural boundaries, played out on a physical stage of immense diversity, its landscapes ranging from open plains and wide river basins to strategic mountains and crucial corridors. Epic battles fought centuries ago remain fresh in the minds of many people living here today; pivotal past migrations are celebrated as though they happened yesterday. Nowhere in Europe is the cultural geography as complex as in the southeastern part of the realm. Illyrians, Slavs, Turks, Magyars, and other peoples converged here from near and far. Ethnic and cultural differences kept them in chronic conflict.

As we shall see, the geographic extent of Europe has always been debatable, and today it is a particularly contentious issue in terms of European Union expansion and with respect to relations with Russia. Europe's eastern boundary is a dynamic one, and it has changed with history. Some would say that there really is no clear boundary, that Europe's atmosphere, so to speak, just gets thinner toward the east. For now, our definition places Europe's eastern boundary between Russia and its numerous European neighbors to the west. This definition is based on several geographic factors including European-Russian contrasts in territorial dimensions, geopolitical developments, cultural properties, and history.

Climate and Resources

From the balmy shores of the Mediterranean Sea to the icy peaks of the Alps, and from the moist woodlands and moors of the Atlantic fringe to the semiarid prairies north of the Black Sea, Europe presents an almost infinite range of natural environments (Fig. 1A-2).

Europe's peoples have benefited from a large and varied store of raw materials. Whenever the opportunity or need arose, the realm proved to contain what was required. Early on, these requirements included cultivable soils, rich fishing waters, and wild animals that could be domesticated; in addition, extensive forests provided wood for houses and boats. Later, coal and mineral ores propelled industrialization. More recently, Europe proved to contain substantial deposits of oil and natural gas.

Landforms and Opportunities

In the Introduction chapter, we noted the importance of physical geography in the definition of geographic realms. The natural landscape with its array of landforms (such as mountains and plateaus) is a key element in the total physical geography—or **physiography** [1]—of any part of the terrestrial world. Other physiographic components include climate and the physical features that mark the natural landscape, such as vegetation, soils, and water bodies. Europe's area may be small, but its physical landscapes are varied and complex. Regionally, we identify four broad units: the Central Uplands, the southern

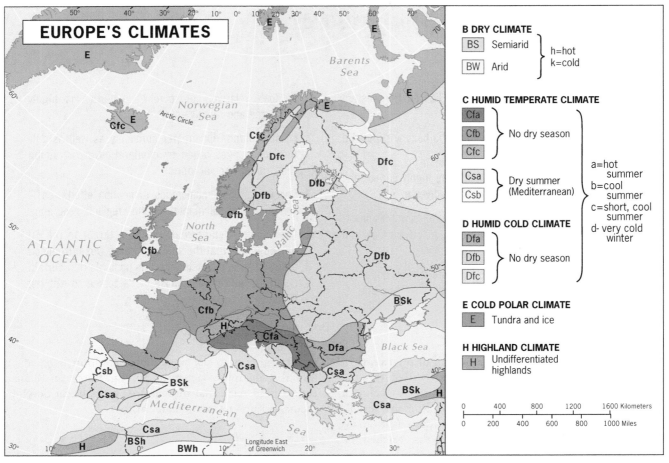

EUROPE'S CLIMATES

B DRY CLIMATE

| BS | Semiarid | } h=hot |
| BW | Arid | k=cold |

C HUMID TEMPERATE CLIMATE

Cfa	
Cfb	} No dry season
Cfc	

| Csa | } Dry summer |
| Csb | (Mediterranean) |

a=hot summer
b=cool summer
c=short, cool summer
d- very cold winter

D HUMID COLD CLIMATE

Dfa	
Dfb	} No dry season
Dfc	

E COLD POLAR CLIMATE

| E | Tundra and ice |

H HIGHLAND CLIMATE

| H | Undifferentiated highlands |

0   400   800   1200   1600 Kilometers
0   200   400   600   800   1000 Miles

FIGURE 1A-2

© H. J. de Blij, P. O. Muller, and John Wiley & Sons, Inc.

From the Field Notes . . .

© Jan Nijman

"Driving across the Swiss Alps, I entered the mini-state of Liechtenstein and drove up to the town of Triesenberg to get a panoramic view of an upper stretch of the Rhine River, flowing from left to right. This is western Europe's leading river and one of its defining geographic features—as a means of transportation, sometimes as a barrier, and frequently as a natural boundary. Here it forms the mini-state's border with Switzerland, located on the far side. Although the river serves primarily as a political boundary, the physical and cultural landscapes on both sides of the Rhine have much in common."

www.conceptcaching.com

Concept Caching

Alpine Mountains, the Western Uplands, and the North European Lowland (Fig. 1A-3).

The **_Central Uplands_** form the heart of Europe. It is a region of hills and low plateaus loaded with raw materials whose farm villages grew into towns and cities when the Industrial Revolution transformed this realm.

The **_Alpine Mountains_**, a highland region named after the Alps, extend eastward from the Pyrenees on the French-Spanish border to the Balkan Mountains near the

Black Sea, and include Italy's Appennines and the Carpathians of eastern Europe.

The **_Western Uplands_**, geologically older, lower, and more stable than the Alpine Mountains, extend from Scandinavia through western Britain and Ireland to the heart of the Iberian Peninsula in Spain.

The **_North European Lowland_** stretches in a lengthy arc from southeastern Britain and central France across Germany and Denmark into Poland and Ukraine, from where it

FIGURE 1A-3 © H. J. de Blij, P. O. Muller, and John Wiley & Sons, Inc.

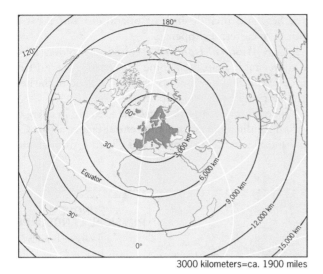

3000 kilometers=ca. 1900 miles

FIGURE 1A-4

© H. J. de Blij, P. O. Muller, and John Wiley & Sons, Inc.

continues well into Russia. Also known as the Great European Plain, this has been an avenue for human migration time after time, so that complicated cultural and economic mosaics developed here and together produced a jigsaw-like political map. As Figure 1A-3 shows, many of Europe's major rivers and connecting waterways serve this populous region, where a number of Europe's leading cities (London, Paris, Amsterdam, Copenhagen, Berlin, Warsaw) are located.

Locational Advantages

Europe also is endowed with some exceptional locational advantages. Its *relative location*, at the crossroads of the land hemisphere [2], creates maximum efficiency for contact with much of the rest of the world (Fig. 1A-4). A "peninsula of peninsulas," Europe is nowhere far from the ocean and its avenues of seaborne trade and conquest. Hundreds of kilometers of navigable rivers, augmented by an unmatched system of canals, open the interior of Europe to its neighboring seas and to the shipping lanes of the world. The Mediterranean and Baltic seas, in particular, were critical in the development of trade in early modern times, and in the emergence of Europe's early trading cities such as Venice (Italy) in the south and Lübeck (Germany) in the north.

And note the scale of the maps of Europe in this chapter. Europe is a realm of moderate distances and close proximities. Short distances and large cultural differences make for intense interaction, the constant circulation of goods and ideas. That has been the hallmark of Europe's geography for more than a millennium.

ANCIENT EUROPE

Modern Europe was peopled in the wake of the Pleistocene's most recent glacial retreat and global warming—a gradual warming that caused tundra to give way to deciduous forest and ice-filled valleys to turn into grassy vales. On Mediterranean shores, Europe witnessed the rise of its first great civilizations, on the islands and peninsulas of Greece and later in what is today Italy.

Ancient Greece and Imperial Rome

Ancient Greece lay exposed to influences radiating from the advanced civilizations of Mesopotamia and the Nile Valley, and in their fragmented habitat the Greeks laid the foundations of European civilization. Their achievements in political science, philosophy, the arts, and other spheres have endured for 25 centuries. One of the essential legacies of ancient Greece involved the formation of city-states [3] such as Athens and Sparta: relatively small territories comprised of cities and their hinterlands that were ruled by elected governments. This is where Western democracy had its origins. But the ancient Greeks never managed to unify their domain, and their persistent conflicts proved fatal when the Romans challenged them from the west. By 147 BC, the last of the sovereign Greek intercity leagues (alliances) had fallen to the Roman conquerors.

The center of civilization and power now shifted to Rome in present-day Italy. Borrowing from Greek culture, the Romans created an empire that stretched from Britain to the Persian Gulf and from the Black Sea to Egypt; they made the Mediterranean Sea a Roman lake carrying armies to distant shores and goods to imperial Rome. With an urban population that probably exceeded 1 million, Rome was the first metropolitan-scale urban center in Europe.

The Romans founded numerous other cities throughout their empire and linked them to the capital through a vast system of overland and water routes, facilitating political control and enabling economic growth in their provinces. It was an unparalleled *infrastructure*, much of which long outlasted the empire itself.

Triumph and Collapse

Roman rule brought disparate, isolated peoples into the imperial political and economic sphere. By guiding (and often forcing) these groups to produce particular goods or materials, the Romans launched Europe down a road for which it would become famous: local functional specialization [4]. The workers on Elba, a Mediterranean island, mined iron ore. Those near Cartagena in Spain produced silver and lead. Certain farmers were taught irrigation to produce specialty crops. Others raised livestock for meat or wool. The *production of particular goods by particular people in particular places* became and remained a hallmark of the realm.

The Romans also spread their language across the empire, setting the stage for the emergence of the **Romance languages**; they disseminated Christianity; and they established durable systems of education, administration, and commerce. But when their empire collapsed in the fifth century AD, disorder ensued and massive migrations soon brought Germanic and Slavic peoples to their present positions on the European stage. Capitalizing on Europe's weakness, the Arab-Berber Moors from North Africa, energized by Islam, conquered most of Iberia and penetrated France. Later the Ottoman Turks invaded eastern Europe and reached the outskirts of Vienna.

EARLY MODERN EUROPE

Europe's revival—its **Renaissance**—did not begin until the fifteenth century. After a thousand years of feudal turmoil marking the "Dark" and "Middle" Ages, powerful monarchies began to lay the foundations of modern states. The discovery of continents and riches across the oceans opened a new era of **mercantilism**, the competitive accumulation of wealth chiefly in the form of gold and silver. Best placed for this competition were the kingdoms of western Europe. Europe was on its way to colonial expansion and world domination.

Even as Europe's rising powers reached for world domination overseas, they fought with each other in Europe itself. Powerful monarchies and landowning ("landed") aristocracies had their status and privilege challenged by ever-wealthier merchants and businesspeople. Demands for political recognition grew; cities mushroomed with the development of industries; the markets for farm products burgeoned; and Europe's population, more or less stable at about 100 million since the sixteenth century, began to increase.

Early modern Europe also was the scene of a growing agricultural sector. As major ports and capital cities boomed, their expanding markets created widening economic opportunities for farmers. This led to revolutionary changes in land ownership and agricultural technology. Improved farming methods, better equipment, superior storage facilities, and more efficient transport to urban markets marked an agrarian revolution in the countryside. Moreover, the colonial merchants brought back new crops (the American potato soon became a European staple), causing market prices to rise and drawing ever more farmers into the economy.

The City-States of Early Modern Europe

From the fourteenth to the seventeenth centuries, growing agricultural production combined with expanding interregional trade to foster the emergence of a considerable number of city-states. These were cities dominated by merchant classes with powerful economic interests. The most important concentrations of city-states were on or near the Mediterranean and Baltic seas, locations that facilitated long-distance commerce. Well-known examples were Venice (for a time the richest place on Earth), Genoa, and Florence in present-day Italy; Lübeck and Hamburg in what is now northern Germany; and Bruges in today's Belgium. These

Visions of Our Land/The Image Bank/Getty Images, Inc.

The Rialto Bridge, one of Venice's famous landmarks, dates from the time that Venice was one of Europe's most powerful and richest city-states. The first bridge over the Grand Canal at this point dates back to the twelfth century; the present span was completed in 1591.

city-states thrived in a Europe in which the modern nation-state had not yet appeared and whose political geography was fragmented at the finest of scales. But in economic terms the realm was being integrated at what were then unprecedented levels; along the shores of the Baltic Sea, the Mediterranean, and the North Sea; in the valleys of the Rhine and other major rivers; and overland.

MODERN HISTORICAL GEOGRAPHY

The Industrial Revolution

The term Industrial Revolution [5] suggests that an agrarian Europe was suddenly swept up in wholesale industrialization that changed the realm in a few decades. In reality, seventeenth- and eighteenth-century Europe had been industrializing in many spheres, long before the chain of events known as the Industrial Revolution began. From the textiles of England and Flanders to the iron farm implements of Saxony (in present-day Germany), from Scandinavian furniture to French linens, Europe had already entered a new era of *local functional specialization*. Nonetheless, by the end of the eighteenth century, industrial Europe took off as never before.

British Primacy

Britain was at the epicenter of this revolution. In the 1780s, the Scotsman James Watt and others devised a steam-driven engine, which was soon adapted to numerous industrial applications. At about the same time, coal (converted into carbon-rich coke) was recognized as a vastly superior substitute for charcoal in smelting iron—and, soon thereafter, far more durable steel. These momentous innovations had a rapid effect. The power loom revolutionized the weaving industry. Iron smelters, long dependent on Europe's dwindling forests for fuel, could now be concentrated near coalfields. Engines could move locomotives as well as power looms. Ocean shipping entered a new age.

Britain had an enormous advantage, for the Industrial Revolution occurred when British influence reigned worldwide and the significant innovations were achieved in Britain itself. The British controlled the flow of raw materials, they held a monopoly over products that were in global demand, and they alone possessed the skills necessary to make the machines that manufactured the products. Soon the fruits of the Industrial Revolution were being exported, and the modern industrial spatial organization of Europe began to take shape. In Britain, manufacturing regions developed near coalfields in the English Midlands, at Newcastle to the northeast, in southern Wales, and along Scotland's Clyde River around Glasgow.

Diffusion Onto the Continent

The Industrial Revolution diffused (spread) eastward from Britain onto the European mainland throughout the middle and late nineteenth century (Fig. 1A-5). Population

skyrocketed, emigration mushroomed, and industrializing cities burst at the seams. European states already had acquired colonial empires before this revolution started; now colonialism gave Europe an unprecedented advantage in its dominance over the rest of the world.

In mainland Europe, a belt of major coalfields extends from west to east, roughly along the southern margins of the North European Lowland, due eastward from southern England across northern France and Belgium, Germany (the Ruhr), western Bohemia in the Czech Republic, Silesia in southern Poland, and the Donets Basin (Donbas) in eastern Ukraine. Iron ore is found in a broadly similar belt and together with coal provides the key raw material for the manufacturing of steel.

As in Britain, this cornerstone industry now spawned new concentrations of economic activity, growing steadily as millions migrated from the countryside to fill expanding employment opportunities. Densely populated and heavily urbanized, these emerging agglomerations became the backbone of Europe's world-scale population cluster (as shown in Fig. G-8).

Two centuries later, this east-west axis along the coalfield belt remains a major feature of Europe's population

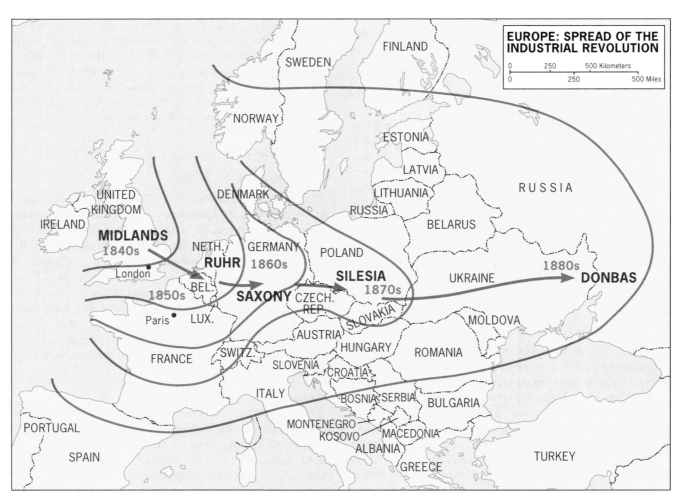

FIGURE 1A-5

© H. J. de Blij, P. O. Muller, and John Wiley & Sons, Inc.

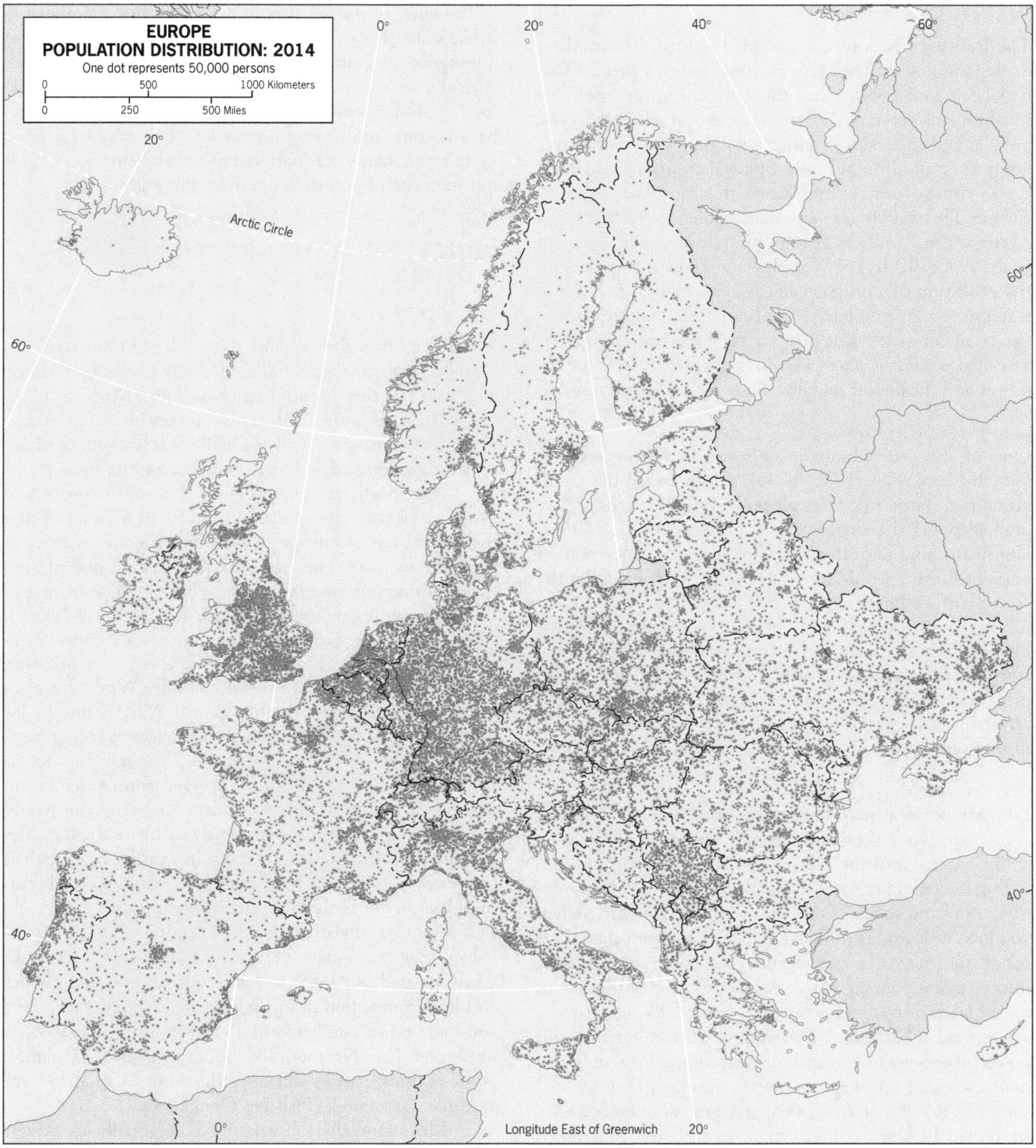

FIGURE 1A-6

© H. J. de Blij, P. O. Muller, and John Wiley & Sons, Inc.

distribution map (Fig. 1A-6). It should also be noted that while industrialization spawned new cities, another set of manufacturing zones arose in and near many existing urban centers. London—already Europe's leading urban focus and Britain's richest domestic market—was typical of these developments. Many local industries were established here, taking advantage of the large supply of labor, the ready availability of capital, and the proximity of so great a number of potential buyers. Although the Industrial Revolution thrust other places into prominence, London did not lose its primacy: industries in and around the British capital multiplied.

Political Revolutions

The Industrial Revolution unfolded against the backdrop of the ongoing formation of national states, a process that had been under way since the 1600s. Europe's political revolutions took many different forms and affected diverse peoples and countries, but in general they involved the ongoing centralization of power by royal courts and the integration of the former city-states within larger national territories. This was often a particularly violent reconfiguration of the realm's political geography. Historians often point to the Peace (Treaty) of Westphalia in 1648 as a key step in the evolution of Europe's state system, ending decades of war and recognizing territories, boundaries, and the sovereignty of countries. But this was only the beginning. The so-called *absolutist states*, in which monarchs held all the power and the people had few if any rights, would not last.

Competing Ideologies

One of the most dramatic episodes to follow was the French Revolution (1789–1795), which ended the era of absolutist states ruled by all-powerful monarchs. More gradual political transformations occurred in the Netherlands, Britain, and the Scandinavian countries. Other parts of Europe would for much longer remain under the control of authoritarian (dictatorial) regimes headed by monarchs or despots. By the late nineteenth century, Europe became the arena for the competing ideologies of *liberalism*, *socialism*, and *nationalism* (national spirit, pride, patriotism). The rise of extreme nationalism (*fascism*) in the twentieth century threw the realm into the most violent wars the world had ever seen.

A Fractured Map

Europe's political map has always been one of intriguing complexity. As a geographic realm, Europe occupies only about 5 percent of the Earth's land area; but that tiny area is fragmented into some 40 countries—more than one-fifth of all the states in the world today. Therefore, when you look at Europe's political map, the question that arises is how did so small a geographic realm come to be divided into so many political entities? Europe's map is a legacy of its feudal and royal periods, when powerful kings, barons, dukes, and other rulers, rich enough to fund armies and powerful enough to extract taxes and tribute from their domains, created bounded territories in which they reigned supreme. Royal marriages, alliances, and conquests actually simplified Europe's political map. In the early nineteenth century, there still were 39 German States; a unified Germany as we know it today would not emerge until the 1870s.

State and Nation

Europe's political revolution produced a form of political-territorial organization known as the nation-state [6], a territorial state embodied by its culturally distinctive population. The term nation [7] refers to a people with a single language, a common history, a similar ethnic background.

In the sense of *nationality*, it relates to legal membership in the state, that is, citizenship. Very few states today are so homogeneous culturally that the culture is conterminous with the state. Europe's prominent nation-states of a century ago—France, Spain, the United Kingdom, Italy—have become multicultural societies, their nations defined more by an intangible "national spirit" and emotional commitment than by cultural or ethnic homogeneity.

CONTEMPORARY EUROPE: A DYNAMIC REALM

Cultural Diversity

The European realm is home to peoples of numerous cultural-linguistic stocks, including not only Latins, Germanics, and Slavs but also minorities such as Finns, Magyars (Hungarians), Basques, and Celts. This diversity of ancestries continues to be an asset as well as a liability. It has generated not only interaction and exchange, but also conflict and war.

It is worth remembering that Europe's territory is just over 60 percent the size of the United States, but that the population of Europe's 40 countries is almost twice as large as America's. This population of around 600 million speaks numerous languages, almost all of which belong to the Indo-European language family [8] (Figs. 1A-7, G-9). But most of those languages are not mutually understandable; some, such as Finnish and Hungarian, are not even members of the Indo-European family. When Europe's unification efforts began after World War II, one major problem was to determine which languages to recognize as "official." That problem still prevails, although English has become the realm's unofficial *lingua franca* (common language). During a visit to Europe, though, you would find that English is more commonly usable in the big cities than in the countryside, and more in western Europe than farther east. Europe's multilingualism remains a rich cultural legacy, but is also a barrier to integration.

Another divisive force confronting Europeans involves religion. Europe's cultural heritage is steeped in Christian traditions, but sectarian strife between Catholics and Protestants, that plunged parts of the realm into bitter and widespread conflict, still divides communities and, as until recently in Northern Ireland, can still arouse violence. Some political parties still carry the name "Christian," for example, Germany's Christian Democrats.

More generally, Christianity has gradually lost adherents since secularization gathered momentum in the late 1960s, especially in western Europe. The Roman Catholic Church, long very powerful in much of Europe, has been losing its grip on society, and many church institutions—schools, universities, unions, political parties, charities, clubs—have been hollowed out. Moreover, many churches have closed down or have been converted into art galleries, public meeting halls, and even corporate offices.

Today, a new factor roils the religious landscape: the rise of Islam. In southeastern Europe, this takes the form

LANGUAGES OF EUROPE

0 200 400 600 Kilometers
0 100 200 300 Miles

ICELANDIC

Arctic Circle

FAEROESE

ATLANTIC OCEAN

SCOTS GAELIC

ENGLISH

North Sea

IRISH GAELIC

ENGLISH

ENGLISH

ENGLISH

BRETON 14

FRENCH

WALLOON

DUTCH

FRYSIAN

GERMAN

DANISH

NORWEGIAN

SWEDISH

SAAMI

SAAMI (LAPP)

SAAMI

SAAMI (LAPP)

FINNISH

KARELIAN

SAMOYEDIC

KOMI

RUSSIAN

Baltic Sea

ESTONIAN 25

LATVIAN 25

LITHUANIAN 25

BELARUSSIAN 25

POLISH

CZECH 40

SLOVAK 40

UKRAINIAN 26

26

25

25

HUNGARIAN 40

ROMANIAN 45

45

25

SLOVENE 29

SERBO-CROATIAN 40

BULGARIAN 40

Black Sea

MACEDONIAN 40

ALBANIAN

GREEK

TURKISH

GALICIAN 11

BASQUE 11

PROVENÇAL

PORTUGUESE

CATALAN 11

SPANISH 40

CATALAN

CORSICAN-ITALIAN

SARDINIAN-ITALIAN

ITALIAN 40

Adriatic Sea

Mediterranean Sea

Longitude West of Greenwich Longitude East of Greenwich

MAJOR INDO-EUROPEAN BRANCHES

GERMANIC GROUP

WESTERN GERMANIC
1 Dutch
2 German
3 Frysian
4 English

NORTHERN GERMANIC
5 Danish
6 Swedish
7 Norwegian
8 Icelandic
9 Faeroese

ROMANCE GROUP

10 Portuguese
11 Spanish
12 Catalan
13 Provençal
14 French
15 Italian
16 Rhaeto-Romansch
17 Romanian
18 Corsican-Italian
19 Sardinian-Italian
20 Walloon

SLAVIC GROUP

WEST SLAVONIC
21 Polish
22 Slovak
23 Czech
24 Lusatian

EAST SLAVONIC
25 Russian
26 Ukrainian
27 Belarussian

SOUTH SLAVONIC
28 Slovene
29 Serbo-Croatian
30 Macedonian
31 Bulgarian

OTHER INDO-EUROPEAN BRANCHES

CELTIC GROUP

BRITANNIC
32 Breton
33 Welsh

GAELISH
34 Irish Gaelic
35 Scots Gaelic

BALTIC GROUP

36 Latvian 37 Lithuanian

HELLENIC

38 Greek

THRACIAN/ILLYRIAN GROUP

39 Albanian

INDO-IRANIAN GROUP

40 Romani (dispersed)

URALIC LANGUAGE FAMILY

FINNO-UGRIC GROUP

41 Finnish
42 Karelian
43 Saami
44 Estonian
45 Hungarian
46 Komi

SAMOYEDIC GROUP

47 Samoyedic

ALTAIC LANGUAGE FAMILY

TURKIC GROUP

48 Turkish

OTHER LANGUAGES

BASQUE

49 Basque

Areas with significant concentrations of other languages (usually adjacent national languages)

Boundary between languages

After Murphy, 1998.

FIGURE 1A-7

© H. J. de Blij, P. O. Muller, and John Wiley & Sons, Inc.

of new Islamic assertiveness in an old Muslim bastion: the (Turkish) Ottoman Empire left behind millions of converts from Bosnia to Bulgaria among whom many are demanding greater political representation and power. In the west, this Islamic resurgence results from the relatively recent infusion of millions of Muslim immigrants from former colonies in North Africa and other parts of the far-flung Islamic world. Here, as mosques overflow with the faithful, churches stand nearly empty as a witness to secularism among Europeans.

For so small a realm, Europe's cultural geography is sharply varied. The popular image of Europe tends to be formed by British pageantry, the French wine country, or historic cities such as Venice or Amsterdam—but go beyond this core area, and you will find isolated Slavic communities in the mountains facing the Adriatic Sea, Muslim towns in poverty-mired Albania, Roma (Gypsy) villages in the interior of Romania, farmers using traditional methods unchanged for centuries in rural Poland. That map of 40 countries does not begin to reflect the diversity of European cultures.

Spatial Interaction

If not a single culture, then what does unify Europe? The answer lies in the realm's outstanding opportunities for productive interaction. The European realm is best understood as an enormous **_functional region_**, an interdependent realm that is held together through highly developed, spatial economic and political networks. Modern Europe has seized on the realm's abundant geographic opportunities to create a huge, intensively used network of spatial interaction linking places, communities, and countries in countless ways. This interaction operates on the basis of two key principles.

First, regional complementarity [9] means that one area produces a surplus of a commodity required by another area. The mere existence of a particular resource or product is no guarantee of trade: it must be needed elsewhere. When two areas each require the other's products, we speak of _double complementarity_. Europe exhibits countless examples of this complementarity, from local communities to entire countries. Industrial Italy needs coal from western Europe; western Europe needs Italy's farm products.

Second, the ease with which a commodity can be transported by producer to consumer defines its transferability [10]. Distance and physical obstacles can raise the cost of a product to the point of unprofitability. But Europe is small, distances are short, and the Europeans have built the world's most efficient transport system of roads, railroads, and canals linking navigable rivers. Taken together, Europe's enormously diverse economic regions and its particularly efficient transportation infrastructure make for a highly interdependent economic realm.

From the Field Notes . . .

"If you were to be asked what city is shown here, would Paris spring to mind? Most images of the French capital show venerable landmarks such as the Eiffel Tower or Notre Dame Cathedral. I took this photo from the top of the famous Arc de Triomphe, looking toward another Paris, the northwestern business district just beyond the city line named _La Défense_. There, Paris escapes the height restrictions and architectural limitations of the historic center and displays an ultramodern face. Glass-box skyscrapers reflect the vibrant global metropolis this is, and there the landmark is the "Cube," a huge open structure admired as well as reviled (as was the Eiffel Tower in its time). _La Défense_ is ingeniously incorporated into Paris's urban design, with a straight-line, broad avenue connecting it to the Arc de Triomphe and then connecting, via the _Champs Élysées_ to the Place de la Concorde (see the first photo in this chapter). In terms of a grand geographic layout, Paris is hard to beat."

© Jan Nijman

www.conceptcaching.com

A Highly Urbanized Realm

About three of every four Europeans live in towns and cities, an average that is far exceeded in the west (see the Data Table in Appendix B) but not yet attained in much of the east. Large cities are production centers as well as marketplaces, and they also form the crucibles of their nations' cultures. Europe's major cities tend to have long histories and are compact, and in general the European cityscape looks quite different from its North American counterpart.

Seemingly haphazard inner-city street systems impede traffic; central cities may be picturesque, but they are also cramped. European city centers tend to be more vibrant today than those in the United States. They offer a mix of businesses, government functions, shopping facilities, educational and art institutions, and entertainment as well as housing for upper-income residents.

Wide residential sectors radiate outward from the central business district (CBD) across the rest of the central city, often inhabited by particular income groups. Beyond the central city lies a sizeable suburban ring, but even here residential densities are much higher than those in the United States because the European tradition is one of setting aside recreational spaces (in "greenbelts") and living in apartments rather than in detached single-family houses. There also is a greater reliance on public transportation, which further concentrates the suburban development pattern. That has allowed many nonresidential activities to suburbanize as well, and today ultramodern outlying business centers increasingly compete with the CBD in many parts of urban Europe (see photo).

A CHANGING POPULATION

Negative Natural Population Growth

There was a time when Europe's population was (in the terminology of population geographers) exploding, sending millions to the New World and the colonies and still growing at home. But today Europe's native population, unlike most of the rest of the world's, is actually shrinking. To keep a given population from declining, the (statistically) average woman must bear 2.1 children. For Europe as a whole that figure was 1.6 in 2012. Several countries recorded numbers at or below 1.3, including Poland, Portugal, Hungary, and Latvia. Such negative population growth poses serious challenges for any nation. When the population pyramid becomes top-heavy, the number of workers whose taxes pay for the social services of the aged goes down, leading to reduced pensions and dwindling funds for health care.

The Growing Multicultural Challenge

Meanwhile, immigration is partially offsetting Europe's population deficit. But it could be a mixed blessing, wherein demographic stability comes at the risk of social disruption. Millions of Turks, Turkish Kurds, Algerians, Moroccans, West Africans, Pakistanis, and West Indians are changing the social fabric of what once were homogeneous nation-states, especially France, Germany, the United Kingdom, Belgium, and the Netherlands. As noted earlier, one key dimension of this change is the spread of Islam in Europe. Muslim populations in eastern Europe (such as Albania's, Kosovo's, and Bosnia's) are indigenous communities converted during the period of Ottoman rule. The Muslim sectors of western European countries, on the other hand, represent more recent immigrations.

The majority of these immigrants are generally more religious than the Christian natives. They arrived in a Europe where native populations are stagnant or declining, where religious institutions are weakened, and where certain cultural norms are incompatible with Islamic traditions. Integration and assimilation of Muslim communities into

A 2009 referendum in Switzerland on new minaret construction produced some ugly symbolism (note the rocket-like depiction of minarets on the Swiss flag). The Swiss electorate approved a law that prohibits the construction of minarets (read: mosques). A majority of the Swiss seemed to feel that their culture was under threat from Islam and that this type of mosque architecture gave expression to an overly assertive minority—even though there were only *four* minarets in the entire country! No doubt, Switzerland's nearly 500,000 Muslims (just over 6 percent of the population, mainly Turks, and not known to be particularly zealous) must have felt uneasy about the vote.

© AP/Wide World Photos

the national fabric has been slow, their education and income levels considerably lower than average. In western European countries particularly, Islamic immigrants are highly concentrated in metropolitan areas. Thus in cities like Hamburg, London, and Brussels, the proportion of Muslim populations is considerably higher than the national average.

The social and political implications of Europe's cultural transformation are numerous and far-reaching. Long known for tolerance and openness, European societies are now trying to restrict immigration in various ways, and political parties with anti-immigrant platforms are gaining ground in several countries.

EUROPEAN UNIFICATION

Realms, regions, and countries can all be subject to dividing and unifying forces that cause them to become more or less cohesive and stable political units. Where the region or country is home to diverse populations with different political agendas, it may prove difficult to avoid divergence and territorial fragmentation. Political geographers use the term centrifugal forces [11] to identify and measure the strength of such division, which may result from religious, racial, linguistic, political, economic, or other regional factors.

Centrifugal forces are measured against centripetal forces [12], the binding, unifying glue of the state or region. General satisfaction with the system of government and administration, legal institutions, and other functions of the state (notably including its treatment of minorities) can ensure stability at the state level. However, in the case of the former Yugoslavia, the centrifugal forces unleashed after the end of the Cold War exceeded the weak centripetal forces in that relatively young state, and it disintegrated with dreadful consequences.

Since World War II ended in 1945, Europe has witnessed a steady process of integration and unification at a much broader geographic scale. A growing majority of European states and their leaders recognize that closer association and regional coordination form the key to a more stable, prosperous, and secure future. A realmwide union has been in the making now for nearly three-quarters of a century. Despite relentless challenges and occasional setbacks, centripetal forces have thus far prevailed.

Background

At the end of World War II, much of Europe lay shattered, its cities and towns devastated, its infrastructure wrecked, its economies ravaged. If this was one of the world's most developed realms at the beginning of the twentieth century, its economic prowess had been almost completely destroyed by 1945. One of the primary motives for integration and collaboration among western European countries, therefore, was rapid economic recovery.

The United States played a leading role, initially, in spurring on such cooperation. In 1947, U.S. Secretary of State George C. Marshall proposed a European Recovery Program designed to help counter all this dislocation and to create stable political conditions in which democracy would survive. Over the next four years, the United States provided about $13 billion in assistance to Europe (more than $125 billion in today's money). The United States was driven by economic and political motives. It had become the largest producer in the world of manufactured goods and was eager to restore European markets. Politically, the ending of World War II witnessed accelerating tensions with the Soviet Union, which had taken control over the bulk of eastern Europe. In addition, communist parties seemed poised to dominate the political life of major western European countries. The United States was intent, through the Marshall Plan, to have a firm hand in western Europe and keep communist influences at bay. The Marshall Plan applied solely to 16 European countries, including defeated (West) Germany and Turkey.

Northwestern European countries themselves were also driven by political considerations. The two world wars had clearly shown the dangers of excessive nationalism and had laid bare the devastating problems that can arise from a lack of political cooperation and collaborative efforts (if the Allies had acted as one sooner, Hitler might have been stopped before things escalated into war in 1939). From the perspective of countries like France, the Netherlands, and Belgium, one of the key issues was to control Germany in the postwar years, and this could only be done through close political cooperation. Thus European integration was from the start both an economic and a political affair, and concerns about Germany played a major part.

As the economies recovered and Germany became firmly embedded in a pan-European structure, the motives for European unification received a different emphasis. Increasingly, the process has been driven by the need to facilitate an ever larger and more efficient open market that can compete globally with the United States, China, and Japan. Politically, the goals today are more and more about stabilizing a much larger and diverse Europe that now approaches the Russian frontier. It is not just about Germany anymore but rather about a much bigger and more complicated geopolitical zone that has to accommodate a large number of (still) sovereign states and at the same time maintain good relations with the Russian giant next door.

The Unification Process

The Marshall Plan did far more than stimulate European economies. It confirmed European leaders' conclusion that their countries needed a joint economic-administrative structure. Such a structure was needed not only to coordinate the financial assistance, but also to ease the flow of resources and products across Europe's mosaic of boundaries, to lower restrictive trade tariffs, and to seek ways to improve political cooperation.

SUPRANATIONALISM IN EUROPE

1944   Benelux Agreement signed.

1947   Marshall Plan created (effective 1948–1952).

1948   Organization for European Economic Cooperation (OEEC) established.

1949   Council of Europe created.

1951   European Coal and Steel Community (ECSC) Agreement signed (effective 1952).

1957   Treaty of Rome signed, establishing European Economic Community (EEC) (effective 1958), also known as the Common Market and "The Six." European Atomic Energy Community (EURATOM) Treaty signed (effective 1958).

1959   European Free Trade Association (EFTA) Treaty signed (effective 1960).

1961   United Kingdom, Ireland, Denmark, and Norway apply for EEC membership.

1963   France vetoes United Kingdom EEC membership; Ireland, Denmark, and Norway withdraw applications.

1965   EEC–ECSC–EURATOM Merger Treaty signed (effective 1967).

1967   European Community (EC) inaugurated.

1968   All customs duties removed for intra-EC trade; common external tariff established.

1973   United Kingdom, Denmark, and Ireland admitted as members of EC, creating "The Nine." Norway rejects membership in the EC by referendum.

1979   First general elections for a European Parliament held; new 410-member legislature convenes in Strasbourg. European Monetary System established.

1981   Greece admitted as member of EC, creating "The Ten."

1985   Greenland, acting independently of Denmark, withdraws from EC.

1986   Spain and Portugal admitted as members of EC, creating "The Twelve." Single European Act ratified, targeting a functioning European Union in the 1990s.

1987   Turkey and Morocco make first application to join EC. Morocco is rejected; Turkey is told that discussions will continue.

1990   Charter of Paris signed by 34 members of the Conference on Security and Cooperation in Europe (CSCE). Former East Germany, as part of newly reunified Germany, incorporated into EC.

1991   Maastricht meeting charts European Union (EU) course for the 1990s.

1993   Single European Market goes into effect. Modified European Union Treaty ratified, transforming EC into EU.

1995   Austria, Finland, and Sweden admitted into EU, creating "The Fifteen."

1999   European Monetary Union (EMU) goes into effect.

2002   The euro is introduced as historic national currencies disappear in 12 countries.

2003   First draft of a European Constitution is published to mixed reviews from member-states.

2004   Historic expansion of EU from 15 to 25 countries with the admission of Cyprus, the Czech Republic, Estonia, Hungary, Latvia, Lithuania, Malta, Poland, Slovakia, and Slovenia.

2005   Proposed EU Constitution is rejected by voters in France and the Netherlands.

2007   Romania and Bulgaria are admitted, bringing total EU membership to 27 countries. Slovenia adopts the euro.

2008   Cyprus and Malta adopt the euro.

2009   Slovakia adopts the euro.

2010   Financial crisis strikes heavily indebted Greece, requiring massive EU bailout. Later in the year, Ireland follows and raises fears of similar crises in Portugal, Spain, and Italy. The future of the EMU is clouded; the value of the euro declines after a long rise against the dollar.

2011   Estonia adopts the euro.

2012   Fiscal Compact agreement (effective 2013) signed by 20 member-states (and ratified by 16) stipulates their tight adherence to rules of fiscal responsibility. The agreement sparked intense debate in various countries and some had not ratified the agreement by mid-2013.

2013   Croatia admitted as the 28th EU member-state. Politicians in several member-states, including the United Kingdom and the Netherlands, demand a national referendum on leaving the EU.

2014   Latvia adopts the euro, increasing eurozone membership to 18 countries.

For all these needs, Europe's governments had some guidelines. While in exile in Britain, the leaders of three small countries—Belgium, the Netherlands, and Luxembourg—had been discussing an association of this kind even before the end of the war. There, in 1944, they formulated and signed the Benelux Agreement, intended to achieve total economic integration. When the Marshall Plan was launched, the Benelux precedent helped speed the creation of the Organization for European Economic Cooperation (OEEC), which was established to coordinate the investment of America's aid (see the box entitled "Supranationalism in Europe").

Soon the economic steps led to greater political cooperation as well. In 1949, the participating governments created the Council of Europe, the beginnings of what was to become a European Parliament meeting in Strasbourg, France. Europe was embarked on still another political revolution, the formation of a multinational union involving a growing number of European states. This is a classic example of supranationalism [13], which geographers define as a voluntary association in economic, political, or cultural spheres of three or more independent states willing to yield some measure of sovereignty for their mutual benefit.

Under the Treaty of Rome, six countries joined to become the European Economic Community (EEC) in 1958, also called the "Common Market." In 1973 the United Kingdom, Ireland, and Denmark joined, and the renamed European Community (EC) now encompassed nine members. As Figure 1A-8 shows, membership reached 15 countries in 1995, after the organization had been renamed yet one more time to become the ***European Union (EU)***. Since

then the number of member-states has climbed to 28, with Croatia the latest to join in mid-2013.

The EU's administrative, economic, and even political framework has become so advanced that the organization now has a headquarters with many of the trappings of a capital city. Early on, EU planners chose Brussels (already the national capital of Belgium, a member of Benelux) as the organization's center of governance. But in order to avoid giving Brussels too much prominence, they chose Strasbourg (located near the German border in the northeastern corner of France) as the seat of the European Parliament, whose elected membership represents all EU countries.

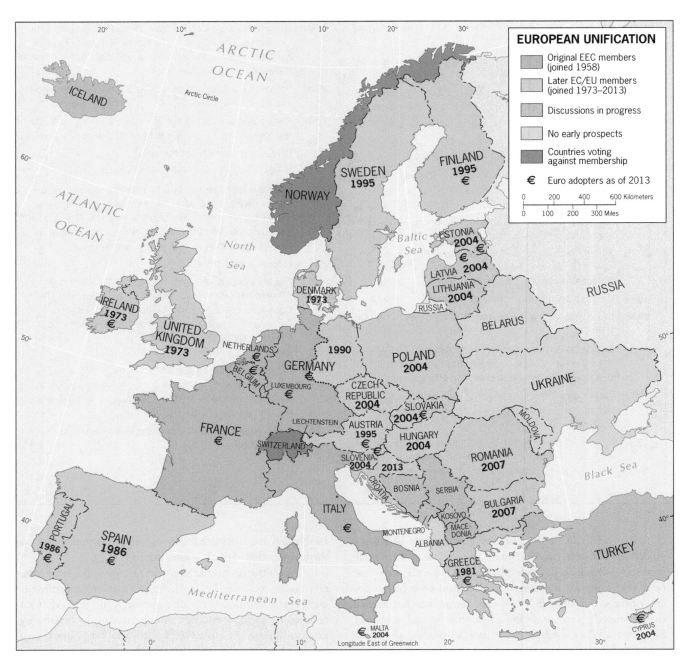

FIGURE 1A-8

© H. J. de Blij, P. O. Muller, and John Wiley & Sons, Inc.

CONSEQUENCES OF UNIFICATION

The European Union is not just a paper organization. It has a major impact on national economies, on the role of individual states, and on the daily lives of its member-countries' citizens.

One Market

EU directives are aimed at the creation of a single market for producers and consumers, businesses and workers. Corporations should be able to produce and sell anywhere within the Union without legal impediments, whereas workers should be able to move anywhere in the EU and find employment without legal restrictions. In order to make this happen and to keep things manageable, member-states have had to harmonize a wide range of national laws from taxation to the protection of the environment to educational standards. One major step came with the introduction of a single central bank (with considerable power over, for instance, interest rates) and a single currency, the *euro*. The single currency was also meant to symbolize Europe's strengthening unity and to establish a counterweight to the once almighty American dollar. In 2002, twelve of the (then) 15 EU member-countries withdrew their currencies and began using the euro, with only the United Kingdom, Denmark, and Sweden staying out (Fig. 1A-8). More recently, Slovakia in 2009, Estonia in 2011, and Latvia became the eighteenth adopter—and member of the eurozone—in 2014. The single currency, hailed as a major triumph at its inception, has in reality become a major bone of contention as it implied a significant reduction in the members' freedom to formulate fiscal policies (more so than was initially realized). We will return to the evolving 'euro crisis' shortly.

A New Economic Geography

The establishment and continuing growth of the European Union have generated a new economic landscape that today not only transcends the old but is fundamentally reshaping the realm's regional geography. By investing heavily in new infrastructure and by smoothing the flows of money, labor, and products, European planners have dramatically reduced the divisive effects of their national boundaries. And by acknowledging demands for greater freedom of action by their provinces, States, departments, and other administrative units of their countries, European leaders unleashed a wave of economic energy that transformed some of these subnational units into powerful engines of growth (Fig. 1A-9). Four of these growth centers are especially noteworthy, to the point that geographers refer to them as the Four Motors of Europe [14]: (1) France's southeastern *Rhône-Alpes Region*, centered on the country's second-largest city, Lyon; (2) *Lombardy* in north-central Italy, focused on the industrial metropolis of Milan; (3) *Catalonia* in northeastern Spain, anchored by the cultural and manufacturing center of Barcelona;

and (4) *Baden-Württemberg* in southwestern Germany, headquartered by the high-tech city of Stuttgart.

Another change in regional economic geography involves agricultural activities and is closely related to deliberate policies designed in Brussels. Taxes tend to be high in Europe, and those collected in the richer member-states are used to subsidize growth and development in the less prosperous ones. This is one of the burdens of membership that is not universally popular in the EU, to say the least. But it has strengthened the economies of Portugal, Spain, and other national and regional economies to the betterment of the entire organization. Some countries also object to the terms and rules of the Common Agricultural Policy (CAP), which, according to some critics, supports farmers far too much and, according to others, far too little. (France in particular obstructs efforts to move the CAP closer to consensus, subsidizing its agricultural industry relentlessly while arguing that this protects its rural cultural heritage as well as its farmers.)

Despite economic integration and the harmonization of policies, Figure 1A-9 also shows that major differences persist among Europe's regions as well as within EU member-states. This is an important reminder that, as noted in the introductory chapter, uneven development is an unyielding phenomenon that plays out at various geographic scales.

Diminished State Power and New Regionalism

As states relinquish some of their power to Brussels and express agreement with the ideal of realmwide integration, some of the provinces and regions *within* states have seized the opportunity to assert their cultural identity and particular economic interests. Often, the local governments in these subregions simply bypass the governments in their national capitals, dealing not only with each other but even with foreign governments as their expanding business networks span the globe. In this they are imitated by other provinces, all seeking to foster their local economies and, in the process, strengthen their political position relative to the state.

Provinces, States, and other subnational political units on opposite sides of international boundaries can now also cooperate in pursuit of shared economic goals. Such cross-border cooperation creates a new economic map that seems to ignore the older political one, creating economically powerful regions that are more or less independent of surrounding national states. Note how European unification seems to simultaneously erode the power of states from above and from below: in order to retain membership, states are more or less compelled to concede major decision-making power to Brussels while at the same time the growing demands of subnational (and cross-national) regional authorities, from Catalonia to Lombardy, eat away at their territorial control at home.

Thus even as Europe's states have been working to join forces in the EU, many of those same states are confronting

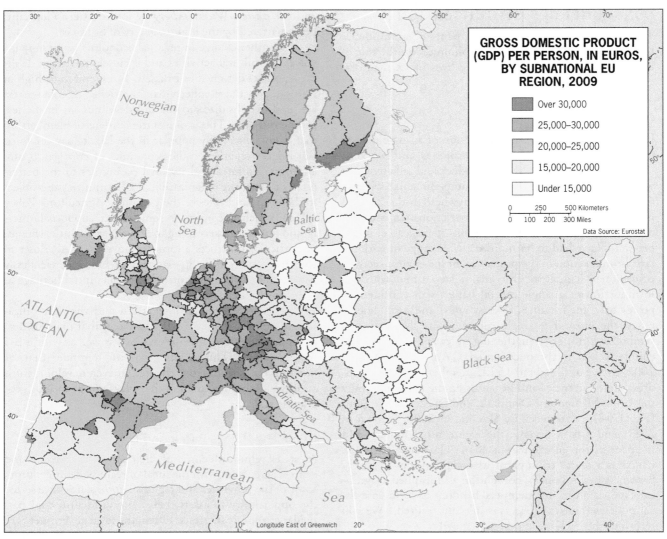

FIGURE 1A-9

© H. J. de Blij, P. O. Muller, J. Nijman, and John Wiley & Sons, Inc.

severe centrifugal stresses. The term devolution [15] has come into use to describe the powerful centrifugal forces whereby regions or peoples within a state, through negotiation or active rebellion, demand and gain political strength and sometimes autonomy at the expense of the center. Most states exhibit some level of internal regionalism, but the process of devolution is set into motion when a key centripetal binding force—the nationally accepted idea of what a country stands for—erodes to the point that a regional drive for autonomy, or for outright secession, is launched. As Figure 1A-10 shows, numerous European countries are affected by devolution.

States respond to devolutionary pressures in various ways, ranging from accommodation to suppression. One way to deal with these centrifugal forces is to give historic regions (such as Scotland or Catalonia) certain rights and privileges formerly held exclusively by the national government. Another answer is for EU member-states to create new administrative divisions that will allow the state to

meet regional demands, often in consultation with, or under pressure of, the *European Commission* (the name of the EU's central administration based in Brussels). We elaborate further in Chapter 1B, highlighting subnational autonomy movements faced by the governments of the United Kingdom, Spain, and Italy.

DEFINING EUROPE: DIFFICULT CHOICES

Widening or Deepening?

Expansion has always been an EU objective, and the subject never fails to arouse passionate debate. Will the incorporation of weaker economies undermine the strength of the whole? Should the ties and cooperation between existing members be deepened and solidified before other, less prepared countries are invited to join? Remember that member-states must adhere to strict economic policies and harmonize their political systems. This is much easier

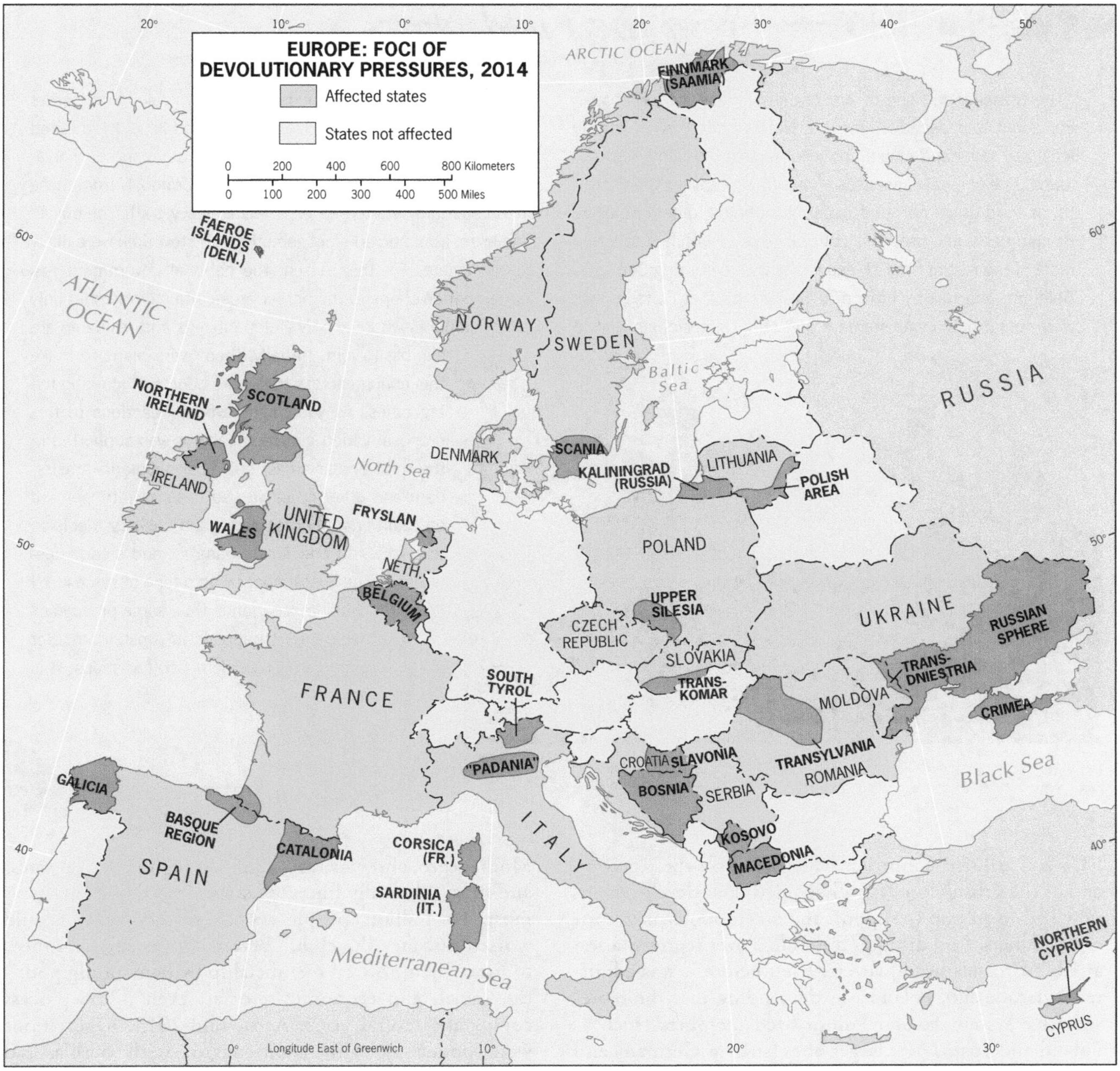

EUROPE: FOCI OF DEVOLUTIONARY PRESSURES, 2014

FIGURE 1A-10

© H. J. de Blij, P. O. Muller, and John Wiley & Sons, Inc.

for prosperous countries with longstanding democratic traditions than for poorer nations with a volatile political past.

Despite such misgivings, negotiations to expand the EU have long been in progress, and the gains of the past decade are mapped in Figure 1A-8. In 2004, a momentous milestone was reached: ten new members were added, creating a greater European Union with 25 member-states. Geographically, these ten fell into three groups: three Baltic states (Estonia, Latvia, and Lithuania); five contiguous states in eastern Europe, extending from Poland and the Czech Republic through Slovakia, Hungary, and Slovenia; and two

Mediterranean island-states, the mini-state of Malta and the still-divided state of Cyprus. In 2007, both Romania and Bulgaria were incorporated, raising the number of members to 27 and extending the Union to the shores of the Black Sea. The newest and 28th member-state, Croatia, joined in 2013, the second component of former Yugoslavia (Slovenia was first) to be admitted to the EU.

Numerous structural implications arise from this expansion, affecting all EU countries. A common agricultural policy became even more difficult to achieve, given the poor condition of farming in most of the member-countries added since 2003. Also, some of the pre-2004

From the Field Notes . . .

"The Grasshopper, one of Amsterdam's many 'coffee shops.' For about four decades now, the Netherlands has effectively legalized sales and consumption of modest amounts of marijuana. The general consensus is that marijuana is not as harmful as hard drugs and that legalization helps to decriminalize its commerce and use. This policy is at odds with legislation in most of the rest of the EU, especially with bordering Germany, Belgium, and nearby France. It used to be that coffee shops were found only in Amsterdam and other major cities, but in recent years they have opened in small towns along the border to attract a foreign clientele (another byproduct of heightened cross-border interaction). As a result, once quiet and conservative rural villages (where lifestyles differ enormously from those in Amsterdam) started to experience heavy traffic of buyers and users from abroad—not something the townfolk were likely to appreciate. For this reason, the national government has turned coffee shops in the border areas into membership-only establishments whereby only Dutch citizens and residents are eligible to join. Initially, there were plans to make this change across the entire country, including the big cities. As you might expect, reactions to this proposal varied geographically: it was supported in the rural border areas, but most people in Amsterdam and other cities viewed it as an infringement on traditional liberties and a bad business decision to boot. Said one Amsterdammer and steady customer of The Grasshopper with a tone of sarcasm: 'I never thought I'd experience this: some provincials trying to decide what happens in Amsterdam. Not in my lifetime!' In Amsterdam's coffee shops, it is business as usual."

© Jan Nijman

www.conceptcaching.com

EU's less affluent countries, which were on the receiving end of the subsidy program that aided their development, now had to pay up to support the much poorer new eastern members. And disputes intensified over representation at EU's Brussels headquarters. Even before it was admitted a decade ago, Poland was demanding that the representative system favor medium-sized members (such as Poland and Spain) over larger ones (such as Germany and France).

The Remaining Outsiders

This momentous expansion has generated major geographic consequences for all of Europe, and not just the EU. As Figure 1A-8 shows, following the admission of Croatia in 2013, a number of countries and territories still remain outside the Union, and their prospect of joining seems a mixed bag. The first group includes the 5 remaining states that have emerged out of former Yugoslavia, plus Albania. In this cluster of western Balkan states, a majority are troubled politically and economically. Only Slovenia and Croatia have achieved full membership; the rest—Serbia, Bosnia and Herzegovina, Macedonia, Montenegro, and Kosovo—rank among Europe's poorest and most ethnically fractured states, but they contain almost 16 million people whose circumstances could worsen outside "the club." Better, EU leaders reasoned, to move them toward membership by demanding political, social, and economic reforms, even if the process could take several years. As of mid-2013, negotiations were underway with Montenegro, with Serbia and Macedonia still in the pre-negotiation stage after formally applying for membership. Elsewhere, ethnically and politically divided Bosnia as well as Albania have signed preliminary agreements with the EU, and their applications are expected in due course. Kosovo, however, remains in limbo following its incompletely-recognized declaration of independence from Serbia in 2008. Note, too, that this area of less-prepared countries just happens to be the most Islamic corner of Europe, which could be another impediment to accession.

The second group of outsiders is comprised of Ukraine and its neighbors. Four former Soviet republics in Europe's "far east" could some day join the EU (even Belarus, until recently the most disinterested, may now be reconsidering). The government of Ukraine has shown

Once Again: In Search of Europe's Eastern Boundary

In the past, "Eastern Europe" incorporated all of Europe east of Germany, Austria, and Italy; north of Greece; and south of Finland. The Soviet communist domination of Eastern Europe (1945–1990) behind an ideological and strategic "Iron Curtain" served to reinforce the division between "west" and "east." The collapse of the Soviet Empire in the early 1990s freed the European countries that had been under Soviet rule, and they swiftly turned their gaze from Moscow to the west. Meanwhile, the European Union had been expanding eastward, and membership in the EU became an overriding goal for the majority of the liberated eastern states. Today, with the Soviet occupation a rapidly fading memory and the European Union stretching from Ireland to the Black Sea, the boundary between western and eastern Europe has disappeared, at least in a political sense. Economically, significant contrasts remain between west and east (see the Data Table in Appendix B; compare, for instance, Bulgaria and France); but in this respect, too, things are evening out.

During the Cold War, Europeans, especially in the west, were preoccupied with the Iron Curtain (see the box titled "EU versus NATO"), and much less so with the question of the eastern boundary of Europe as a whole. After all, eastern Europe was drawn so tightly into the Soviet orbit politically, militarily, economically, and even culturally (the main foreign language taught in schools was Russian) that it seemed a moot point. But deep down, most of those eastern components remained quite European in spirit and tradition, and possessed historical ties that could not be easily erased. So now we are once again left to contemplate where, between Moscow and Vienna, Europe's eastern boundary lies or should be placed. More than anything else, it is the eastward expansion of the EU that is testing this question.

© Tomasz Grzyb/Demotix/CORBIS

For weeks in November 2012, protesters took to the streets of Athens to protest the Greek government's austerity measures to comply with EU bailout plans. This is part of the crowd of an estimated 40,000 people that turned out for the rally at Syntagma Square near Greece's Parliament, their banners screaming "NO".

interest, although its electorate is strongly (and regionally) divided between a pro-EU west and a pro-Russian east. Moldova views the EU as a potential supporter in a struggle against devolution along its eastern flank, and in 2006 a country not even on the map—Georgia, across the Black Sea from Ukraine—proclaimed its interest in EU membership for similar reasons: to find an ally against Russian intervention in its internal affairs.

Third and last, we should take special note of another important candidate for EU membership: Turkey. Some EU leaders would like to include a mainly "Muslim country" in what Islamic states sometimes call the "Christian club," but others are convinced that Turkey is just not European enough. Interestingly, the growing economic troubles inside the EU over the past few years contrast sharply against some eye-catching economic advances in Turkey—so it should come as no surprise that the Turks today are losing interest in joining the European Union.

The Fiscal Crisis

The challenges to ongoing European integration are considerable, and they seem to be magnified during times of economic distress. Since 2009, the "euro crisis" has been an almost standard news item throughout the realm and is often reported in global news media as well. It was initially triggered by the financial crisis that erupted in the United States in 2008 and quickly reverberated around the globe, hitting Europe particularly hard. Economic growth rates plunged; unemployment rose; government deficits in certain cases skyrocketed; and politics in many countries became increasingly polarized.

But then the crisis took on its own form in Europe because it laid bare the limitations that accompanied the shift to a common currency and a common monetary policy. The evolving problems are not just about the euro

EU Versus NATO

FIGURE 1A-11

© H. J. de Blij, P. O. Muller, J. Nijman, and John Wiley & Sons, Inc.

THE EMPHASIS PLACED nowadays on developments in the EU tends to overshadow another very important pan-European construct, the ***North Atlantic Treaty Organization (NATO)***. This alliance partially overlaps with the EU and includes many European countries (Fig. 1A-11). But NATO is an altogether different creature. First, it is primarily concerned with politics and security and not with economics: NATO's purpose is to provide military security to its members. Second, NATO is led by the United States, which provides the bulk of the alliance's military muscle, and also includes Canada. Third, NATO includes non-EU member Turkey, a critically important country because it is strategically located on Europe's southeastern edge and close to the Middle East (one can almost hear the Turks think "if we are good enough for NATO, why aren't we welcome in the EU?").

NATO was created in 1949 to provide a security umbrella for western Europe under U.S. leadership (in response, the Soviets and their satellites forged the Warsaw Pact). When the Cold War ended in 1991 with the disintegration of the Soviet Union, NATO became a more general security organization that would provide stability across Europe—and now opened its doors to membership for eastern European countries. This eastward expansion is not unlike that of the EU; the latest to join were Croatia and Albania in 2009, making for a current total of 28 member-states (Fig. 1A-11). Today, NATO is more concerned with the possibility of twenty-first-century types of threats to its members: terrorism, attacks by "rogue" states with weapons of mass destruction, and cyberwarfare (a very real and growing security danger with crucial global implications).

This also means that the alliance, while still mainly focused on Europe, is increasingly active on the global scene. For instance, one of the items atop its agenda is the possible nuclear missile threat from Iran. In the past few years, the largest military operation of the alliance (employing U.S. and European troops under a single command) has been far away from Europe, in Afghanistan. NATO intervention and air power also played a vital role in the support of Libyan rebels and subsequent defeat of the Qadhafi dictatorship in 2011.

Of course, both economic issues (EU) and security issues (NATO) are deeply political and are therefore often intertwined. Having separate organizations to deal with these two spheres adds another layer of complexity to the European realm. Economically, the United States and Europe are often perceived as competitors, and the Europeans expressly go their own way. But where security is concerned, the United States still functions as the guarantor of peace in the realm, with most Europeans happy to defer to the Americans who pick up the lion's share of the bill. The United States, in turn, views strategic involvement in Europe as fundamental to its own security interests.

itself but about the inability or unwillingness of individual countries to comply with fiscal standards (e.g., not running government deficits) and their inability to apply solutions on an individual country basis. Keep in mind that EU countries still have their own budgets, their own revenues and expenditures, and that the EU budget is still quite small (about 1 percent of the EU's GDP)—but the budget *rules* are in a number of crucial ways determined by Brussels.

The economic difficulties faced by several European national governments became more intractable because they had (only recently) introduced the single European currency and significantly constrained their policy options. Some of the EU's weaker member-states, such as Greece, accumulated enormous debts that violated terms in the agreements that established the eurozone. Moreover, having a single currency implied that countries could no longer independently pursue such monetary policies as devaluations (a common approach to promoting exports) or the lowering of interest rates (used to stimulate the economy). In other words, countries like Greece and Spain faced growing economic problems, but their hands were tied because of their dependence on the European Central Bank.

Greece accumulated such a massive government deficit that it required a bailout from Brussels in 2010 to avoid bankruptcy and chaos. A year later, it was Ireland's turn: the country that not long ago had been hailed as one of Europe's major success stories had to be rescued from imminent financial collapse. Portugal required a similar bailout in 2011, and Greece received a second one in 2012. By then, fiscal problems had also emerged in Italy (where the prime minister was forced to resign), in France (where austerity measures triggered widespread public protests), and even in the Netherlands (where a coalition government fell when it could not agree on severe budget cuts). Given the integrated financial system that the EU has become, the contagion of failing banks and faltering governments is a now a huge concern—as if Europe constituted a precarious row of dominoes. Not surprisingly, the future of the euro as a stable global currency has been thrown into uncertainty.

By mid-2012, fears of a breakup of the eurozone reached a peak when it seemed likely that Greece was about to exit. That country needed such enormous long-term bailouts that the richer EU member-states no longer appeared willing to provide economic support while the Greek government was unable to convince its constituents to accept the austerity measures that were part of the bailout agreement. The reason a breakup did not occur was that the consequences of a Greek exit would threaten the integrity of the EU as a whole. It would open the door to other countries leaving, an unraveling that could greatly undermine the very idea of a single European union—which is why the European Central Bank declared on July 26, 2012 that it would do "whatever it takes" to preserve the euro. This vow underscores the strong political will in much of Europe to stick together and bear the burden—but whether it endures will heavily depend on the economic direction Europe takes in the years immediately ahead.

Future Prospects of the EU

Europe's quest for enduring unity continues even as the fiscal crisis demonstrates that integration and unification is far more difficult to maintain during economic recessions. To be sure, unification of a realm of this size and complexity will always face recurring structural challenges. Even in good times, the sense of have and have-not, core and periphery, continues to pervade EU operations and negotiations. The European Union consists of a large number of countries of bewildering diversity, and for all to get along infinite patience, gigantic bureaucracies, and a penchant for compromise are essential.

The European Union now reaches deeply into eastern Europe; encompasses 28 members; has a common currency and a parliament; is developing a constitution; has facilitated political stability as well as economic progress for more than half a century; and is even considering expansion beyond the realm's borders. All this constitutes a tremendous achievement in this historically volatile and fractious part of the world. The EU now has a combined population of nearly 510 million that constitutes one of the world's richest markets; its member-states account for more than 40 percent of the world's exports.

Europe's leaders, by averting the 2012 breakup of the eurozone, have reinforced the political will to maintain the Union. Whether European integration stays on course will not only depend on the direction the realm's economy will take but also on the ability of Europe's political leadership to legitimize the cost of integration to their citizens. The problem of the so-called 'democratic deficit' is a serious one: from Germany to Greece, people often do not

Regional ISSUE
Should the Eurozone Be Maintained at All Costs?

A VIEW FROM GERMANY

"As a school teacher, I have followed the issues surrounding the euro crisis pretty closely. In a way it is amazing how my country's role has changed in the past couple of decades in the EU. In the old days, most Europeans used to be worried about us, especially after World War II. Now we are in the driver's seat, whether we like it or not. Germany has the strongest economy in Europe and when other countries are in trouble, from Greece to Portugal, everybody is looking to us for help.

I do think that European integration, overall, is a good thing and for Germany as well, because our economy has developed strong ties all over the continent and in recent years especially to the east. But I want to remind you how we got here: with very hard work and discipline. Our economy was in a shambles after the war and it took great efforts to rebuild it. Then, with reunification in the early 1990s, we had to reintegrate impoverished East Germany back into our society. If we are Europe's biggest economy and one of the most prosperous countries, it is because of hard work and dedication.

Now look at Greece: what a mess they have made of it there. And the same could be said of Portugal as well as Ireland, and it seems the same problems are surfacing in Italy and even France. Why did they let things get so far out of hand? Government finances are a disaster because their leaders just accumulated debt, spending their way into re-election time and again. They just have not been responsible and they have been living beyond their means for a long time. You know what? I am afraid this attitude was made possible because they think they can rely on the EU to bail them out.

If it is a one-time deal, we should make the sacrifice and help other countries by paying their debt for them. But it really worries me that this only makes them more dependent. When the European Central Bank comes up with these rescue plans (with our money!) they demand, rightly so, that these countries tidy up their finances and cut expenditures that they could not afford in the first place. But look at the angry mobs in Athens protesting these measures! What do these people want?

The EU is important and should be kept together, but not at any price. There are limits to our means, and we do have to look out for ourselves. We will not pay indefinitely for other people's lack of responsibility. Our next elections take place in the autumn of 2013 and I am going to listen closely to what our politicians have to say about this."

A VIEW FROM GREECE

"I am a student in Athens and I took part in the demonstrations in November of 2012 against the austerity measures imposed on us by the EU. Our government was required to enact three rounds (!) of budget cuts in order to appease the EU. They barely got enough votes in Parliament, but they passed new legislation that is just going to kill us financially. Can't they see that we are at the end, that there is just nothing more to give by the people who have to make ends meet every day?

I and most other Greeks believe in the idea of Europe and European integration. Of course we do: Greece is the cradle of European civilization. Greek philosophy and the notion of Western democracy come from us and we have shared it with the rest of the continent. We have been members of the EU for more than 30 years, long before other countries were let in, and we joined the eurozone at its outset. But some of the richer countries in the EU just cannot see what the impact is on less affluent member-states. Perhaps it was a mistake for Greece to join the euro and be subordinated to policies made in Germany or France.

As I see it, the fiscal crisis is the result of the rich members forcing the entire Union to abide by rules that the more vulnerable countries just cannot sustain. Like the 'law' that members are not allowed more than a 3 percent deficit on their annual budgets—that is a lot easier for rich countries than it is for we poorer ones. With a tax base like Germany's, it is easy enough. But if you are Greece or Portugal, it's an entirely different proposition. In the end, it is the more vulnerable people in countries like Greece that pay dearly for the lofty ideas coming from Brussels.

Did you know that the Greek economy has for the past five years shrunk by fully one-fifth? How do you expect us cover our necessary expenditures without running up debt? And now with these austerity packages, things will get even worse because everything from student loans to rent subsidies will decrease. And the economy is forced into a downward spiral because nobody can afford to buy anything anymore. Unemployment among Greek youths is now well above 50 percent and I can't see how there will be a job for me when I graduate from college.

When I hear comments from Brussels that we are being irresponsible or irrational, it makes me angry and I feel we should walk away from the EU altogether. Whatever happened to democracy? There are limits to our suffering. And I will not support another Greek government that dances to the tunes being played in Brussels."

Vote your opinion at www.wiley.com/go/deblijpolling

feel they are being heard and national governments need their votes to support the Union (see the *Regional Issue Box* "Should the Eurozone Be Maintained at all Costs?"). In early 2013, the British prime minister announced he was in favor of a referendum on continuing EU membership; but if the United Kingdom were to leave, even though it has always been a reluctant member, that would deal a serious blow to the Union. Debates also continue as to whether membership should be more flexible, wherein countries would not have to commit on all fronts in the same way. But others say that such a "Europe *à la carte*" would lead to endless negotiations and also undercut the entire notion of unity.

And yet, the EU has been very resilient and, thus far, has been able to avert any major reversals no matter how messy the process has been. Overall, it is truly remarkable what has been accomplished in little more than five decades. Some of the EU's leaders want more than an economic union: they envisage a United States of Europe, a political as well as an economic competitor for the United States. To others, such a "federalist" notion is an abomination not even to be mentioned (the British most of all are particularly wary of such an idea). Whatever the outcome, Europe is clearly undergoing still another of its revolutionary transformations, and when you study its evolving map you are looking at history in the making.

⬤ POINTS TO PONDER

- Germany has the strongest economy in Europe and now dominates much of the realm as well as EU policies, including efforts to deal with the fiscal crisis.

- Some western European countries accepted relatively large numbers of religious Muslim immigrants at a time when secularization among Europe's native population reached a peak.

- NATO's main purpose is to provide security to its member-states in Europe plus the United States and Canada; yet its most important military operations in recent years took place far outside the realm in Afghanistan and Libya.

- If Greece or any other fiscally troubled country were to leave the eurozone, a dangerous precedent would be set that could undermine the entire EU project.

- Unemployment rates among youths in Greece and Spain are well over 50 percent. What are the prospects of college graduates there?

TIC OCEAN

North Land
(Severnaya Zemlya)
Kosomolets I.

Bolshevik I.

PENINSULA

Nordvik

NORTH SIBERIAN LOWLAND

CENTRAL

YAKUTSK
BASIN

SIBERIAN

PLATEAU

Tura

Vilyuy

Mirnyy

Lensk

Angara

Ust Ilimsk

Ust Kut

Tayshet

Bratsk

Lake
Baykal

Ust-Ordynskiy

Angarsk   Irkutsk

Chita

Ulan-Ude

Aginskoye

MOUNTAINS

Mt. Munku Sardyk
491 m, 11,453 ft.)

HANGAYN MOUNTAINS

Ulaanbaatar

MONGOLIA

MONGOLIAN
PLATEAU

Laptev
Sea

Gulf of
Yana

New Siberian Islands

Kotelnyy I.

Novaya
Sibir I.

Malyy Lyakhovskiy I.

Bolshoy Lyakhovskiy I.

Begichev I.

Tiksi

East
Siberian
Sea

Wrangel I.

Chukchi
Sea

CHUKCHI
PENINSULA

Bering Strait

UNITED
STATES

St. Lawrence I.

Gulf of
Anadyr

St. Matthew I.

Arctic Circle

Pevek

Ambarchik

Anadyr

CHUKCHI
RANGE

KORYAK RANGE

Mt. Ledyanaya
(2,562 m, 8,406 ft.)

Karaginsky I.

UNITED STATES

Commander
Islands
RUSSIA

VERKHOYANSK RANGE

CHERSKIY RANGE

Lena

Ust Nera

Mt. Mus Khaya
(2,959 m, 9,708 ft.)

KOLYMA RANGE

Kolyma

Omolon

Gizhiga

Palana

KAMCHATKA
PENINSULA

Mt. Klyuchevskaya
(4,750 m, 15,584 ft.)

Petropavlovsk-
Kamchatsky

Namtsy

Yakutsk

Ust Maya

Aldan

SIBERIA

Magadan

Okhotsk

Shelikhov
Gulf

Sea
of
Okhotsk

Bolsheretsk

Cape Lopatka

Paramushir I.

Kurile Islands

Suntar

Lena

DZHUGDZHUR RANGE

Uda Bay

Shantar
Islands

Nogliki

Sakhalin
Island

Urup

STANOVOY RANGE

Mt. Skalistyy
(2,467 m, 8,094 ft.)

Skovorodno

Komsomolsk

Amur

Vanino

Lazarevo

Tatar
Strait

Yuzhno-Sakhalinsk

Korsakov

La Perouse Strait

Etorofu

Kunashiri

Shikotan

Habomai

YABLONOVYY RANGE

Heihe

Blagoveshchensk

Birobidzhan

Mt. Tardoki-Yani
(2,090 m,
6,857 ft.)

Khabarovsk

STIKHOTE-ALIN RANGE

Dalnegorsk

Vladivostok

Nakhodka

Wakkanai

SAPPORO

Hokkaido

Aomori

JAPAN

PACIFIC
OCEAN

GREATER KHINGAN RANGE

HARBIN

Songhua

Lake
Khanka

NORTHEAST
CHINA PLAIN

CHANGCHUN

JILIN

Yilan

SHENYANG

Liao

NORTH
KOREA

PYONGYANG

East Sea
(Sea of Japan)

Mt. Fuji
(3,776 m,
12,388 ft.)

SENDAI

TOKYO

KAWASAKI

YOKOHAMA

NAGOYA

KYOTO

KYOTO

FIGURE 2A-1   © H. J. de Blij, P. O. Muller, and
John Wiley & Sons, Inc.

Every geographic realm has a dominant, distinguishing feature: Europe's jigsaw-puzzle map of 40 countries, South America's familiar triangle, Subsaharan Africa's straddling of the equator, Southeast Asia's thousands of islands and peninsulas. But the Russian geographic realm has what is perhaps the most distinctive hallmark of all—its gigantic territorial size. Almost (but not quite) all of this realm is constituted by the state that dominates it, which is why we call this the Russian realm. By itself, Russia is nearly twice as large as Canada, the world's second-largest country. Russia is three times as big as neighboring Europe. Stretching east-west from the Pacific Ocean to the Baltic Sea, Russia has *nine* time zones. When Russians are getting ready for bed in Moscow, they're having breakfast in Vladivostok.

DEFINING THE REALM

As Figure 2A-1 reveals and a globe shows even better, Russia's entire northern coast, from its border with Norway in the west to the Bering Strait in the east, faces the Arctic Ocean, with all the climatic consequences you would expect. And for all its huge dimensions, most of the Russian realm lies at high latitudes, shut out by mountains and deserts from the warmer and moister parts of Eurasia. That has been a geographic problem for Russian rulers and governments for as long as Russia has existed as a state. Russia's ports on the Pacific Ocean in the east lie about as far from

where most Russians live as they could be. And in the west, where Russia's core area is situated, every maritime outlet is restricted in some way. The Arctic ports operate on seasonal access. The Baltic Sea ports lie far from the open ocean. The Black Sea ports (some leased from Ukraine) require navigation through narrow straits across Turkish territory simply to reach the eastern Mediterranean Sea.

The Russian realm is vast, but its human numbers are modest. As the Data Table in Appendix B reports, this entire realm's population of barely 160 million is now smaller than

major geographic qualities of
RUSSIA

1. Russia is the largest territorial state in the world. Its area is nearly twice as large as that of the next-ranking country (Canada).

2. Russia is the northernmost large and populous country in the world; much of it is cold and/or dry. Extensive rugged mountain zones separate Russia from warmer subtropical air, and the country lies open to Arctic air masses.

3. Russia is by far the "widest" realm on Earth, stretching from west to east for some 10,000 kilometers (over 6000 mi) and spanning nine time zones.

4. Russia was one of the world's major colonial powers. Under the czars, the Russians forged the world's biggest contiguous empire; the Soviet rulers who succeeded the czars expanded that empire.

5. For so large a territory, Russia's shrunken population of just under 143 million is comparatively small. The population remains heavily concentrated in the westernmost one-fifth of the country.

6. Development in Russia is concentrated west of the Ural Mountains; here are the major cities, leading industrial regions, densest transport networks, and most productive farming areas. National integration and economic development east of the Urals extend mainly along a narrow corridor that stretches from the southern Urals region to the southern Far East around Vladivostok.

7. Russia is a multicultural state with a complex domestic political geography and administrative structure.

8. Its huge territorial size notwithstanding, Russia faces land encirclement within Eurasia; it has few good and suitably located ports.

9. Regions long part of the Russian and Soviet empires are still realigning themselves in the post-communist era. Eastern Europe and the heavily Muslim Southwest Asia realm are encroaching on Russia's imperial borders.

10. The failure of the Soviet communist system left Russia in economic disarray. It is often considered to be one the world's major emerging economies, but its growth is fragmentary and precarious. Russia is overly dependent on exports of oil and natural gas.

Courtesy of Dr. Elena Grigorieva, ICARP FEB RAS, Birobidzhan, Russia

The mid-winter landscape beyond Siberia in far eastern Russia. This is the World War II Memorial in the city of Birobidzhan, one of the more than 70,000 such monuments the Soviets erected all across the USSR in the postwar era. No country suffered greater losses (26.6 million) during that "Great Patriotic War" of the early 1940s, a human catastrophe that will forever scar Russian history.

those of such individual countries as Nigeria and Pakistan. Moreover, the realm's population has declined substantially since 1990 before leveling off at the beginning of this decade. For a combination of reasons we will examine later, the 1991 collapse of the Soviet Union created political, economic, and social conditions that continue to produce negative demographic effects today. This issue has come to the forefront in Russia at a time when the country's leaders want to restore Russia's power and prestige in the wider world. To accomplish that restoration, Russia will need to strengthen its social institutions, diversify its economy, and restore the confidence lost when the Soviet system disintegrated. The Russian geographic realm as defined by our framework consists of four political entities: the giant Russian state itself plus three small countries in Transcaucasia, the mountainous area between the Black Sea and the Caspian Sea. Georgia, Armenia, and Azerbaijan are small in size, and their combined population is just under 11 percent of the realm's total. They are located in a historically turbulent zone of conflict between Russian and non-Russian peoples.

Take a look at the Russian realm in Figure G-3, and you will note that many of Russia's neighbors, even those countries that formed part of the former Soviet Union, are now absorbed into other realms. The Baltic states, for example, have become an integral part of Europe as members of the European Union. The Central Asian countries once under Moscow's sway, such as Kazakhstan and Uzbekistan, now form a discrete region in an adjoining realm in which Islam is resurgent. But the three Transcaucasian states are not collectively European (although Georgia has European aspirations), or Islamic (only in Azerbaijan does Islam have a strong foothold), or Russian. What these three states have in common is Russia's still-powerful influence in one form or another. Georgia endures Russian political, economic, and even military intervention; Azerbaijan seeks ways to avoid having to depend on Russian transit for its energy exports; and Armenia continues to view Russia as its most dependable ally. For these reasons, elaborated in the following discussion, we map these states as part of the Russian geographic realm.

Even though our first task is to look in some detail at the giant physical stage on which the Russian geographic realm is built, we should note that the human geography of this realm is not neatly defined by sharp boundaries. Look again at Figure G-3, and you will see that the margins of the Russian realm in two prominent places (and elsewhere not shown at that map's small scale) are marked by **transition zones**. There, geographic features of this realm spill over into neighboring realms, sometimes creating social and political problems for the adjacent countries affected. But first, let us examine the physical landscapes, climate, and ecologies of the Russian realm.

PHYSICAL GEOGRAPHY OF THE RUSSIAN REALM

Physiographic Regions

The first feature you notice when looking at the physiographic map of the Russian realm is a prominent north-south trending mountain range that extends from the Arctic Ocean southward to Kazakhstan (Figs. 2A-1 and 2A-2), dividing Russia into two parts: the Russian Plain to the west and Siberia to the east. This range, the Ural Mountains, is sometimes designated as the "real" eastern boundary of Europe, but as we noted in Chapters 1A and 1B, Russia is not Europe. Cultural life to the east of the Urals is pretty much the same as it is to the west, and there is no geographic justification for putting the city of Samara (see Fig. 2A-1) in Europe but Chelyabinsk, on the other side of the Urals, outside of it. Neither is European; both are Russian.

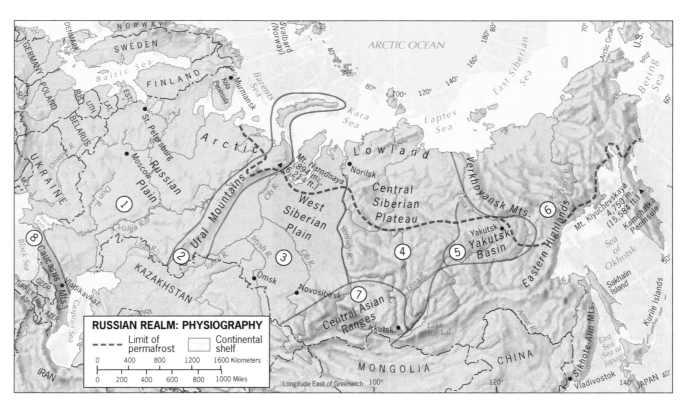

FIGURE 2A-2

© H. J. de Blij, P. O. Muller, and John Wiley & Sons, Inc.

The Russian Plain

The Russian Plain, which lies west of the Ural Mountains, is the eastward continuation of the North European Lowland, and here lies Russia's *core area*. Travel northward from the centrally located capital of Moscow, and the countryside soon changes to coniferous (needleleaf) forests like those of Canada. Centuries ago, those forests afforded protection to the founders of the Russian state when invaders on horseback from eastern Asia swept into this region. The Volga River, Russia's Mississippi, flows southward in a wide arc across the plain from the forested north—but unlike the Mississippi, the Volga drains into a landlocked lake, the Caspian "Sea." Travel southward from Moscow today, and the land is draped in grain fields and pastures. Eastward, the Ural Mountains form a range not tall enough to create a major barrier to transportation, but it is prominent because it separates two vast expanses of low *relief* (elevation range).

In geopolitical texts, the western Russian Plain has also been dubbed the Eurasian heartland [1] because it lies deep within the world's greatest landmass and because it has had a major influence throughout history on the shaping of societies to the west (Europe), southeast (Central Asia), and far east (China, Japan, Korea, and even across the Bering Strait into North America). But this exceptional geographic position not only provides opportunities for expansion; it also implies potential vulnerability and a sense of encirclement. This apparent contradiction has been a feature of the realm for centuries.

Siberia

The West Siberian Plain, on the far side of the Urals, is often described as the world's largest unbroken lowland, and here the rivers flow north, not south. Over the last 1600 kilometers (1000 mi) of its course to the Arctic Ocean, the Ob River falls less than 90 meters (300 ft) in huge meanders flanked by forests until the trees give way in the near-Arctic cold to mosses and lichens. Follow an imaginary trail eastward, and in just about the middle of Russia the West Siberian Plain gives way to the higher relief of the Central Siberian Plateau, one of the most sparsely populated areas in the habitable world. Where the West Siberian Plain meets the Central Siberian Plateau, the Yenisey River, also flowing northward into the Arctic Ocean, marks the change of landscape.

Continuing our eastward transect, we next encounter the Yakutsk Basin, drained by the Lena River and forming the last vestige of moderate *topography* (surface configuration). Now we approach the realm's mountainous eastern perimeter (look again at Fig. 2A-1), where the few roads and railroads must wend their way through tunnels and valleys with hairpin turns. We map this jumble of ranges collectively as the Eastern Highlands, but this is one of the most spectacular, diverse, and still-remote regions on Earth.

Kamchatka and Sakhalin

In its farthest eastern reaches, the Russian realm makes contact with the Pacific Ring of Fire (see Fig. G-5). There are no active volcanoes in Siberia and earthquakes are rare, but the Kamchatka Peninsula has plenty of both. This is one of the most volatile segments of the Pacific Ring of Fire, with more than 60 volcanoes, many of them active or dormant, forming the spine of the peninsula. Nothing here resembles Siberia (the climate is moderated by the Pacific waters offshore; the vegetation is mixed, not coniferous). It is one of the most difficult places on Earth to live, virtually disconnected from the rest of Russia (and entirely so overland).

Also on the Pacific fringe of the Russian realm is an island named Sakhalin, where earthquakes rather than volcanic activity are the leading environmental

The village of Tara on the Irtysh River in the Omsk Region of the Siberian Federal District displays little or no evidence of modernization. Czarist-era wooden houses and wobbly sheds are seen here on a sunny summer day. But even though this is one of Russia's southernmost administrative units (see Fig. 2B-2), it lies exposed to the harsh Siberian winter; when the river freezes over, you can walk to the inhabited meander knoll seen in the near distance. The short growing season allows cultivation of spring wheat and some other early-ripening crops, and small farm settlements like this dot the flat landscape.

© Jon Arnold Images Ltd/Alamy

hazard. Long a battleground between Russians and Japanese, Sakhalin finally fell to the Russians at the end of World War II. In subsequent decades the island and its maritime environs proved to contain substantial reserves of oil and natural gas, making it a valuable asset in Russia's energy-based export economy.

The Southern Perimeter

A final look at Figures 2A-1 and 2A-2 reminds us that mountainous topography encircles much more than just the eastern edge of the Russian realm. Some of the highest relief in Eurasia prevails in the southern interior, where the Eastern Highlands meet the Central Asian Ranges; here lies Lake Baykal in a tectonic trough that is more than 1500 meters (5000 ft) deep—the deepest lake of its kind in the world. And between the Caspian Sea and the Black Sea, the Caucasus Mountains, geologically an extension of Europe's Alps, rise like a wall between Russia and the lands beyond—a multi-tiered barrier over which Russians have fought with their neighbors for centuries.

When you approach the forbidding Caucasus ranges from the low relief of the Russian Plain to the north, they seem impenetrable, and you realize why so few routes cross them, even today. It is also clear why Russia's armies had such difficulty pushing across the Caucasus into the areas beyond. At present, these mountains shelter insurgents defying Russia's authority in such territories as Chechnya and Ingushetiya. And the zone beyond is no easy target: to the south of the Caucasus, high relief dominates all the way into neighboring Turkey and Iran.

Harsh Environments

The historical geography of Russia is the story of Slavic expansion from its populous western heartland across interior Eurasia to the east, and into the mountains and deserts of the south. This eastward march was hampered not only by vast distances but also by harsh natural conditions. As the northernmost populous country on Earth, Russia has virtually no natural barriers against the onslaught of Arctic air. Moscow lies farther north than Edmonton, Canada, and St. Petersburg lies at latitude 60° North—the latitude of the southern tip of Greenland. Winters are long, dark, and bitterly cold in most of Russia; summers are short and growing seasons limited. Many a Siberian frontier outpost was doomed by cold, snow, and hunger.

It is therefore useful to view Russia's past, present, and future in the context of its climate. Even today, in this age of global warming, Russia still suffers from severe cold and associated drought. Precipitation, even in western Russia, ranges from modest to minimal because the warm, moist air carried across Europe from the North Atlantic Ocean loses much of its warmth and moisture by the time it reaches Russia. Figure 2A-3 reveals the consequences.

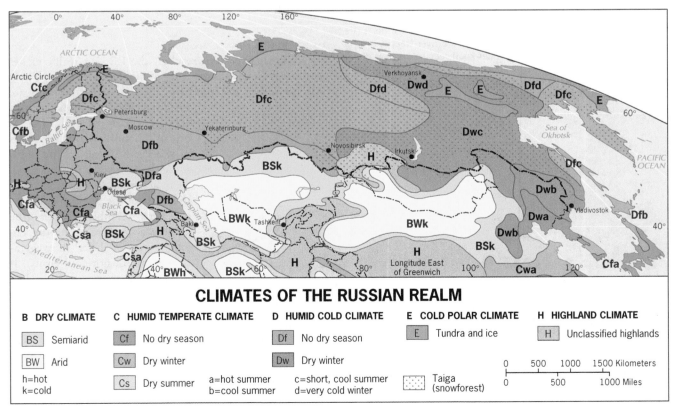

CLIMATES OF THE RUSSIAN REALM

B DRY CLIMATE	**C HUMID TEMPERATE CLIMATE**	**D HUMID COLD CLIMATE**	**E COLD POLAR CLIMATE**	**H HIGHLAND CLIMATE**
BS Semiarid	Cf No dry season	Df No dry season	E Tundra and ice	H Unclassified highlands
BW Arid	Cw Dry winter	Dw Dry winter		
h=hot k=cold	Cs Dry summer	a=hot summer b=cool summer	c=short, cool summer d=very cold winter	Taiga (snowforest)

0 500 1000 1500 Kilometers
0 500 1000 Miles

FIGURE 2A-3

© H. J. de Blij, P. O. Muller, and John Wiley & Sons, Inc.

DEA/C. SAPPA/Getty Images

As Figure 2A-3 shows, Siberia is cold and, in Russia's far northeast, dry as well. In the north lies the tundra, treeless and windswept, and beyond is the ice of the Arctic. But where somewhat more moderate conditions prevail (moderate being a relative concept in northwestern Russia and Siberia), coniferous forests known as *taiga* cover the countryside. Also called boreal (cold-temperate) forests, these evergreen, needleleaf pines and firs create a dense and vast high-latitude girdle of vegetation across northern Eurasia as well as northern North America. This view from the air shows how tightly packed the trees are; they are slow-growing, but long-lived. Most of the world's taiga forest, among the largest surviving stands of primary forest on the planet, remains protected by distance from the threat of exploitation—but lumbering is nevertheless taking its toll. Recent studies indicate that climate change in high latitudes is enabling the forest to expand northward at a faster rate than it diminishes due to lumbering activities elsewhere, a rare case of good news relating to global warming.

nently frozen, creating an even more formidable obstacle to settlement and infrastructure than the severe weather alone. It is referred to as permafrost [3], and it affects other high-latitude environments as well (Alaska, for example). Where the permafrost ends, seasonal temperature changes cause alternate thawing and freezing, with destructive impacts on buildings, roads, railroad tracks, and pipelines.

Examine Figure 2A-3 carefully, and you will see two ecological terms: *tundra* and *taiga*. Tundra [4], as the map suggests, refers to both climate and vegetation. The blue area mapped as **E** marks the coldest and ice-affected environmental zone in Russia and elsewhere in the high Arctic: this is frigid, treeless, windswept, low-elevation terrain where bare ground and rock prevail and mosses, lichens, patches of low grass, and a few hardy shrubs are all that grows. Taiga [5], the stippled area on the map, a Russian word meaning "snowforest" (also called boreal forest), extends across vast reaches of Eurasia as well as northern North America and is dominated by coniferous (as in pine cone) trees. As the map shows, the taiga extends southward into relatively moderate environs, and there it becomes a mixed forest of coniferous and deciduous trees. Although the taiga prevails from northern Scandinavia to the Russian Far East, this is the vegetative landscape most often associated with Siberia: endless expanses of rolling countryside draped in dense stands of evergreen pine trees (see photo).

Climates and Peoples

Climate and weather (there is a distinction: *climate* refers to a long-term average, whereas *weather* describes a set of immediate atmospheric conditions at a given place and time) have always challenged the peoples of this realm. The high winds that drive the bitter Arctic cold southward deep into the landmass, the blizzards of Siberia, the temperature extremes, rainfall variability, and short and undependable growing seasons even in the more moderate western parts of this realm have always made farming difficult. That was true during the time of the ruling czars, when the threat of famine never receded. It was also a constant problem during the Soviet-communist period, when Moscow was the capital of an empire far larger than this realm and the non-Russian sectors of that empire (such as Ukraine and parts of Central Asia) produced food staples Russia needed. Despite a massive effort to restructure agriculture throughout the Soviet Empire by means of collectivization and irrigation projects, the Russians often had to import grain.

Russia's climatic continentality [2] (inland climatic environment remote from moderating and moistening maritime influences) is expressed by its prevailing *Dfb* and *Dfc* conditions. Compare the Russian map to that of North America (Fig. G-7), and you note that, except for a small corner off the Black Sea, Russia's climatic conditions resemble those of the Upper Midwest of the United States and interior Canada. Along its entire northern edge, Russia has a zone of **E** climates, the most frigid on the planet. In these Arctic latitudes originate the polar air masses that dominate its environments.

The Russian realm's harsh northern climates affect people, animals, plants—and even the soil. In Figure 2A-2 you can find a direct consequence of what you see in Figure 2A-3: a dashed blue line that starts at the shore of the Barents Sea, crosses Siberia eastward, and reaches the coast of the Pacific Ocean north of the neck of the Kamchatka Peninsula. North of this line, water in the ground is perma-

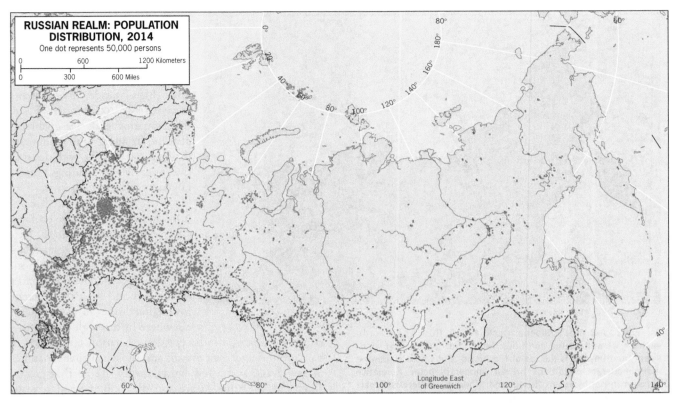

RUSSIAN REALM: POPULATION DISTRIBUTION, 2014
One dot represents 50,000 persons

FIGURE 2A-4

© H. J. de Blij, P. O. Muller, and John Wiley & Sons, Inc.

As we noted in the Introduction, and as we will observe time and again throughout this book, humankind's long-term dependence on agriculture remains etched on the population map, even as our planet becomes ever more urbanized and its economy more globalized. By studying the climates of the Russian realm, we can begin to understand what the map of population distribution communicates (Fig. 2A-4). The overwhelming majority of the realm's 160 million inhabitants remain concentrated in the west and southwest, where environmental conditions were least difficult at a time when farming was the mainstay of most of the people. To the east, the population is sparser and tends to cluster along the southern margin of the realm, becoming even more thinly distributed east of Lake Baykal. If you consider that three-quarters of this realm's population today lives in cities and towns, it is not difficult to imagine just how empty vast stretches of countryside must be—especially in frigid northern latitudes.

Climate Change and Arctic Prospects

As every map of this high-latitude realm shows, its northern coast lies entirely on the polar side of the Arctic Circle. Such a lengthy coastline on the Arctic Ocean does not exactly constitute an advantage: most of the Arctic Ocean is frozen much of the year, and only some warmth from the North Atlantic Drift ocean current keeps the western ports of Murmansk and Arkhangelsk open a bit longer. Ports like this (and even St. Petersburg on the Gulf of Finland, an arm of the Baltic Sea) would never have developed the way they did if Russia had better access to the world ocean; but as we noted, this has been one of the country's historic impediments.

Now it looks as though nature may give Russia a helping hand. If, as most climatologists anticipate, global warming causes long-term melting of large portions of the Arctic Ocean's ice cover, that body of water may come to play a new and different role in this realm's future. Milder atmospheric conditions may shrink the area of permafrost mapped in Figure 2A-2; moister air masses may improve agriculture on the Russian Plain; warmer water may keep Arctic ports open year-round; and the so-called Northern Sea Route (also known as the Northeast Passage) might even open up between the Bering Strait and the North Sea (see Fig. 12-5), shortening some international sea routes by thousands of kilometers and ushering in a new era of trade.

That, at least, is how many Russians like to envision global warming—as a potential advantage nature has long denied them. And indeed, the Arctic provides much evidence for such warming: the melting of parts of the Greenland Ice Sheet, the shrinking of the average extent of permanent Arctic Ocean ice, and the reduced incidence of icebergs. Russian economic planners look at the shallow waters offshore along the Arctic Ocean coastline (see the white- and light-blue areas in Fig. 2A-1) and hope that oil and gas reserves beneath those waters will come within reach of exploitation.

These developments may even have the effect of expanding the Russian geographic realm far into the Arctic. As we note when we discuss the polar areas in greater detail in Chapter 12, states with coastlines in the Arctic are likely to demand certain exclusive rights not only over waters offshore but also the resources on and beneath the ocean floor. It is therefore in their interest to extend those rights as far from shore as possible, even hundreds of (nautical) miles outward. In 2007, the Russian government even placed a metal Russian flag at the North Pole on the seafloor, under the permanent ice of the Arctic Ocean, symbolizing its intentions (see final photo in Chapter 12). The map of the northern perimeter of the Russian realm is changing—but not always for the better.

Ecologies at Risk

If, as computer models predict, global warming continues and perhaps intensifies in the polar latitudes, these ecologically sensitive environments are sure to be severely affected. Animals as well as humans have long adapted to prevailing climatic conditions, and such adaptations would be significantly disrupted by environmental change. The intricate web of relationships among species and their environments on the one hand, and among species themselves on the other, can be quickly damaged by temperature change. The polar bear is just one prominent example: it depends on ample floating sea ice to hunt as well as raise cubs. When sea ice contracts and wider stretches of open water force polar bears to swim greater distances during the cub-rearing season, fewer infants make it to adulthood. If ice-free Arctic summers are indeed in the offing, the polar bear could become extinct in your lifetime. Rapid ecosystem change would also endanger seal, bird, fish, and other Arctic wildlife populations.

Such changes affect human populations as well. For example, Inuit (formerly called Eskimo) communities still pursuing traditional lives in parts of the Arctic domain (though not in the Russian realm) are similarly adapted to the harsher environments of the past. Their traditions, already under pressure from political and economic forces resulting from their incorporation into modern states, would be further threatened by environmental changes that are likely to alter, or even destroy, the ways of life they developed over thousands of years.

And if a new era of oil and natural gas exploration and exploitation is indeed about to open, already-fragile offshore environments face even greater peril. As technologies of recovery put ever more of these reserves within reach, oil platforms, drills, pumps, and pipelines will make their appearance—along with risks of oil spills, pollution, disturbance, and damage of the kind we have seen all over the lower-latitude world. Clearly, the forces of globalization are finally penetrating a part of the world long protected from it by distance and nature.

RUSSIA'S NATURAL RICHES

Given the enormous territorial dimensions of the Russian realm, it is not surprising that its natural resources are vast and varied. The Russians today are excited about the energy reserves that are to be found and exploited beneath Arctic waters, but this realm already is a major producer and exporter of oil and natural gas from a growing number of fields dispersed across Russia from the North Caucasus in the west to the island of Sakhalin in the east and from the Arctic shore of Siberia in the north to the Caspian Basin in the south (Fig. 2A-5).

And petroleum and natural gas are not the only underground riches of this realm. Deposits of so many minerals lie within Russian territory that virtually all of the raw materials required by modern industry are present. Nor are oil and natural gas the only energy reserves. Major coalfields are found east as well as west of the Urals, and in Siberia as well as in more southerly latitudes (the string of mines producing high-quality coal along the Trans-Siberian Railroad corridor were vital in Russia's industrial development and its successful war against Nazi Germany). Large deposits of iron ore, too, lie widely scattered across this enormous realm, from the so-called Kursk Magnetic Anomaly near the border with Ukraine to the remotest corners of Siberia's Arctic north. And when it comes to other metallic ores, this realm has it all—or almost all—from gold to lead and from aluminum to zinc. Moreover, one of the world's largest concentrations of nonferrous (noniron) metals lies in and around the Ural Mountains, where Russia's metallurgical industries emerged.

And there is likely to be much more. Vast reaches of this far-flung realm have not yet been fully explored, especially in the far northeast. Given such material assets, you would imagine that this realm has always been in the forefront of industrial production and economic diversification. But, as we shall also see, the availability of raw materials is only one part of such development. You are likely to buy Chinese and Japanese products on an almost daily basis—but you are likely to own very few if any items of Russian manufacture. That is part of the story we relate in Chapter 2B.

Environment—in the form of climate, relief, vegetation, and other elements—has much to do with the way Russia evolved as the dominant power over this vast realm. To better understand the map, let us briefly trace the historical geography of Russia, its defenders, and rulers who eventually pushed Russian influence far beyond the Russian Plain—even into western North America. It may come as a surprise to many Americans that Russians not only colonized Alaska, but even reached central California and built a fort not very far north of present-day San Francisco. So let us focus first on place and time in Russia's evolution.

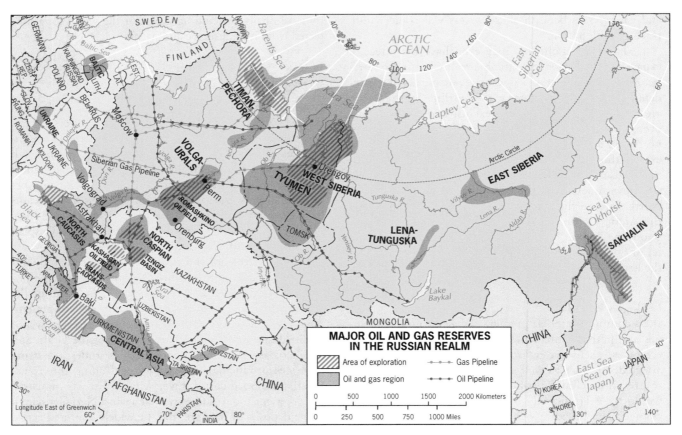

FIGURE 2A-5

© H. J. de Blij, P. O. Muller, and John Wiley & Sons, Inc.

RUSSIAN ROOTS

A thousand years ago, Eurasian peoples of many ethnic sources and cultural backgrounds were migrating across the plains south of the taiga (coniferous snowforest) in search of new and secure homelands; Scythians, Sarmatians, Goths, Huns, and others came, fought, settled, survived, absorbed neighbors, or were driven off. Eventually the Slavs, comparative latecomers to this turbulent stage, established settlements in the area of present-day Ukraine, north of the Black Sea and in the southwestern corner of the physiographic region we have defined as the Russian Plain (Fig. 2A-2).

Here the Slavic peoples found fertile soils, a relatively moderate climate, and a physical landscape with many advantages and opportunities: the Dnieper River and its tributaries, stands of forest, relatively low relief, and easy contact among settlements. The Slavs used the name **Rus** to designate such settlements, and the largest and most successful of these early Russes was the one located where the capital of modern Ukraine, Kiev (Kyyiv), lies today. This is one reason why many "Russians" today cannot imagine an independent, Europe-oriented Ukraine: this, after all, is their historic heartland. And from this southern base, the Slavs expanded their domain across the Russian Plain, first establishing their northern headquarters at Novgorod on Lake Ilmen (see Fig. 2A-1). This northern Rus

was well positioned to benefit from the trade between the Hanseatic ports on the Baltic Sea and the trading centers on the Black and Mediterranean seas. During the eleventh and twelfth centuries, the Kievan Rus and the Novgorod Rus combined to form a large and prosperous state astride both the northern forest and southern steppe [6] (semi-arid grassland).

The Mongol Invasion

Prosperity attracts attention, and knowledge about the Russes spread far and wide. In the distant east, north of China, another successful state had been building: the empire of the Mongol peoples under Genghis Khan. Also under the sway of this legendary ruler was a group of nomadic, Turkic-speaking peoples known as the Tatars. Together, Mongol-Tatar armies rode westward on horseback into the domain of the Russes to challenge the power of the Slavs.

Geography had much to do with their early success: on the open steppes of the southern Russian Plain, the Russes lay exposed to the fast-charging Mongol forces, and by the middle of the thirteenth century, the Kievan Rus had fallen. Slavic refugees were fleeing into the northern forests, where they reorganized to face their enemies in newly built Russes. The forest environment was their ally: Mongol tactics were effective for the open plain, but not in the woods. What ensued was not a victory for either side,

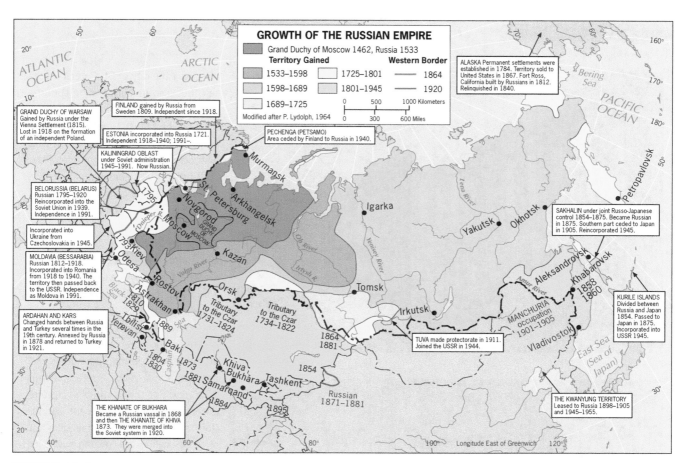

FIGURE 2A-6

© H. J. de Blij, P. O. Muller, and John Wiley & Sons, Inc.

but a standoff: the Tatars threatened and tried to lay siege, but they could not win outright. So the leaders of the forest-based Russes paid tribute to the Mongol-Tatar invaders, and in exchange they were left alone.

One of these Russes was Moscow, deep in the forest on the Moscow River and destined to become the capital of a vast empire. On a defensible site and in a remote situation, Moscow's leaders began to establish trade links with even safer Novgorod, and the city grew and thrived. When the Mongols, worried about Moscow's growing power and influence, attacked and were successfully repulsed, Moscow emerged as the leader among Russes, its destiny assured. The Mongol-Tatar campaign had essentially failed.

Before we go on, we should take note of a crucial geographic development. Whereas the Mongols and Tatars fought together, their failure to conquer the Slavic-Russian heartland had both cultural and geographic consequences that have endured into the present. Although most of the Mongols withdrew following their unsuccessful fourteenth-century assault on Moscow, many Tatars remained on what, at the time, was the periphery around the Slavic/Russian core in such places as the Volga River Basin, the Crimean Peninsula, and other smaller pockets. There they were converted in the wave of Islam that was rolling into the Black Sea Basin and beyond, creating a new kind of division between Christian Slavs and their old-time adversaries.

Grand Duchy of Muscovy

During the fourteenth century, the Grand Duchy of Muscovy rose to preeminence under the rule of princes or dukes. They extended Moscow's trade links from the Baltic to Black Sea shores and forged valuable religious ties with the leadership of the Eastern Orthodox Church in Constantinople. Then, from around 1450, there began a period lasting more than three centuries during which powerful Russian rulers etched their imprints on the map of Russia, Eurasia, and, by extension, the world (Fig. 2A-6).

By the sixteenth century, during the reign of Ivan IV, better known as the infamous *Ivan the Terrible*, the Grand Duchy of Muscovy had been transformed into a major military power and an imperial state. He expanded Moscow's empire by conquering the Islamic regions to the south and gaining control over present-day Estonia and Latvia on the Baltic Sea. It was a time of almost continuous warfare, and Ivan the Terrible acquired his reputation from the reign of terror he unleashed in his pursuit of military discipline, centralized administrative control, and retaliation against many members of the nobility.

From the Field Notes . . .

© H.J. de Blij

"Not only the city of St. Petersburg itself, but also its surrounding suburbs display the architectural and artistic splendor of czarist Russia. The czars built opulent palaces in these outlying districts (then some distance from the built-up center), among which the Catherine Palace, begun in 1717 and completed in 1723 followed by several expansions, was especially majestic. During my first visit in 1994, the palace, parts of which had been deliberately destroyed by the Germans during World War II, was still being restored; large black and white photographs in the hallways showed what the Nazis had done and chronicled the progress of the repairs during communist and postcommunist years. A return visit in 2000 revealed the wealth of sculptural decoration on the magnificent exterior (top) and the interior detail of a set of rooms called the 'golden suite,' of which the ballroom (bottom) exemplifies eighteenth-century Russian Baroque at its height."

www.conceptcaching.com

© H.J. de Blij

BUILDING THE RUSSIAN EMPIRE

Czarist Russia

When Peter the Great became czar (he ruled from 1682 to 1725), Moscow already lay at the center of a great empire—great, at least, in terms of the territories it controlled. The Islamic threat had been ended with the defeat of the Tatars. The influence of the Russian Orthodox Church was represented by its distinctive religious architecture and powerful bishops. Peter consolidated Russia's gains and endeavored to make a modern, European-style state out of his loosely knit country. He built St. Petersburg as a forward capital [7] on the doorstep of Swedish-held Finland, fortified it with major military installations, and made it Russia's leading port.

Peter the Great, an extraordinary leader, was in several ways the founder of modern Russia. In his desire to remake Russia—to pull it from the forests of the interior to the seas of the west, to open it to outside influences, and to relocate its population—he left nothing to chance. Prominent merchant families were forced to move from other cities to St. Petersburg. Ships and wagons entering the city had

Russians in North America

THE FIRST WHITE settlers in Alaska were Russians, not western Europeans, and they came across Siberia and the Bering Strait, not across the Atlantic and North America. Russian hunters of the sea otter, valued for its high-priced pelt, established their first Alaskan settlement at Kodiak Island in 1784. Moving south along the North American coast, the Russians founded a chain of additional villages and forts to protect their tenuous holdings until they reached as far as the area just north of San Francisco Bay, where they built Fort Ross in 1812.

But these Russian settlements were isolated and vulnerable. European fur traders began to put pressure on their Russian competitors, and St. Petersburg soon found the distant settlements a burden and a risk. In any case, American, British, and Canadian hunters were decimating the sea-otter population, and profits declined. When U.S. Secretary of State William Seward offered to purchase

Russia's North American holdings in 1867, St. Petersburg quickly agreed—for $7.2 million (more than $100 million in today's dollars). Thus Alaska, including its lengthy southward coastal extension, became U.S. territory and, in 1959, the forty-ninth State. Although Seward was ridiculed for his decision—Alaska was called "Seward's Folly" and "Seward's Icebox"—he was vindicated when gold was discovered there in the 1890s. The twentieth century further underscored the wisdom of Seward's action, strategically as well as economically. At Prudhoe Bay off Alaska's northern Arctic slope, large oil reserves were tapped in the 1970s and are still being exploited. And like Siberia, Alaska probably contains yet unknown riches. From the point of view of the United States, besides the 24 dollars allegedly paid to acquire Manhattan Island, this $7.2 million transaction is often regarded as the most lucrative real estate deal in world history.

to bring building stones as an entry toll. The czar himself, aware that to become a major power Russia had to be strong at sea as well as on land, went to the Netherlands to work as a laborer in the famed Dutch shipyards to learn the most efficient method for building ships. Meanwhile, the czar's forces continued to conquer people and territory: Estonia was incorporated in 1721, widening Russia's window to the west, and in Siberia major expansion soon occurred south of the city of Tomsk (Fig. 2A-6).

Under Czarina Catherine the Great, who ruled from 1760 to 1796, Russia's empire in the Black Sea Basin grew at the expense of the Ottoman Turks. The Crimea Peninsula, the port city of Odesa (Odessa), and the entire northern coastal zone of the Black Sea fell under Russian control. Also during this period, the Russians made a fateful move: they penetrated the corridor between the Black and Caspian seas, whose spine is the mountainous Caucasus with its dozens of ethnic and cultural groups, many of which were Islamized. The cities of Tbilisi (now in Georgia), Baki (Baku) in Azerbaijan, and Yerevan (Armenia) were captured. Eventually, the Russian push toward an Indian Ocean outlet was thwarted by the British, who held sway in Persia (modern Iran), and also by the Turks.

Meanwhile, Russian colonists (descendants of Cossacks who originally hailed from Ukraine and southwestern Russia) had advanced far to the east, settling along the southeastern frontier, crossing the Bering Strait, and entering Alaska in 1784 (see the box titled "Russians in North America"). Catherine had made Russia a huge colonial power, but within a century the Russians gave up on their North American outposts. The sea-otter pelts that had attracted the early pioneers were running out, European and white American hunters were cutting into the profits, and indigenous Ameri-

can resistance was growing. When the United States offered to purchase Russia's Alaskan holdings in 1867, the Russian government swiftly agreed—setting Alaska on a new course that culminated in its joining the U.S. as the forty-ninth State in 1959.

Nineteenth-Century Expansion

Although Russia had withdrawn from North America, Russian expansionism during the nineteenth century continued in Eurasia. While extending their empire southward, the Russians also took on the Poles, old enemies to the west, and succeeded in taking most of what is today the Polish state, including the capital of Warsaw. To the northwest, Russia took over Finland from the Swedes in 1809.

During most of the nineteenth century, however, the Russians were preoccupied with Central Asia—the region between the Caspian Sea and western China—where Tashkent and Samarqand (Samarkand) came under St. Petersburg's control (Fig. 2A-6). The Russians here were still bothered by raids of nomadic horsemen, and they sought to establish their authority over the Central Asian drylands as far as the edges of the high mountains that lay to the south. Thus Russia gained many Muslim subjects, because this was Islamic Asia they were penetrating. Under czarist rule, though, these people retained some autonomy.

Much farther to the east, a combination of Japanese expansionism and a decline of Chinese influence led Russia to annex from China a number of provinces north and southeast of the Amur River. Soon thereafter, in 1860, the Russians founded the port of Vladivostok on the Pacific. Now began the series of events that were to lead to the first involuntary halt in the Russian drive for territory. As

Figure 2A-1 shows, the most direct route from western Russia to the port of Vladivostok lay across northeastern China, the territory then still called Manchuria. The Russians had begun construction of the Trans-Siberian Railroad in 1892, and they wanted China to permit the tracks to cross Manchuria. But the Chinese resisted. Then, taking advantage of the Boxer Rebellion in China in 1900 (see Chapter 9A), Russian forces occupied Manchuria so that railway construction might proceed.

That move, however, threatened Japanese interests in this area, and Japan confronted Russia in the Russo-Japanese War of 1904–1905. Not only were the Russians beaten and forced out of Manchuria: Japan even took possession of the southern portion of Sakhalin Island, which they named Karafuto and retained until 1945.

Thus Russia, like Britain, France, and other European powers, expanded through *imperialism*. Whereas the other European powers expanded overseas, Russian influence traveled overland into Central Asia, Siberia, China, and the Pacific coastlands of the Far East. What emerged was not the greatest empire but the largest territorially contiguous empire in the world.

The czars embarked on their imperial conquests in part because of Russia's relative location: Russia always lacked warm-water ports. Had the early-twentieth-century Revolution not intervened, their southward push might have reached the Persian Gulf or even the Mediterranean Sea. Czar Peter the Great envisaged a Russia open to trading with the entire world; he developed St. Petersburg on the Baltic Sea into Russia's leading port. But in truth, Russia's historical geography is one of remoteness from the mainstreams of change and progress, as well as one of self-imposed isolation.

A Multinational Empire

Centuries of Russian expansionism did not confine itself to empty land or unclaimed frontiers. The Russian state became an imperial power that annexed and incorporated numerous nationalities and cultures. This was done by employing force of arms, by overthrowing uncooperative rulers, by annexing territory, and by stoking the fires of ethnic conflict. By the time the ruthless Russian regime had begun to confront revolution among its own citizens, czarist Russia controlled peoples representing more than 100 nationalities. The winners in the revolutionary struggle that ensued—the communists who forged the Soviet Union—did not liberate these subjugated peoples. Rather, they changed the empire's framework, binding the peoples colonized by the czars into a new system that would in theory give them autonomy and identity. In practice, it doomed those peoples to bondage and, in certain cases, extinction. The Soviet Union, which arose in the wake of the communist revolution of 1917, constituted another effort to incorporate all these peoples and regions into this vast multinational state, notwithstanding the mantra-like socialist condemnations of imperialism.

THE SOVIET UNION

Communism found fertile ground in the Russia of the 1910s and 1920s. In those days Russia was infamous for the wretched serfdom of its peasants, the cruel exploitation of its workers, the excesses of its nobility, and the ostentatious palaces and riches of the czars. Ripples from the European Industrial Revolution introduced a new age of misery for those laboring in factories. There were workers' strikes and ugly retributions, but when the czars finally tried to better the lot of the poor, it was too little too late.

There was no democracy, and the people had no way to express or channel their grievances. Europe's democratic revolution had passed Russia by, and its economic revolution touched the czars' domain only slightly. Most Russians, as well as tens of millions of non-Russians under the czars' control, faced exploitation, corruption, starvation, and harsh subjugation. When the people began to rebel in 1905, there was no hint of what lay in store; even after the full-scale Revolution of 1917, Russia's political future hung in the balance.

The Political Framework

Russia's great expansion had brought many nationalities under czarist control; now the revolutionary government sought to organize this heterogeneous ethnic mosaic into a smoothly functioning state. The czars had conquered, but they had done little to bring Russian culture to the peoples they ruled. In 1917, when the old order was overthrown, the Russians themselves constituted only about one-half of the population of the entire empire.

In the wake of the Revolution, the first response of many of Russia's subject peoples was to proclaim independent republics, as occurred in Ukraine, Georgia, Armenia, Azerbaijan, and even Central Asia. But Vladimir Lenin, the communist leader and chief architect of the new political system, had no intention of permitting the Soviet state to break up. In 1923, when his blueprint for the new Soviet Union went into effect, the last of these briefly independent units was fully absorbed into the sphere of the Moscow regime.

The political framework for the Soviet Union was based on the ethnic identities of its many incorporated peoples. Given the size and cultural complexity of the empire, it was impossible to allocate territory of equal political standing to all the nationalities (the communists controlled the destinies of well over 100 peoples, both large nations and small isolated groups). It was decided to divide the vast realm into 15 *Soviet Socialist Republics* (*SSRs*), each of which was delimited to correspond broadly to one of the major nationalities (Fig. 2A-7). As was noted, Russians constituted only about half of the developing Soviet Union's population, but they also were (and still are) the most widely dispersed ethnic group in the realm (see Fig. 2A-8). The Russian Republic, therefore, was by far the largest designated SSR, encompassing just over three-quarters of the total Soviet territory.

FIGURE 2A-7

© H. J. de Blij, P. O. Muller, and John Wiley & Sons, Inc.

Within the SSRs, smaller minorities were assigned political units of lesser rank. These were called Autonomous Soviet Socialist Republics (ASSRs), which in effect were republics within republics; other areas were designated as Autonomous Regions or other nationality-based units. It was a complicated, cumbersome, often poorly designed framework, but in 1924 it was launched officially under the banner of the ***Union of Soviet Socialist Republics (USSR)***.

A Phantom Federation

The Soviet planners called their system a federation [8]. Federalism involves the sharing of power between a country's central government and its political subdivisions (provinces, States, or, in the Soviet case, "Socialist Republics"). Study the map of the former Soviet Union (Fig. 2A-7) and an interesting geographic corollary emerges: every one of the 15 SSRs had a boundary with a non-Soviet neighbor. This seemed to give geographic substance to the notion that any Republic was free to leave the USSR if it so desired. Reality, of course, was quite different, and Moscow's absolute control over the SSRs made the Soviet Union a federation in theory only.

In practice, it was very difficult to accommodate the shifting multinational mosaic of the Soviet realm. The republics quarreled among themselves over boundaries and territory. Demographic change, forced migrations, war, and economic factors soon made much of the layout of the 1920s obsolete. Moreover, the communist planners made it Soviet policy to relocate entire peoples from their homelands in order to better fit the grand design, and to reward or punish—sometimes capriciously. The overall effect, however, was to move minority peoples eastward and to replace them with Russians. This Russification [9] of the Soviet Empire produced substantial ethnic Russian minorities in all the non-Russian republics.

The centerpiece of the tightly controlled Soviet "federation" was the Russian Republic. With half of the vast state's population, the capital city, the realm's core area, and 76 percent of the Soviet Union's territory, Russia was the empire's nucleus. In other republics, "Soviet" often was simply equated with "Russian"—it was the reality with which the lesser republics lived. Russians came to the other republics to teach (Russian was taught in the colonial schools), to organize (and frequently dominate) the local Communist Party, and to implement Moscow's economic decisions. This was colonialism, but somehow the communist disguise—how could socialists, as the communists called themselves, be colonialists?—and the contiguous spatial nature of the empire made it appear to

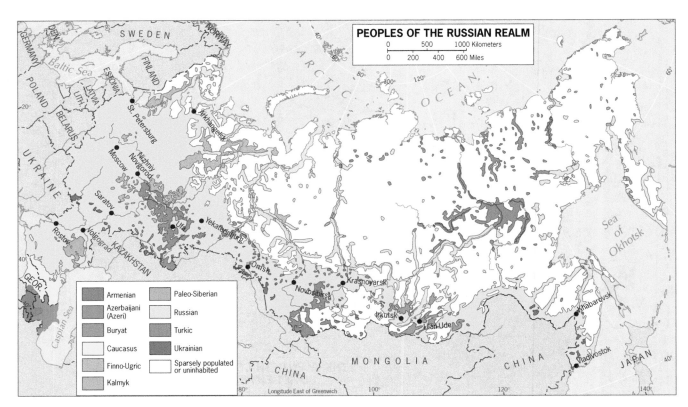

FIGURE 2A-8

© H. J. de Blij, P. O. Muller, and John Wiley & Sons, Inc.

the rest of the world as something else. Indeed, on the world stage the Soviet Union became a champion of oppressed peoples, a force in the decolonization process. It was an astonishing contradiction that would, in time, be fully exposed.

The Soviet Economic Framework

The geopolitical changes that resulted from the establishment of the Soviet Union were accompanied by a gigantic economic experiment: the conversion of the empire from a czarist autocracy with a capitalist veneer to communism. From the early 1920s onward, the country's economy would now be *centrally planned*—the communist leadership in Moscow would make all decisions regarding economic planning and development. Soviet planners had two principal objectives: (1) to accelerate industrialization, and (2) to **collectivize** agriculture. For the first time ever on such a scale, an entire country was organized to work toward national goals prescribed by a central government.

The Soviet planners believed that agriculture could be made more productive by organizing it into huge state-run enterprises. The holdings of large landowners were expropriated, private farms were taken away from their farmers, and the land was consolidated into collective farms. Initially, all such land was meant to be part of a **sovkhoz**, literally a grain-and-meat factory in which agricultural efficiency, through maximum mechaniza-

tion and minimum labor requirements, would be at its peak.

Soviet agriculture never attained such productivity and those who obstructed the communists' grand design suffered a dreadful fate. It has been estimated that between 30 and 60 million people lost their lives from imposed starvation, constant political purges, Siberian exile, and forced relocation. The Soviet grand experiment amounted to an incalculable human tragedy, but the secretive character of Soviet officialdom made it possible to hide everything from the world.

The USSR practiced a **command economy [10]**, in which state planners assigned the production of particular manufactures to particular places, often disregarding the rules of economic geography. For example, the manufacture of railroad cars might be assigned (as indeed it was) to a factory in Latvia. No other factory anywhere else would be permitted to produce this equipment—even if supplies of raw materials would make it cheaper to build them near, say, Volgograd 2000 kilometers (1250 mi) away. Yet, despite an expanded and improved transportation network (see Fig. 2A-9), such practices made manufacturing in the USSR extremely expensive, and the absence of competition made managers complacent and workers far less productive than they might have been.

Of course, the Soviet planners never imagined that their experiment would fail and that a market-driven economy would replace their command economy. When that happened, the transition was predictably difficult;

indeed, it is far from over and continues to severely stress the now more democratic, post-communist state.

THE NEW RUSSIA

On December 25, 1991, the inevitable occurred: the Soviet Union disintegrated. The centrally planned economy went into structural failure, the arms race with the United States during the Cold War had drained resources, and efforts at Russification had only fueled the drive for independence among so many of the peoples that had been forcibly incorporated into the Union. The last Soviet president, Mikhail Gorbachev, resigned, and the Soviet hammer-and-sickle flag flying atop the Kremlin was lowered for the last time and immediately replaced by the white, red, and blue Russian tricolor. A new and turbulent era began—but Soviet institutions and systems will long cast their shadows over transforming Russia.

When the Soviet system failed and the Soviet Socialist Republics became independent states in 1991, Russia was left without the empire that had taken centuries to build and consolidate—and that contained crucial agricultural and mineral resources. No longer did Moscow control the farms of Ukraine and the oil and natural gas reserves of Central Asia. But look at Figures 2A-1 and especially 2B-2 and you will see that, even without its European and Central Asian colonies, Russia remains an empire. Russia lost the "republics" on its periphery, but Moscow still rules over a domain that extends from the borders of Finland to North Korea. Inside that domain Russians are in the overwhelming majority, but many subjugated nationalities, from Tatars to Yakuts, continue to inhabit ancestral homelands. Accommodating these many indigenous peoples is still one of the challenges facing the Russian Federation today.

A Complex Cultural Mosaic

Although Russia's dominance of this geographic realm justifies our naming it as such, this is a culturally and ethnically diverse part of the world whose traditions and customs spill over into neighboring realms even as neighbors have come to live here. Ethnic Russians still form the great majority, but sizeable parts of this realm are home to non-Russian peoples—and not just along the borders. As Figure 2A-8 shows, the Russian realm contains Finnish, Turkic, Armenian, and dozens of other "nationalities," but the scale of this map cannot reflect the complexity of the overall ethnic mosaic. Here is an interesting example: in the southwest, facing the Caspian Sea, lies a small "republic" that is part of modern Russia, named Dagestan (which achieved notoriety in 2013 in conjunction with the Boston Marathon bombings). It is half the size of Maine, has a population of 3 million, and contains nearly 30 ethnic "nationalities" speaking their own languages, most of which are variants of languages spoken in the Caucasus, Turkey, and Iran.

As the map shows, the Slavic peoples known collectively as the Russians not only form the majority of the population but also are the most widely dispersed. Although the Russian Plain is the core area of the Russian state and was its historic hearth, Russian settlement extends from the shores of the Arctic Sea to the Black Sea coast and from St. Petersburg on the Gulf of Finland to Vladivostok on the Sea of Japan. Discontinuous nuclei and ribbons of Russian settlement are scattered across Siberia, but as we noted in Figure 2A-4, the population, Russian and non-Russian, tends to concentrate in the southern sector of the realm.

Russians are not the only Slavic peoples. More than one thousand years ago, when many ethnic groups struggled to establish themselves in Europe, the early Slavs, whose original home may have been on the North European Plain in the area north of the Carpathians, achieved stability and security in a homeland that expanded steadily, not only eastward into what is today Russia, but also westward and southwestward into the valley of the Danube and beyond. As we noted in Chapters 1A and 1B, the Serbs, Croats, Slovaks, and Czechs are Slavic peoples, as are the Poles, Ukrainians, and Belarussians, among others (see Fig. 1B-14). Today you can discern evidence of this distant past in the Slavic languages these descendants speak (see Fig. 1A-7), which still have much in common despite centuries of divergence.

Even as the early Russian state consolidated, non-Russian peoples incubated in and beyond the Caucasus Mountains in the corridor between the Black and Caspian seas. Georgians, Armenians, Azeris, and many others created a jigsaw mosaic of nationalities in this region (the aforementioned Dagestan is only a tiny part of it). Then, after about AD 1400, Islam propagated by the Ottoman Empire pushed northward here, and by 1500 Islam's vanguards were challenging Slavic peoples along the northern shore of the Black Sea. Remnants of such advances and invasions still remain on the cultural map (Fig. 2A-8): look at the crescent of Turkic peoples (shaded red) extending from near the city of Nizhniy Novgorod to the border of Kazakhstan, and you see part of the evidence. Today, Russia has a far higher percentage of Muslims in its population than western European countries do; although the data are not precise, the consensus is that roughly 15 percent of Russia's inhabitants are Muslims.

Long before Islam appeared on the scene, Slavic peoples from one end of their domain to the other had accepted the teachings of the Eastern Orthodox Church, and in the Russian realm the Russian church became Eastern Orthodoxy's dominant institution. It stayed that way until the triumph of the communist revolutionaries, who in 1917 put an end to rule by the Russian czars and began the disestablishment of the church. For more than seven decades, atheism was official policy—until the communist system imploded. Since the early 1990s, the Russian Orthodox Church has made a vigorous comeback, attended by nationalist and ethnic propaganda.

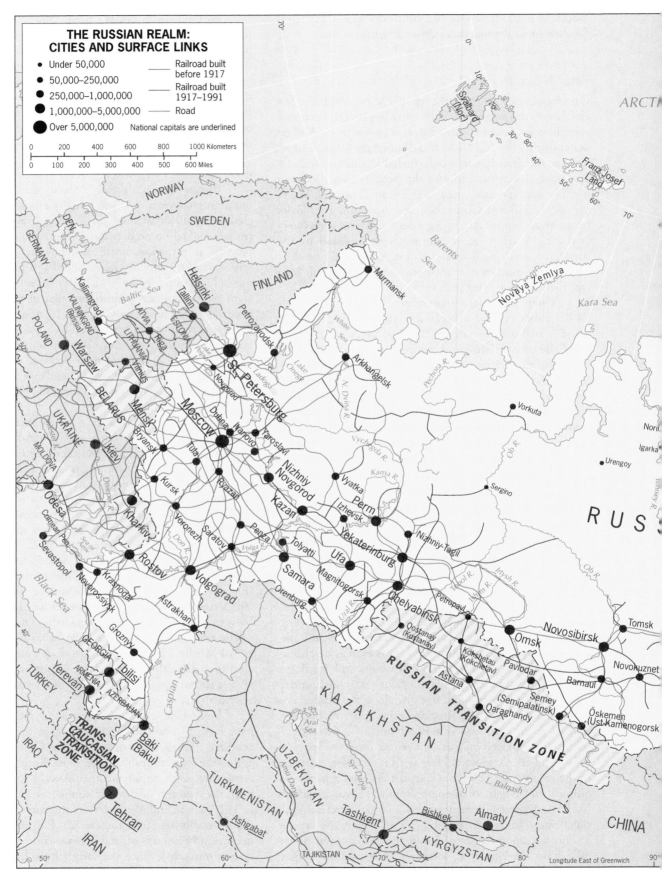

FIGURE 2A-9

© H. J. de Blij, P. O. Muller, and John Wiley & Sons, Inc.

Cities Near and Far

When the czars ruled Russia, people living in villages and on homesteads in the countryside far outnumbered those residing in towns and cities. It is not that the czars intended to keep it that way, however their policies—social, economic, and otherwise—obstructed change and suppressed opportunities that draw people to urban areas. Even under Peter the Great, who admired urbanizing western Europe and wanted to make St. Petersburg a glittering Russian window on the wider world, Russia's urbanization lagged well behind Europe's. Compare Russia's level of urbanization today (74 percent) to that of western Europe (84 percent), and this contrast endures. Figure 1A-5 reminds us that the Industrial Revolution came late to this realm, and that its impact was slowed until the revolutionary communist organizers who succeeded the czars in the 1920s undertook a massive effort to catch up.

The three countries that form the Transcaucasus region are even less urbanized than Russia: in both Azerbaijan and Georgia only 53 percent of the people live in urban areas, and even in Armenia urbanization lags (see the Data Table in Appendix B to compare these numbers to, say, East Asia or South America). Here the twentieth-century period of Russian influence did little to dislodge rural traditions or stimulate change.

Nonetheless, the cities, when mapped by size (Fig. 2A-9), reveal much about this realm's expansive regional geography. Primate-city Moscow and northerly but coastal St. Petersburg decidedly anchor the Russian core area. Consider this: the three airports of Moscow combined (which serve around 65 million passengers a year) handle more than half of the total number of Russia's air passengers. With St. Petersburg second at about 11 million passengers annually, the dominance of the Core, and particularly its two leading cities, is overwhelming.

Elsewhere in the Core region, historic urban centers like Novgorod, Kazan, and Yekaterinburg mark cru-

cial episodes in Russia's historical geography; and the cities on the Volga River spearheaded the country's post-czarist transformation. As the ribbon of cities and towns thins out eastward beyond the Urals, we observe the names associated with the communist Soviet Union's industrial might and heroic resistance against the Nazi penetration: Omsk, Krasnoyarsk, and chill-inducing Novosibirsk. In the Russian Far East, Vladivostok symbolized Soviet naval power, which has today given way to a new era of Russian indifference. And on the Kamchatka Peninsula, people are streaming away from Petropavlovsk, once an outpost favored by the Soviets but now abandoned by Moscow.

As for Transcaucasia, its three leading cities, also the capitals of their respective republics, all signify a singular, dominant issue: oil and its export routes in Baki (Baku), Azerbaijan; conflict with Russia in Tbilisi, Georgia; and landlocked weakness in Yerevan, Armenia.

The Near Abroad

The ending of the Cold War in the early 1990s implied an abrupt termination of Soviet geopolitical strategies that had been aimed at confronting U.S.-led alliances in Europe, the Middle East, and South Asia as well as Southeast

The landscape of Tula, a city of 505,000 about 150 kilometers (100 mi) south of Moscow, is typical of urban centers in western Russia. Tula's townscape today is a mixture of pre-Soviet historic buildings, drab Soviet-era tenements, and scattered post-Soviet high-rises and single-family houses. The urban cultivators in the foreground are a common sight in a country with limited agricultural land and short growing seasons. Fresh produce is particularly coveted and is widely used for bartering among friends and neighbors in exchange for other hard-to-get commodities. Informal farming on fertile plots of urban land has increased since 1991 as the redistribution of population has channeled rural migrants into cities, where their slow absorption into urban society often requires them to fall back on their food production and preservation skills to supplement their diets and make meager incomes stretch further.

Mauro Galligani/Contrasto/Redux Pictures

Regional ISSUE

What Are Russia's Rights in the Near Abroad?

IN FAVOR OF STRONG RUSSIAN INFLUENCE

"I am delighted that [former] President Medvedev showed the world that we Russians will protect ourselves and our allies in the Near Abroad wherever it's necessary. Those Georgians who think they can ride roughshod over our friends the Ossetians have learned a lesson, and I hope they heed it. As a former officer in the Soviet Army, I have no doubt that nations have to show their strength or they'll get trampled on. I'm still sorry we left Afghanistan in 1989 the way we did. And even if the USSR is no more, we Russians earned the right not to be bullied by upstart leaders like that dreadful Saakashvili in Georgia or that supposedly democratically-elected Yushchenko in Ukraine. Have those people forgotten what we did for them and their countries? We created their national identities, established their republics, built their economies, put them on the map. We built their roads, railroads, bridges, and airports; we taught them Russian and nourished their cultures. We saved the Armenians from the Turks, the Estonians from the Germans, the Mongolians from the Chinese. If the Americans hadn't armed the Afghan extremists, we wouldn't have the Taliban threatening the place today.

"So what thanks do we get? Saakashvili starts a war in South Ossetia and kills Russian soldiers and Ossetian villagers. Chechen terrorists kill Russians in the Caucasus, and all we hear about is that we mistreat minorities. The Latvians insult and offend us at every turn, treating its Russian-speaking residents as second-class citizens. The Ukrainians are cozying up to the European Union even though the millions of Russians in the country oppose it. Now the Americans want to put so-called missile defense systems in Poland and the Czech Republic, and I'm pleased that our president played our Kaliningrad card. I've had it with the high-handed treatment we're getting around our perimeter, and it's time to put a stop to it.

"You can look at the Near Abroad in two ways: as the ring of countries that encircles us or as the Slavic outposts that persist from Kazakhstan to Kosovo. Whichever way you define it, we Russians reserve the right to take care of our own, and we will not stand by as our kinspeople are mistreated, or our homeland threatened, by those who think we are weak and impotent. I hope the Ukrainians and the Moldovans and the Albanians and others who might miscalculate learn a lesson from what happened in Georgia. If we have to, we will take appropriate action, and that includes military action. Our military forces suffered during the Yeltsin years, but those days are over. We have the money to rebuild our forces and we're doing so. We will not be pushed around, and it would be a grave mistake for the rest of the world to see us as weak or lacking resolve. The Soviet Union may have collapsed, but Russia will always be a force to reckon with."

OPPOSED TO STRONG RUSSIAN INFLUENCE

"Talk about the Near Abroad is all the rage in Russia these days. Whether it's the television news, the magazines and newspapers, or talk radio, the Near Abroad is the topic that gets everyone riled up. In truth, this is nothing new—it started even before the USSR broke up two decades ago. Not only were Russians marooned in the former republics, but their friends and allies among the locals had a tough time as well. Those who tried to help save the situation Gorbachev had created were seen as traitors to their people, and in places like Lithuania and Georgia it got pretty ugly.

"As a history teacher, I try to put things in long-term perspective. I don't care what state or nation it is, when you've got the power you tend to abuse it, and even if you don't, you're accused of doing so by association. That certainly was true of the western European colonial powers. Look at France and its 'Near Abroad' in its former colony of Algeria. How many tens of thousands of Frenchmen were killed in the run-up to Algeria's independence, and how many afterward? We Russians feel that we weren't in a similar situation, because our Soviet republics really were not colonies. But millions of Russians did go to the republics to govern, to build infrastructure, to teach, or just to work for the fatherland, and you can be sure that many locals saw these 'foreigners' as power-hungry outsiders. In the Muslim societies we never managed to persuade the people of the irrelevance of religion. In other republics, Latvia for example, there had been sympathies for Nazi Germany and we were viewed as occupiers. Get this: the Lithuanians not long ago launched a (U.S.) $34 billion claim against us for what they call Russia's '50-year occupation.'

"Make no mistake: I don't like it when I hear or read about the mistreatment of Russians or our allies in countries of the Near Abroad. Trying to force Russians to abandon their citizenship and compelling them to pass difficult language tests as a condition for local citizenship is no way to get over the past. But I feel that nothing is gained by the kind of violence that recently took place in South Ossetia and Abkhazia. Some reports say that Georgia's president started the whole thing by unleashing attacks on Russian protective forces; others tell a different story. But the fact is that Russian forces were within Georgia's international borders even before the conflict took its deadly turn, and that was asking for trouble. I have no doubt that the Georgian regime was guilty of discrimination against South Ossetians (and Abkhazians as well), but we're talking here about only tens of thousands of people in a tiny enclave—was it worth risking a wider war over what is essentially a minority-treatment issue?

"I don't think so, but let me tell you—I'm in a small minority here. The small shooting war in Georgia has galvanized Russians. I hope it's not the beginning of a new era in the Near Abroad."

Vote your opinion at www.wiley.com/go/deblijpolling

Asia. Indeed, Soviet foreign policy and power had been projected beyond the Soviet frontier to other continents, from Africa to Middle America. The collapse of the Soviet Union meant that the new Russia, shorn of satellite states [11] in eastern Europe and abandoned by all of the other former Soviet republics, had to completely rethink its position in the world and most immediately in Eurasia. And it had to do so in the knowledge that a total makeover of its economy was the top priority.

The Russian government in 1992 introduced the term Near Abroad [12] for the newly formed countries that surround Russia today. These are for the most part the other former Soviet republics, from the Baltic states to Kazakhstan. These states may now be located "abroad," but seen from Moscow they are so "near"—and together constitute such a pronounced encirclement of the country—that the Russian government feels entitled to take a special interest in them (compare Figs. 2A-7 and 2A-9). What this really means is that Russia will not allow any of these bordering countries to develop a threat of any sort and that it reserves the right to intervene if necessary. It is not that hard to imagine this sense of territorial encirclement in Russia, particularly with the eastward expansion of the EU (now practically on Russia's western doorstep), Islamic fundamentalism in the south, and the swift rise and growing assertiveness of China in the east.

And then there is the issue of Russian minorities who now find themselves living abroad. Although many Russian nationals have returned from the former SSRs, millions of others stayed on. They lived in areas where Russians were in the majority (for example, in eastern Ukraine and in northern Kazakhstan) and where post-Soviet life was not all that different from what it was during Moscow's rule. But elsewhere, Russians who remained in the former SSRs found themselves mistreated in various ways, and they often appealed to Moscow for help. Thus the concept of a Russian "Near Abroad" found its way into Russian discourse. Beyond Russia's borders but of concern to its leaders and people, the "Near Abroad" became geographic shorthand for a Russian sphere of influence, whereby Moscow stood ready to help its fellow ethnics in case of trouble. On the map, the most vivid example of this is the so-called Russian Transition Zone in northern Kazakhstan (Fig. 2A-9), which was tightly integrated into the adjacent Russian sphere during Soviet times. (A larger-scale map would show similar but smaller Russian clusters in Estonia, Latvia, Moldova, and elsewhere.) And Ukraine, which occupies part of the western transition zone, is of the utmost importance as

well (as noted in Chapter 1B), with its eastern half heavily dominated by Russia and home to a large Russian population.

A REALM IN FLUX

Almost 25 years ago, the Soviet Empire collapsed and disintegrated. What remains today is the massive centerpiece of that empire, the Russian Federation. Two-plus decades may seem like a long time, but the current situation still bears the marks of the Soviet era and this very much remains a realm in flux. Soviet times were repressive and economically stagnant, whereas the new Russia has offered greater freedom and business opportunities. Nonetheless, the benefits of this new era have mostly been limited to the favored few, and income inequality continues to widen. By 2011, the masses were increasingly showing their discontent, most notably in anti-regime street protests in Moscow and other cities. They are frustrated with the widespread corruption as well as a post-communist economy that is not a true free market (it is sometimes derisively referred to as mafia-capitalism) and does not provide any of the securities of the old Soviet system. Indeed, a recent survey among Russians showed that half of the population agreed that it was "a great misfortune that the Soviet Union no longer exists."

Demographically, economically, administratively, politically, and geostrategically, Russia is likely to continue to adjust for many years to come. Ideally, relations with

---

At a soccer match between Russia and Poland during the 2012 Euro Tournament, Russian fans 'greeted' the Polish team with a gigantic banner that left little doubt about their convictions—the game was played in Warsaw, Poland, and those fans knew very well that it was televised around the globe, along with their message. There is plenty of breeding ground in Russia for aggressive foreign policy claims in the Near Abroad and beyond. The game ended in a 1-1 tie.

© Photo ITAR-TASS/Valery Sharifulin/Corbis

the Near Abroad remain cordial and peaceful, the Russian Federation itself maintains cohesion, and overall economic well-being improves. Clearly, this depends on more than decision-making in Moscow. The geography of the Russian realm is such that it finds itself at the heart of the Eurasian continent, the Russian Federation itself bordering no less than 15 countries as well as four other realms. Perhaps, in such circumstances, long-term stability is an illusion. To be sure, it is a formidable challenge to manage a country of this enormous size and diversity. In Chapter 2B, we discuss the evolving administrative (spatial) structure of the new Russia and take a closer look at the regions that constitute this unique realm.

POINTS TO PONDER

- High-speed train travel, urgently needed in this far-flung realm, has been very slow to develop. In 2010 the first such route opened between the capital, Moscow, and the leading port and second city, St. Petersburg.

- All of the major transnational empires that were created in the nineteenth century came to an end in the wake of World War I or World War II—except the Russian Empire, which continued in a different guise after 1917 until it finally imploded in 1991.

- Global warming can have major disruptive effects on the ways that people interact with their habitat. But Russians consider themselves to be potential beneficiaries as Siberia's harsh environments moderate and the Arctic Ocean's ice recedes, probably opening up new sea lanes and improving access to major energy deposits buried beneath the seafloor.

- The Russian Federation borders 15 countries and four other geographic realms. Compare that to the conterminous United States, which borders only two countries and two other realms.

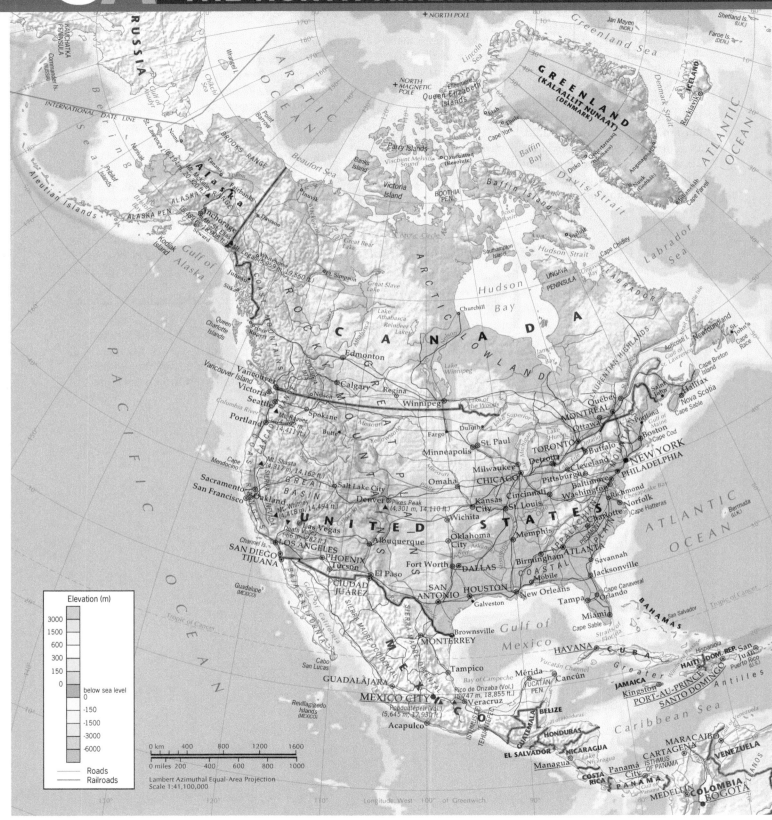

FIGURE 3A-1

© H. J. de Blij, P. O. Muller, and John Wiley & Sons, Inc.

DEFINING the Realm

We turn now to the Western Hemisphere, the two great interconnected continents that separate the Atlantic and Pacific oceans and extend, very nearly, from pole to pole, flanked by numerous islands large and small, indented by gulfs and bays of historic and economic import, and endowed with an enormous range of natural resources. Two continents—North and South—form the Americas, but three geographic realms blanket them (North, Middle, and South). In the context of physical (natural) geography, North America from Canada's Ellesmere Island in the far north to Panama in the south is a continent. In terms of modern human geography, the northern continent is divided into the North American and Middle American realms along a transition zone marked by a political as well as physical boundary between the United States and Mexico (Fig. 3A-1). In Texas, from the Gulf of Mexico to El Paso/Ciudad Juárez, the Rio Grande forms this border. From El Paso westward to the Pacific Ocean, straight-line boundaries, reinforced by fences and walls, separate the North from the Middle. Here, global core and global periphery meet, sometimes contentiously. We begin in North America.

DEFINING THE REALM

North America is constituted by two of the world's most highly advanced countries by virtually every measure of social and economic development. Blessed by an almost unlimited range of natural resources and bonded by trade as well as culture, Canada and the United States are locked in a mutually productive embrace that is reflected by the economic statistics: in an average year of the recent past, about two-thirds of Canadian exports went to the United States, and just over half of Canada's imports came from its southern neighbor. For the United States, Canada is not quite as dominant, but it is still its leading export market and the second biggest importer.

This realm is also defined on the basis of a range of broad cultural traits, from urban landscapes and a penchant for mobility to religious beliefs, language, and political persuasions. Both countries rank among the world's most highly urbanized: nothing symbolizes the North American city as strongly as the skyscrapered panoramas of New York, Chicago, and Toronto—or the vast, beltway-connected suburban expanses of Los Angeles, Washington, and Houston. North Americans are also the most mobile people on Earth. Each year about one out of every eight individuals changes his or her residence, a proportion that has recently declined but still leads the world.

Despite noteworthy multilingualism, in most areas English is both countries' *lingua franca*. And notwithstanding all the religions followed by minorities, the great majority of both Canadians and Americans are Christians. Both states are stable democracies, and both have federal systems of government.

Canadians and Americans also share a passion for the same sports. Baseball and a modified version of American football are popular sports in Canada; more than 20 years ago, the Toronto Blue Jays became the first team outside the United States to win baseball's World Series. Canada's national sport, ice hockey, now has more NHL teams in the U.S. than in Canada, although curling, a slower-paced Canadian pastime, has not exactly captured the American imagination.

No metropolis escaped the U.S. housing crisis of the late 2000s: a foreclosed home on the upscale outskirts of Washington, D.C., 2012.

© Kristoffer Tripplaar/Alamy Limited

major geographic qualities of
NORTH AMERICA

1. North America encompasses two of the world's biggest states territorially (Canada is the second-largest in size; the United States is third).

2. Both Canada and the United States are federal states, but their systems differ. Canada's is adapted from the British parliamentary system and is divided into ten provinces and three territories. The United States separates its executive and legislative branches of government, and it consists of 50 States, the Commonwealth of Puerto Rico, and a number of island territories under U.S. jurisdiction in the Caribbean Sea and the Pacific Ocean.

3. Both Canada and the United States are plural societies. Canada's pluralism is most strongly expressed in regional bilingualism. In the United States, divisions occur largely along ethnic, racial, and income lines.

4. A substantial number of Quebec's French-speaking citizens support a movement that seeks independence for this Canadian province. The movement's high-water mark was reached in the 1995 referendum in which (minority) non-French-speakers were the difference in the narrow defeat of separation. Prospects for a breakup of Canada have been diminishing since 2000 but have not disappeared.

5. North America's population, not large by international standards, is one of the world's most highly urbanized and mobile. Largely propelled by a continuing wave of immigration, the realm's population total is expected to grow by more than one-third over the next half-century.

6. By world standards, this is a rich realm where high incomes and high rates of consumption prevail. North America possesses a highly diversified resource base, but nonrenewable fuel and mineral deposits are consumed prodigiously.

7. North America has long been home to one of the world's great manufacturing complexes that generated a dense, mature urban system. Over the past few decades, North America has come to rely increasingly on a highly advanced information economy and high-technology industries.

8. The two countries heavily depend on each other for supplies of critical raw materials (e.g., Canada is a leading source of U.S. energy imports) and have long been each other's primary trading partners. Today, the North American Free Trade Agreement (NAFTA), which also includes Mexico, is linking all three economies ever more tightly as the remaining barriers to international trade and investment flow are dismantled.

9. Continued immigration and high transnational mobility make for an exceptionally diverse multicultural realm.

Driving from Michigan across southern Ontario to upstate New York does not involve a sharp contrast in cultural landscapes. Americans visiting Canadian cities (and vice versa) find themselves in mostly familiar settings. Canadian cities have fewer impoverished neighborhoods, no ethnic ghettos (although low-income ethnic districts do exist), lower crime rates, and, in general, better public transportation; but rush hour in Toronto very much resembles rush hour in Chicago. The boundary between the two states is porous, even after the events of 9/11. Americans living near the border shop for more affordable medicines in Canada; Canadians who can afford it seek medical treatment in the United States.

None of this is to suggest that Canadians and Americans don't have their differences—they do. Most of these differences may seem subtle to people from outside the realm, but they are important nonetheless, particularly so to Canadians who at times feel dominated by Americans whose political or cultural values they don't always share.

You can even argue over names: if this entire hemisphere is called the Americas, aren't Canadians, Mexicans, and Brazilians as well as others Americans too?

POPULATION CLUSTERS

Although Canada and the United States share many historical, cultural, and economic qualities, they also differ in significant ways, diversifying this realm. The United States, somewhat smaller territorially than Canada, occupies the heart of the North American continent and, as a result, encompasses a greater environmental range. The U.S. population is dispersed across most of the country, forming major concentrations along both the (north-south trending) Atlantic and Pacific coasts (Fig. 3A-2). The overwhelming majority of Canadians, on the other hand, live in an interrupted east-west corridor that extends across southern Canada, mostly within 300 kilometers (200 mi) of the U.S. border. The United States, again unlike Canada, is a

FIGURE 3A-2

© H. J. de Blij, P. O. Muller, and John Wiley & Sons, Inc.

fragmented country in that the broad peninsula of Alaska is part of it (offshore Hawai'i, however, belongs in the Pacific Realm).

Figure 3A-2 reveals that the great majority of both the U.S. and Canadian population resides to the east of a line drawn down the middle of the realm, reflecting the historic core-area development in the east and the later and still-continuing shift to the west, and, in the United States, to the south. Certainly this map shows the urban concentration of North America's population: you can

easily identify cities such as Toronto, Chicago, Denver, Dallas-Fort Worth, San Francisco, and Vancouver. Just under 80 percent of the realm's population is concentrated in cities and towns, a higher proportion even than Europe's.

As the Data Table in Appendix B indicates, the population of the United States, which reached 317 million in 2014, is growing at a rate 25 percent higher than Canada's, and the 400-million mark may be reached as soon as 2050. This is an unusually high rate

Vito Palmisano/Photographer's Choice/Getty Images, Inc.

The central business districts (CBDs) of North America's large cities have distinctive skylines, often featuring architectural icons like the Empire State Building. Indeed, you should have little trouble identifying this CBD: the black profile of Hancock Tower on the shoreline of Lake Michigan just to the right of center is one of the signature structures of downtown Chicago, America's third-largest city. In fact, the only skyscraper more famous than Hancock Tower is Willis Tower, the Western Hemisphere's second-tallest building, from whose 110-story-high Skydeck this photo was taken. Willis Tower??? Absolutely, although it is still far more widely known by its former name of Sears Tower (the original 1973 tenant that relocated its corporate headquarters to suburban Hoffman Estates a quarter-century ago). Today, according to its website, Willis Tower has reinvented itself as one of the world's greenest buildings, in the vanguard of a movement that marks Chicago as the U.S. leader in working toward a more sustainable urban future.

NORTH AMERICA'S PHYSICAL GEOGRAPHY

Physiographic Regions

One of the distinguishing properties of the North American landmass, all of which lies on the North American tectonic plate, is its remarkable variegation into regional physical landscapes. So well defined are many of these landscape regions that we use their names in everyday parlance—for example, when we say that we flew over the Rocky Mountains or drove across the Great Plains or hiked in the Appalachians. These landscapes are called physiographic regions [2], and nowhere else in the hemisphere is their diversity greater than to the north of the Rio Grande (Fig. 3A-3).

In the Far West, the Pacific Mountains extend all the way from Southern California through coastal Canada to Alaska. In the western interior, the Rocky Mountains form a continental backbone from central Alaska to New Mexico. Around the Great Lakes, the low-relief landscapes of the Interior Lowlands and the Great Plains to the west are shared by Canada and the United States, and the international boundary even divides the Great Lakes. In the east, the Appalachian Mountains (as the cross-sectional inset shows, no match for the Rockies) form a corridor of ridges, valleys, and plateaus that represent a familiar topography from Alabama and Georgia to Nova Scotia and Newfoundland. If there is a major physiographic province that belongs to only one of the realm's two countries, it is the Canadian Shield, scoured bare by the Pleistocene glaciers that deposited their pulverized rocks as fertile soil in the U.S. Midwest, that is, in the Interior Lowlands.

Climate

This diversity of landscape is matched by a variety of climates. Take another look at Figure G-7, and you can see the lineaments of landscape mirrored in the contrasts of climate. North America may not have it all—there are no areas of true tropical environment in the North American realm to speak of except at the southern tip of Florida—but does exhibit a great deal of variation. North America contains moist coastal zones and arid interiors, well-watered plains, and even bone-dry deserts. On the world map, *Cf* and *Df* climates are especially good for commercial farming; note how large North America's share of these environments is.

The map leaves no doubt: the farther north you go, the colder it gets, and even though coastal areas derive moderation from warmer offshore waters, which is why there is a Vancouver and a Halifax, the rigors of *continentality* set in not far from the coast. Hot summers, frigid winters, and limited precipitation make high-latitude continental interiors

of growth for a high-income economy, resulting from a combination of natural increase (which leads today) and substantial immigration (expected to lead after 2030).

Although Canada's overall growth rate is significantly lower than that of the United States, immigration contributes proportionally even more to this increase than in the United States. With just over 35 million residents, Canada, like the United States, has been relatively open to legal immigration, and as a result both societies exhibit a high degree of cultural diversity [1] in ancestral and traditional backgrounds. Indeed, Canada recognizes two official languages, English and French (the United States does not even designate English as such); and by virtue of its membership in the British Commonwealth, East and South Asians form a larger sector of Canada's population than Asians and Pacific Islanders do in the United States. On the other hand, cultural diversity in the United States reflects large Hispanic (16.7 percent), African American (13.1 percent), and Asian (5 percent) minorities as well as a wide range of other ethnic backgrounds.

Robust urbanization, substantial immigration, and cultural diversity are defining properties of the human geography of the North American realm. But first we need to become familiar with the physical stage on which the human drama is unfolding.

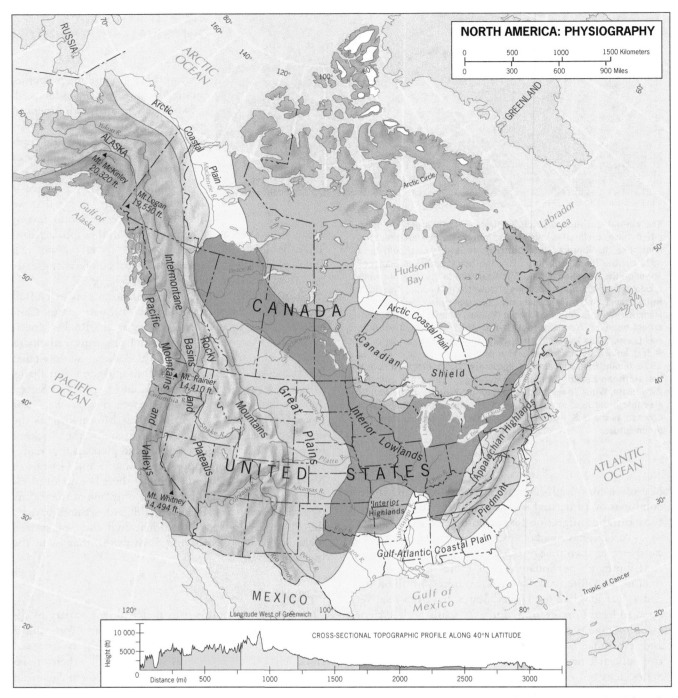

FIGURE 3A-3

© H. J. de Blij, P. O. Muller, and John Wiley & Sons, Inc.

difficult places to make it on the land. Figure G-7 has much to do with the southerly concentration of Canadian population and with the lower densities in the interior throughout the realm.

In the west, especially in the United States, you can see what the Pacific Mountains do to areas inland. Moisture-laden air arrives from the ocean, the mountain wall forces the air upward, cools it, condenses the moisture in it, and produces rain—the rain for which Seattle and Portland as well as other cities of the Pacific Northwest are (in) famous. By the time the air crosses the mountains and descends on the landward side, most of the moisture has been drawn from it, and the forests of the ocean side give way to scrub and brush. This rain shadow effect [3] extends all the way across the Great Plains; North America does not turn moist again until the Gulf of Mexico sends humid tropical air northward into the eastern interior via the Mississippi-Missouri River Basin.

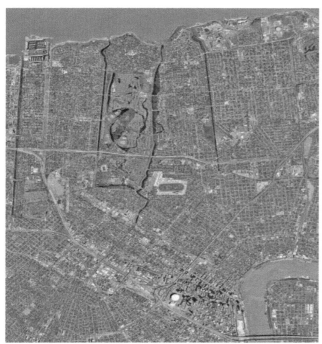 

Digital Globe/Eurimage/Science Source

On August 29, 2005, Category-4 Hurricane Katrina cut a 230,000-square-kilometer (90,000-sq-mi) path of destruction along the Louisiana and Mississippi Gulf Coast after making landfall just west of the mouth of the Mississippi River. Most devastated was the city of New Orleans, 80 percent of which lay underwater in the immediate aftermath of the storm. The pair of aerial photos above shows central New Orleans under normal conditions in the spring of 2004 (left) and two days after the tropical cyclone struck (right). Katrina was by far the most costly natural disaster in U.S. history, and its toll was truly staggering: more than 1800 lives lost, at least 200,000 homes destroyed, nearly a million people displaced, and more than $25 billion in insured property damage. Despite $180 billion in federal aid during the years following the disaster, rebuilding has been patchy and painfully slow. Today, the city's population is still more than 20 percent smaller than before the storm. Tens of thousands of residential properties remain unoccupied, most of them still damaged. The proportion of the population living in poverty stood at 27 percent in 2012, and the number of homeless people in that year was estimated at 6,700, three times the national average. The Big Easy continues to struggle toward an acceptable level of restoration, yet it remains highly vulnerable to hurricanes in the future.

In a very general way, therefore, and not including the coastal strips along the Pacific, nature divides North America into an arid west and a humid east. Again the population map reveals more than a hint of this: draw a line approximately from Lake Winnipeg to the mouth of the Rio Grande, and look at the contrast between the (comparatively) humid east and drier west when it comes to population density. Water is a large part of this story.

Between the Rocky Mountains and the Appalachians, North America lies open to air masses from the frigid north and tropical south. In winter, southward-plunging polar fronts send frosty, bone-dry air masses deep into the heart of the realm, turning even places like Memphis and Atlanta into iceboxes; in summer, hot and humid tropical air surges northward from the Gulf of Mexico, giving Chicago and Toronto a taste of the tropics. Such air masses clash in low-pressure systems along weather fronts loaded with lightning, thunder, and, frequently, dangerously destructive tornadoes. And the summer heat brings an additional threat to the Gulf-Atlantic Coastal Plain (Fig. 3A-3): hurricanes capable of inflicting catastrophic devasta-

tion on low-lying areas (see photo pair above). These tropical cyclones also prune natural vegetation, replenish underground water reservoirs, fill natural lakes, and flush coastal channels.

Great Lakes and Great Rivers

Two great drainage systems lie between the Rockies and the Appalachians: (1) the five Great Lakes that drain into the St. Lawrence River and the Atlantic Ocean, and (2) the mighty Mississippi-Missouri system that carries water from a vast interior watershed to the Gulf of Mexico, where the Mississippi forms one of the world's major *deltas*. Both natural systems have been modified by human engineering. In the case of the St. Lawrence Seaway, a series of locks and canals has created a direct shipping route, via the Great Lakes and their outlet, from the Midwest to the Atlantic. The Mississippi and Missouri rivers have been fortified by artificial levees that, while failing to contain the worst of flooding, have enabled farmers to cultivate the most fertile of American soils.

NATIVE AMERICANS AND EUROPEAN SETTLEMENT

When the first Europeans set foot on North American soil, the continent was inhabited by millions of people whose ancestors had reached the Americas from Asia via Alaska, and possibly also across the Pacific, more than 14,000 years before (and perhaps as long as 30,000 years ago). In search of Asia, the Europeans misnamed them Indians. These Native Americans or *First Nations*—as they are now called, respectively, in the United States and Canada—were organized into hundreds of nations with a rich mosaic of languages and a great diversity of cultures (Fig. 3A-4). Canada's First Nations also include Métis (of mixed native and European descent) and the Inuit (formerly called Eskimos) of the far north.

The eastern nations were the first to bear the brunt of the European invasion. By the end of the eighteenth century, ruthless and land-hungry settlers had driven most of the native peoples living along the Atlantic and Gulf coasts from their homes and lands, initiating a westward push that was to devastate indigenous society. Today, there are only about 3 million remaining Native Americans in the United States and about one-third that number in Canada. In the U.S. they are left with only about 4 percent

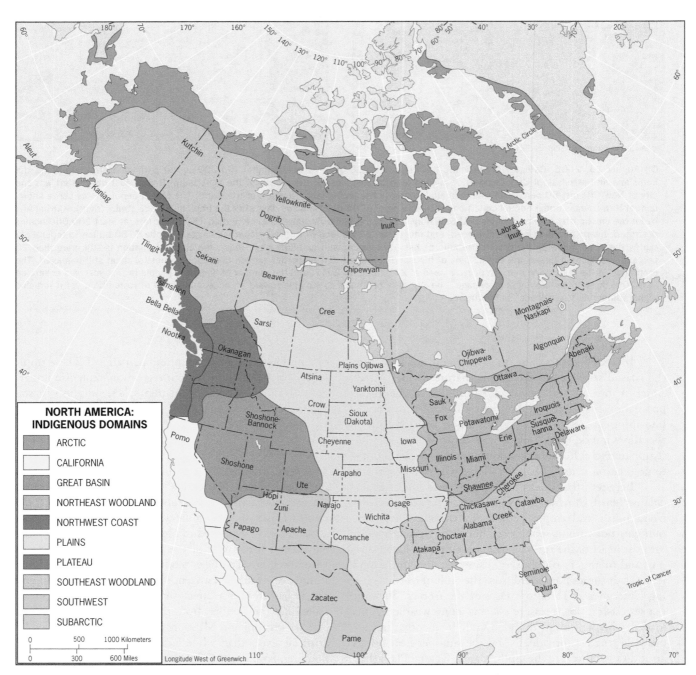

FIGURE 3A-4

© H. J. de Blij, P. O. Muller, and John Wiley & Sons, Inc.

of the national territory in the form of mostly impoverished reservations. Aboriginal peoples today are better off territorially in Canada where they hold titles to large tracts of land, especially in the northern sectors of British Columbia and Quebec (but keep in mind that northern Canada is relatively empty to begin with, and that environmental conditions up north can be quite harsh).

The current population geography of North America is rooted in the colonial era of the seventeenth and eighteenth centuries that was dominated by Britain and France. The French sought mainly to organize a lucrative fur-trading network, while the British established settlements along the coast of what is now the eastern seaboard of the United States (the oldest, Jamestown, was founded in Virginia more than four centuries ago).

The British colonies soon became differentiated in their local economies, a diversity that was to endure and later shape much of North America's cultural geography. The northern colony of New England (Massachusetts Bay and surroundings) specialized in commerce; the southern Chesapeake Bay colony (Virginia and Maryland) emphasized the plantation farming of tobacco; the Middle Atlantic area lying in between (southeastern New York, New Jersey, eastern Pennsylvania) formed the base for a number of smaller, independent-farmer colonies.

These neighboring colonies thrived and yearned to expand, but the British government responded by closing the inland frontier and tightening economic controls. This policy provoked general opposition in the colonies, followed by the revolutionary challenge that was to lead to independence and the formation of the United States of America by the late 1780s. The acquisition of more distant western territories followed in short order (Fig. 3A-5).

CULTURAL FOUNDATIONS

The modern American creed, if one can be identified, has been characterized by urban geographer Brian Berry as exhibiting an adventurous drive, a liking for things new, an ability to move, a sense of individualism, an aggressive pursuit of goals and ambition, a need for societal acceptance, and a firm sense of destiny. These qualities are not unique to modern U.S. culture, of course, but in combination they seem to have created a particular and pervasive mindset that is reflected in many ways in this geographic realm. Generally speaking, these tendencies tend to translate into an intense pursuit of educational and other goals and high aspirations for upward socioeconomic mobility. Thus the *American Dream*, whether a genuine prospect or an ideological fabrication, is very much an expression of this set of cultural values.

Facilitating these aspirations is **language**. None of these goals would be within reach for so many were it not for the use of English throughout most of the realm. In Europe, by contrast, language inhibits the mobility so routinely practiced by Americans: workers moving from Poland to Ireland found themselves at a disadvantage in competition with immigrants from Ghana or Sri Lanka. In North America, a worker from Arkansas would not even consider language to be an issue when applying for a job in Vancouver.

As we shall see, the near-universality of English in North America is diminishing, but English continues to be the dominant medium of interaction. Interestingly, English in the United States is undergoing a change that is affecting it worldwide: in areas where it is the second language it is blending with the local tongue, producing hybrids just as is happening in Nigeria ("Yorlish"), Singapore ("Singlish"), and the Philippines ("Taglish"). English, therefore, may become the Latin of the twenty-first century: Latin also produced blends that eventually consolidated into Italian, French, Spanish, and the other Romance languages.

Also reflecting the cultural values cited above is the role of **religion**, which sets American (more so than Canadian) culture apart from much of the rest of the Western world. The overwhelming majority of North Americans express a belief in God, and a large majority regularly attend church, in contrast to much of Europe. Three out of four people in the United States say they belong to a religion, and four out of ten say they attend a religious service once a week (more than in Iran!). Religious observance is a virtual litmus test for political leaders; no other developed country prints "In God We Trust" on its currency.

Figure 3A-6 shows the mosaic of Christian faiths that blankets the realm, but a map at this scale can only suggest the broadest outlines of what is a much more intricate pattern. Protestant denominations are estimated to number in the tens of thousands in North America, and no map could show them all. Southern (and other) Baptists form the majority across the U.S. Southeast from Texas to Virginia, Lutherans in the Upper Midwest and northern Great Plains, Methodists in a belt across the Lower Midwest, and Mormons in the interior West centered on Utah. Roman Catholicism prevails in most of Canada as well as the U.S. Northeast and Southwest, where ethnic Irish and Italian adherents form majorities in the Northeast and Hispanics in the Southwest. Behind these patterns lie histories of proselytism, migration, conflict, and competition, but tolerance of diverse religious (even nonreligious) views and practices is a hallmark of this realm.

On the other hand, U.S. culture does have its complexities, and one example will suffice. This is in many respects the freest country in the world, and it certainly prides itself as such. Yet the United States also has the largest prison population of the developed Western world: about 2.4 million or 1 for every 100 adults. That is 8 times as many as in Canada, 9 times as many as in Germany, and 12 times as many as in Japan. It is also 3 times the rate in Iran and even exceeds the number in Russia by a wide margin. It wasn't always like this: the proportion of the population behind bars has quadrupled since 1970, mainly as a result of (overly?) harsh laws and sentencing. This may have produced a safer country, but the cost is enormous—financially (at around $25,000 per year per inmate) as well as socially, because incarceration affects so many people (not just the inmates but also their relatives, dependents, and social networks).

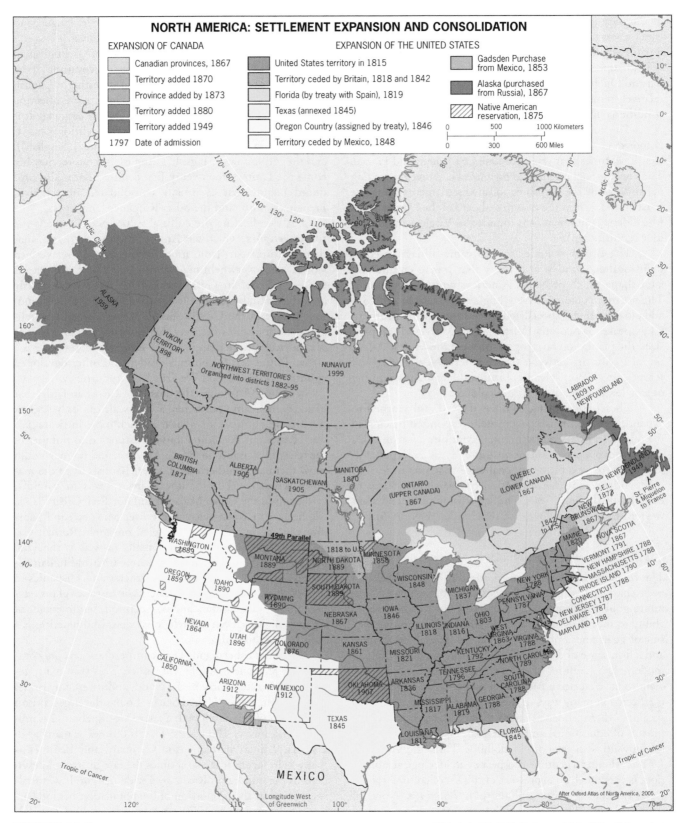

NORTH AMERICA: SETTLEMENT EXPANSION AND CONSOLIDATION

EXPANSION OF CANADA

- Canadian provinces, 1867
- Territory added 1870
- Province added by 1873
- Territory added 1880
- Territory added 1949
- 1797 Date of admission

EXPANSION OF THE UNITED STATES

- United States territory in 1815
- Territory ceded by Britain, 1818 and 1842
- Florida (by treaty with Spain), 1819
- Texas (annexed 1845)
- Oregon Country (assigned by treaty), 1846
- Territory ceded by Mexico, 1848
- Gadsden Purchase from Mexico, 1853
- Alaska (purchased from Russia), 1867
- Native American reservation, 1875

FIGURE 3A-5

© H. J. de Blij, P. O. Muller, and John Wiley & Sons, Inc.

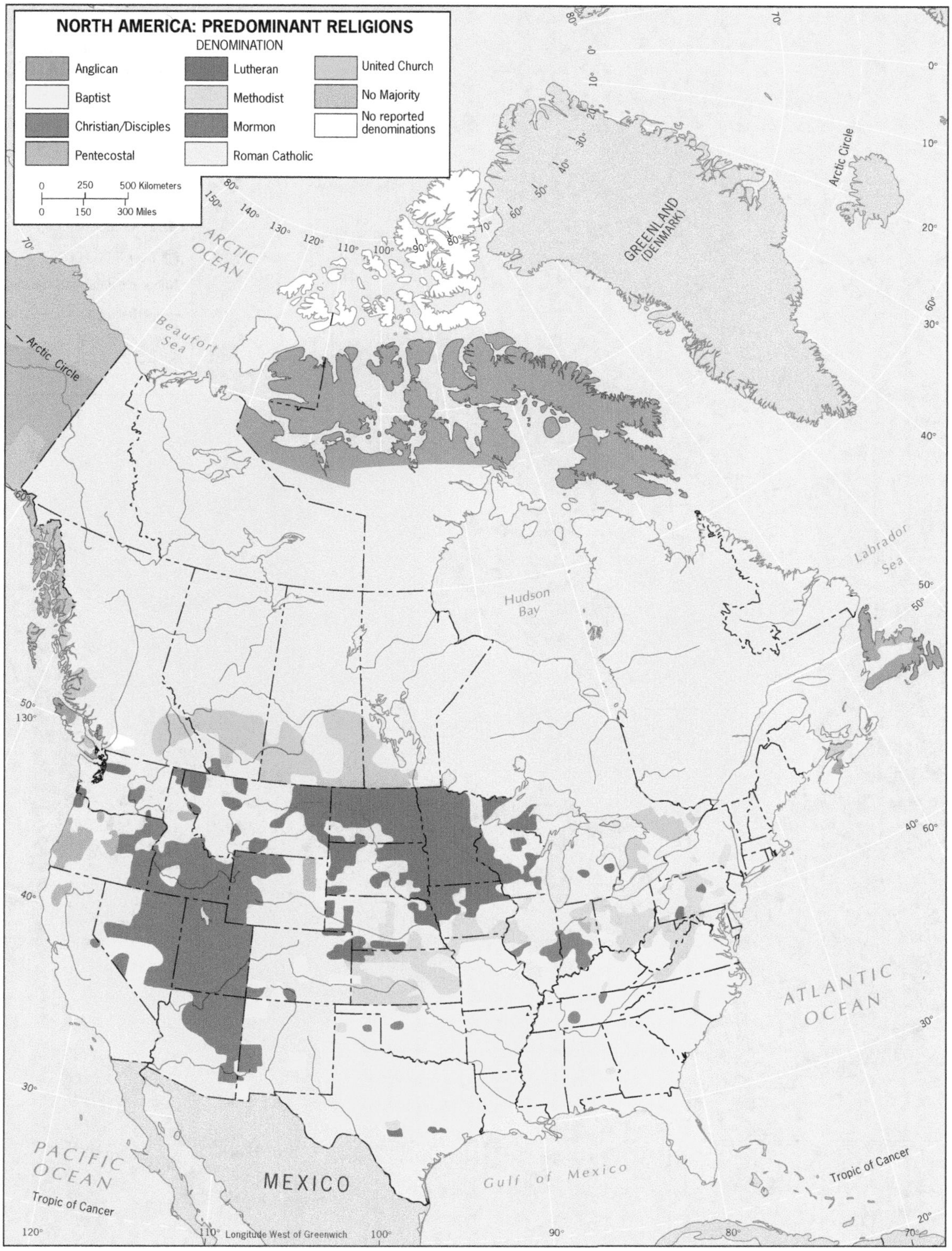

NORTH AMERICA: PREDOMINANT RELIGIONS
DENOMINATION

Anglican
Baptist
Christian/Disciples
Pentecostal
Lutheran
Methodist
Mormon
Roman Catholic
United Church
No Majority
No reported denominations

FIGURE 3A-6

© H. J. de Blij, P. O. Muller, and John Wiley & Sons, Inc.

THE FEDERAL MAP OF NORTH AMERICA

The two states that constitute North America may have arrived at their administrative frameworks with different motives and at different rates of speed, but the result is unmistakably similar: their internal political geographies are dominated by straight-line boundaries of administrative convenience (Fig. 3A-7). In comparatively few places, physical features such as rivers or the crests of mountain ranges mark internal boundaries, but by far the greater length of

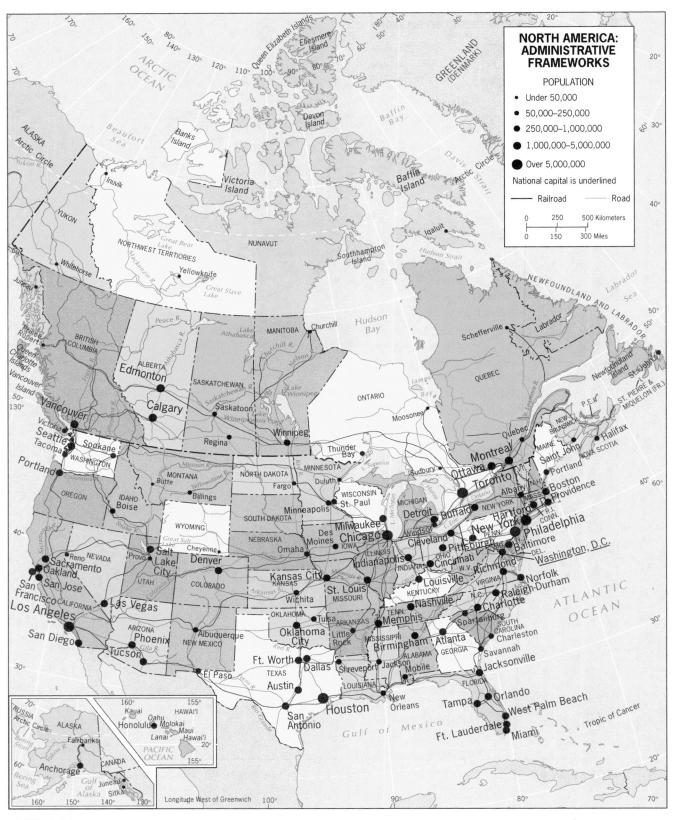

FIGURE 3A-7

© H. J. de Blij, P. O. Muller, and John Wiley & Sons, Inc.

boundaries is ruler-straight. Even most of the international boundary between Canada and the United States west of the Great Lakes coincides with a parallel of latitude, 49°N.

The reasons are all too obvious: the framework was laid out before, in some areas long before, significant white settlement occurred. There was something arbitrary about these delineations, but by delimiting the internal administrative units early and clearly, governments precluded later disputes over territory and resources. In any case, neither Canada nor the United States was to become a unitary (centralized) state: both countries are *federal states*. The Canadians call their primary subdivisions provinces, whereas in the United States they are, as the country's name implies, States.

It is no matter of trivial pursuit to take a careful look at some of the provinces and States that compartmentalize this realm, because some are of greater consequence than others. We have already noted the special significance of mainly French-cultured Quebec, which still occupies a unique position in federal Canada. In many ways the key Canadian province is Ontario, containing the country's largest and most globalized city (Toronto) as well as the capital (Ottawa) on its eastern river border with Quebec. In the United States, key States in the political and economic geography of the federation (indeed the four most populated, in descending order) are California facing the Pacific, Texas bordering Mexico, Florida pointing toward the Caribbean and South America beyond, and New York with its window on the Atlantic.

The rectangular layout of the realm seems to symbolize North America's modernity and its stability, whereas the federal structure itself (with considerable autonomy at the State or provincial level) reflects the culture of freedom and independence. If federalism works within these high-income economies, shouldn't the rest of the world emulate it? Federalism does have its assets, but it also carries some significant liabilities.

THE DISTRIBUTION OF NATURAL RESOURCES

One of these liabilities has to do with the variable allotment of natural resources among the States and provinces. In Canada, Alberta is favored with massive energy reserves (and more may be in the offing), but its provincial government is not always eager to see the federal administration take that wealth to assist less affluent provinces. In the United States, when oil prices are high Texas and Oklahoma benefit while California's budget suffers. So it is important to compare the map of natural resources (Fig. 3A-8) with the one of States and provinces.

Water certainly is a natural resource, and North America as a realm is comparatively well supplied with it

© Jim Havey/Alamy

Wind "farms" are spreading to many more places in North America as the clean-energy campaign to generate electricity from sources other than fossil fuels accelerates. This cluster of modern wind turbines on a cattle ranch in southern Wyoming (the livestock provide a sense of scale) exploits a flat-floored windstream corridor between areas of higher relief.

despite concerns over long-term prospects in the American Southwest and the Great Plains, where some States depend on sources in other States. Another concern focuses on lowering water tables in some of North America's most crucial aquifers (underground water reserves) in which a combination of overuse and decreasing replenishment suggests that supply problems may arise.

North America is endowed with abundant reserves of *minerals* that are mainly found in three zones: the Canadian Shield north of the Great Lakes, the Appalachian Mountains in the east, and the mountain ranges of the west. The Canadian Shield contains substantial iron ore, nickel, copper, gold, uranium, and diamonds. The Appalachians yield lead, zinc, and iron ore. And the western mountain zone has significant deposits of copper, lead, zinc, molybdenum, uranium, silver, and gold.

In terms of fossil fuel [4] energy resources (oil, natural gas, coal), North America is also quite well endowed, though the realm's voracious demand, the highest in the world, cannot be met by domestic supplies alone and necessitates an enormous need for imports. Figure 3A-8 displays the distribution of oil, natural gas, and coal.

The leading *oil*-production areas lie (1) along and offshore from the Gulf Coast, where the floor of the Gulf of Mexico is yielding a growing share of the output; (2) in the Midcontinent District, from western Texas to eastern Kansas; and (3) along Alaska's North Slope facing the Arctic Ocean. An important development is taking place in Canada's northeastern Alberta, where oil is being drawn from deposits of *tar sands* in the vicinity of the boomtown of Fort McMurray. The process is expensive and can reward

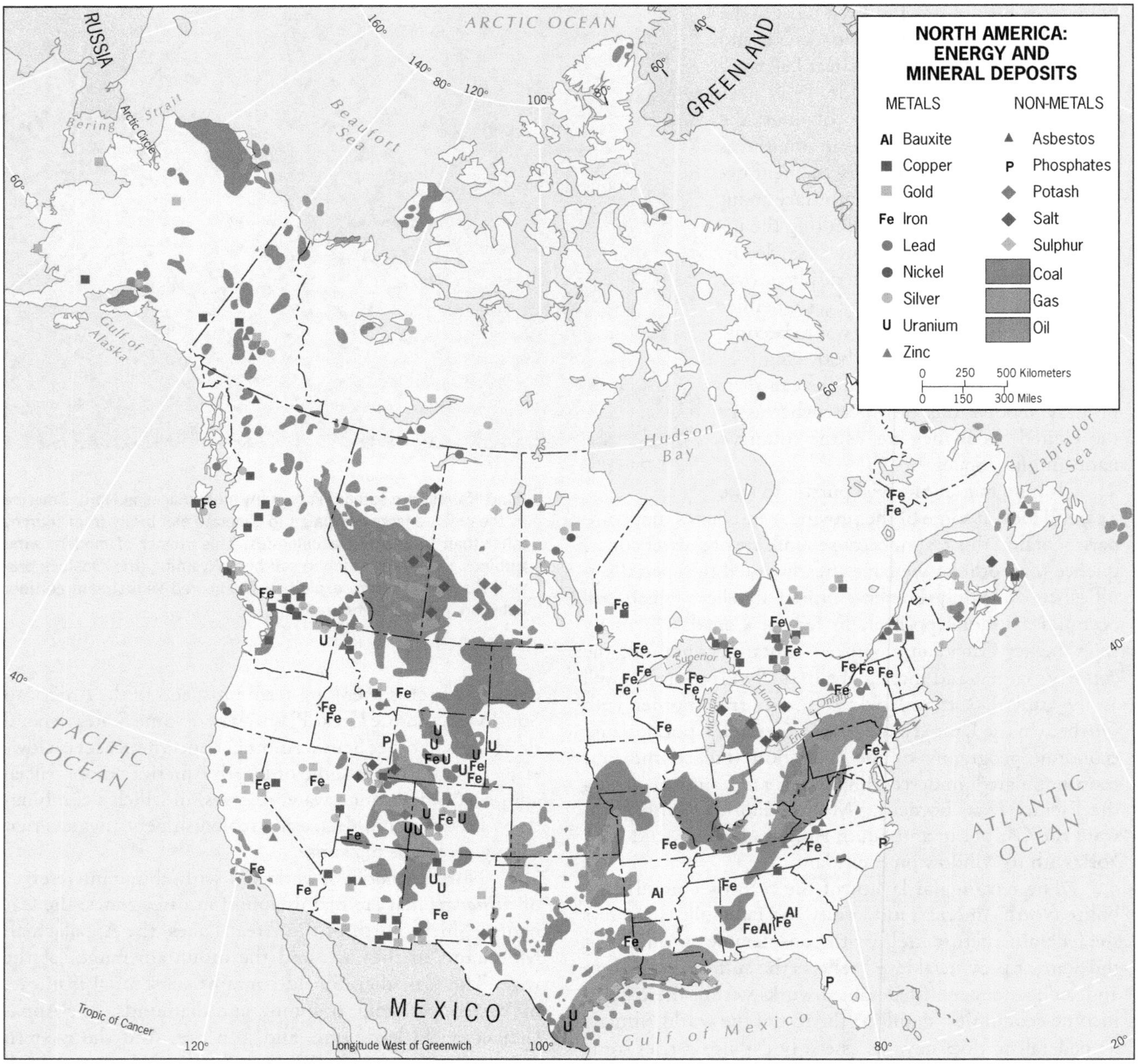

FIGURE 3A-8

© H. J. de Blij, P. O. Muller, J. Nijman, and John Wiley & Sons, Inc.

investors only when the price of oil is comparatively high, but the reserves of oil estimated to be contained here may exceed those of Saudi Arabia (we will have more to say about the impact of Alberta's tar sands in Chapter 3B).

The distribution of **natural gas** reserves resembles that of oilfields because petroleum and natural gas tend to be found in similar geological formations (i.e., the floors of ancient shallow seas). What the map cannot reveal is the volume of production, in which this realm leads the world (Russia and Iran lead in proven reserves). That output has risen dramatically since 2000 as natural gas has become the fuel of choice for electricity generation in North America. Driving this expansion has been the widespread application

of hydraulic fracturing (*fracking*) technology. By injecting pressurized fluids into deeply buried shale rocks to create fractures, vast quantities of trapped gas can be extracted, resulting in surging supplies and nosediving prices.

The **coal** reserves of North America, perhaps the largest on the planet, are found in Appalachia, beneath the Great Plains of the United States as well as Canada, and in the southern Midwest among other places. These reserves guarantee an adequate supply for centuries to come, although coal has become a less desirable fuel due its polluting emissions that contribute to global warming.

Given the relative scarcity of oil and the geopolitical disadvantages of having to import nearly half of what is needed in the United States (ca. 40 percent in 2012), you might expect nuclear energy to be more ubiquitous, especially since it is relatively cheap to produce. There are just over 100 nuclear power plants in the United States providing about one-fifth of all electrical energy (Canada has 19 plants that produce 15 percent of the country's electricity). But ever since the notorious leak and near-calamity at Three Mile Island (Pennsylvania) in 1979, the fear of nuclear accidents is pervasive. Since then, not a single new nuclear plant has been approved by the government.

URBANIZATION AND THE SPATIAL ECONOMY

Industrial Cities

When the Industrial Revolution crossed the Atlantic and touched down in America in the 1870s, it took hold so successfully and advanced so robustly that only 50 years later North America was surpassing Europe as the world's mightiest industrial complex. Industrialization progressed in tandem with urbanization as manufacturing plants in need of large labor supplies were built in and near cities. This, in turn, propelled rural-urban migration (including the migration of African Americans from the South to northern cities during the first half of the twentieth century) and the growth of individual cities. At a broader scale, a *system* of new cities emerged that specialized in the collection and processing of raw materials and the distribution of manufactured products. This urban system [5] was interconnected through a steadily expanding network of railroads, themselves a product of the Industrial Revolution.

As new technologies and innovations emerged, and specializations such as Detroit's automobile industry strengthened, an American Manufacturing Belt [6] (that extended into southern Ontario) evolved into the foundation of a North American Core (Fig. 3A-9). This core area, on the way to becoming the world's most productive and important, contained the majority of the realm's industrial activity and leading cities, including New York, Chicago, Toronto, and Pittsburgh (the "steel city").

In the course of intertwined urbanization and industrialization, the spatial economy of North America underwent profound changes. The ***primary*** sector, involving the extraction of raw materials from nature (agriculture, mining, fishing), was rapidly mechanized, and the workforce in this sector shrank considerably. Employment in the ***secondary*** sector, using the input of raw materials and manufacturing them into finished products, grew rapidly. The ***tertiary*** sector, entailing all kinds of services to support production and consumption (banking, retail, transport) expanded as well. Both the secondary and tertiary sectors were overwhelmingly concentrated in cities.

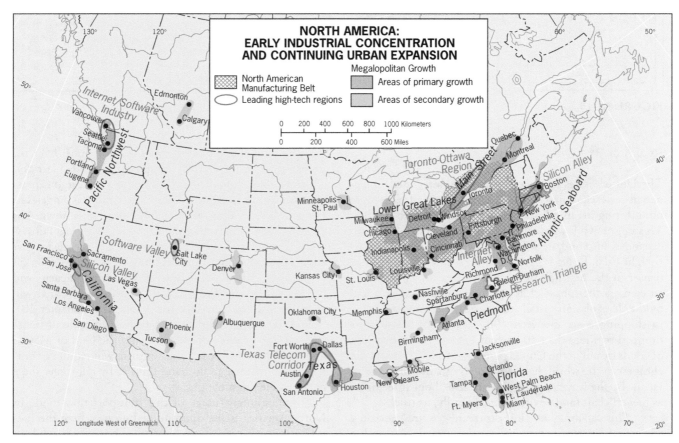

FIGURE 3A-9

© H. J. de Blij, P. O. Muller, and John Wiley & Sons, Inc.

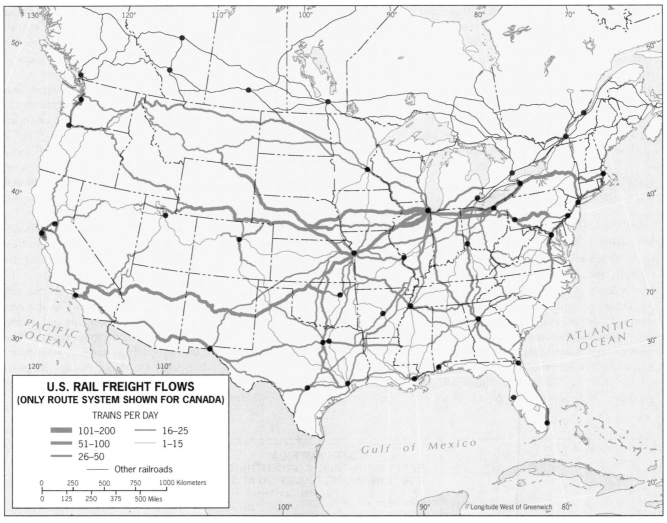

FIGURE 3A-10

© H. J. de Blij, P. O. Muller, J. Nijman, and John Wiley & Sons, Inc.

Realm of Railroads

The United States first became a single, integrated, continental-scale economy when long-distance railroads were built during the middle decades of the nineteenth century. This rail network was launched in the Northeast and soon expanded into and across the Midwest, the realm's industrial heartland (Fig. 3A-10). The realm's network grew denser in the first half of the twentieth century and then entered another phase of development after 1980, marked by the deregulation of rail transport services and a decline in shipping costs. Between 1981 and 2012, those costs dropped by more than 50 percent, making the movement of goods by rail in the United States and Canada among the cheapest in the world, half of what it costs in Europe or in Japan. By the way, freight trains are also about three times as fuel efficient (and environment-friendly) as trucks.

This far-flung rail infrastructure requires not only constant maintenance but also frequent updating—another advantage of the privatized North American rail system is that the individual rail companies pay for (most of) this. One example is the recently completed Alameda Corridor, a major project involving a 20-mile-long rail cargo express line that links the ports of Long Beach and Los Angeles to the Southern California mainlines near downtown Los Angeles (which from there connect to the national rail system). It consists of a series of bridges and underpasses that allow fast and uninterrupted transport, separated from all other traffic. And in this decade, even more rail capacity will be needed. For instance, in 2015 the Panama Canal will open its enlarged third lane (diagrammed in Chapter 4B). That is bound to translate into a major increase of trans-Pacific cargo headed for U.S. ports on the Gulf of Mexico and the Atlantic seaboard; this, in turn, will require a commensurate increase in overland transfer by rail to get these goods to their destinations.

Interestingly, usage of this transportation mode in North America is the opposite of Europe's: here the railroads primarily carry cargo rather than passengers, while in the European realm it is the other way around. Rail freight in North America accounts for about 42 percent of the entire freight market (that also includes trucking, shipping, and air transport), which ranks it among the highest in the world's wealthy countries. Although the largest single cargo share is claimed by coal (38 percent and dropping), the fastest growing category of cargo is what is called "intermodal"— truck-trailer containers stacked onto railroad flatcars at ports and other break-of-bulk points.

Deindustrialization and Suburbanization

Cities continued to evolve, along with the nature of the economy and with the development of new transportation and communication technologies. The mass introduction of automobiles and the accompanying construction of a large-scale highway system, especially after World War II, had two major effects on cities. First, it resulted in much higher mobility and interconnectedness among cities. Second, it propelled a process of *suburbanization*—the transformation from compact city to widely dispersed metropolis through the evolution of residential suburbia into a complete outer city [7] with its own businesses and industries, sports and entertainment complexes, and myriad other amenities. As the newly urbanized suburbs increasingly captured major economic activities, many central cities saw their comparative status diminish.

Importantly, this transformation coincided with the deindustrialization [8] that hit American cities after 1970: the loss of manufacturing (and jobs) due to automation and the relocation of production to countries with lower wages.

While the suburban outer cities became the destination of intrametropolitan migrants and of economic activity and employment in the service sector, many once-thriving and predominant CBDs were now all but reduced to serving the less affluent populations that increasingly dominated the central city's close-in neighborhoods. The fate of Detroit is often cited as exemplifying this sequence of events, but to a certain degree all major U.S. cities suffered.

The Information Economy and City Regions

Since the 1980s, a number of North American cities (but not all) have bounced back from the destructive effects of deindustrialization and unemployment. The ***information economy***—embodied in the *quaternary* sector—had arrived. Many northern cities had lost population and underwent "hollowing out" for nearly two decades, but the tide turned again. Employment in the tertiary sector started to grow rapidly, especially in high-technology, producer services (such as consulting, advertising, and accounting), finance, research and development, and the like. Indeed, with the onset of the digital era, most of these information-rich services evolved into quaternary activities. The geography of the information economy is quite different from that of the old manufacturing industries and is still not fully understood. Some of it concentrates in established CBDs like Midtown Manhattan; some of it locates around important hubs of the Internet infrastructure to benefit from maximum bandwidth (e.g., North Dallas); and still other activities cluster in suburban areas containing large pools of highly skilled workers such as

From the Field Notes . . .

"Monitoring the urbanization of U.S. suburbs for the past four decades has brought us to Tyson's Corner, Virginia on many a field trip and data-gathering foray. It is now hard to recall from this recent view that less than 50 years ago this place was merely a near-rural crossroads. But as nearby Washington, D.C. steadily decentralized, 'Tyson's' capitalized on its unparalleled regional accessibility (its Capital Beltway location at the intersection with the radial Dulles Airport Toll Road) to attract a seemingly endless parade of high-level retail facilities, office complexes, and a plethora of supporting commercial services. Today, this suburban downtown ranks among the largest business districts in all of North America. But it also exemplifies urban sprawl, and in 2009 its developers, tenants, and county government formed a coalition to transform Tyson's into a true city characterized by smarter, greener development."

© Andy Ryan Photography

www.conceptcaching.com

Silicon Valley or North Carolina's Research Triangle. The largest and best known high-technology clusters in North America are mapped in Figure 3A-9.

Northern California's **Silicon Valley**—the world's leading center for computer research and development, and the headquarters of the United States' microprocessor industry—exquisitely illustrates the locational dynamics of this newest sector of the spatial economy. Proximity to Stanford, a world-class research university; adjacent to cosmopolitan San Francisco; the major local concentration of highly educated and skilled workers; a strong business culture; ample local investment capital; high-quality housing; and a scenic area with good weather—all combining to make Silicon Valley a prototype for similar developments elsewhere, and not just in North America. Under different names (*technopolis* is used in Brazil, France, and Japan; *science park* in China, Taiwan, and South Korea), such ultramodern, campus-like complexes symbolize the digital economy just as the smoke-belching factory did the industrial age of the past.

Polycentric Cities

Fly into any large American metropolitan region, and you will see the high-rises of suburban downtowns encircling the old central-city CBD, some of them boasting their own impressive skylines (see photo in *From the Field Notes*). In Canada, where such deconcentration has had more to do with lower land values outside the city centers, this spatial pattern has become common as well, although most Canadian cities remain more compact than the far-flung U.S. metropolis.

Thus the overall structure of the modern North American metropolis is polycentric and resembles a pepperoni pizza (Fig. 3A-11) in its general form. The traditional CBD still tends to be situated at the center, much of its former cross-traffic diverted by beltways; but the outer city's CBD-scale nodes are both ultramodern and thriving. Efforts to attract businesses and higher-income residents back to the old CBD sometimes involve the construction of multiple-use high-rises that often displace low-income residents, resulting in conflicts and lawsuits. The revitalization and upgrading—or gentrification [9]—of crumbling downtown-area neighborhoods increases real estate values as well as taxes, which tends to drive lower-income, long-time residents from their homes. The revival of old CBDs and/or part of their immediate surroundings is happening in numerous urban areas, from Manhattan's Harlem to downtown Seattle; but the growth and development of large interconnected metropolitan regions marked by multiple urban centers is certain to continue.

Effects of the Great Recession

The financial crisis that erupted in the United States in 2008, and soon assumed global proportions, was concentrated in the banking sector; it had much to do with excessive mortgage lending and borrowing, and with the increasingly nontransparent trade in mortgages. Although

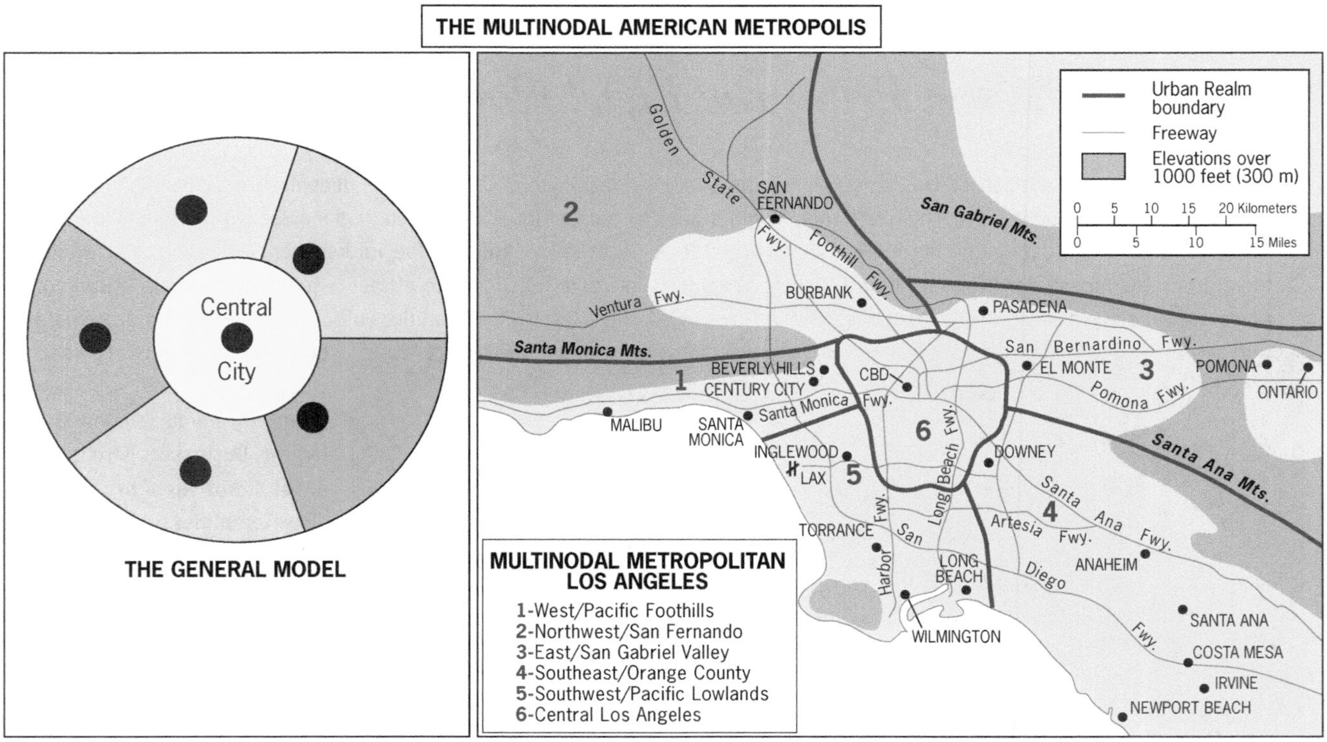

THE MULTINODAL AMERICAN METROPOLIS

THE GENERAL MODEL

MULTINODAL METROPOLITAN LOS ANGELES
1-West/Pacific Foothills
2-Northwest/San Fernando
3-East/San Gabriel Valley
4-Southeast/Orange County
5-Southwest/Pacific Lowlands
6-Central Los Angeles

A   B

© H. J. de Blij, P. O. Muller, and John Wiley & Sons, Inc.

FIGURE 3A-11

many banks got into serious trouble for having accumulated what were clinically labeled "toxic assets," millions of American households fell victim as their mortgages became ever more difficult to afford. The crisis was in large part a housing (or mortgage), crisis and one of the lessons learned from it was how essential this sector has become to the twenty-first-century economy.

The resulting major economic downturn—quickly dubbed the Great Recession—took on unusually clear geographical dimensions precisely because it was so closely connected to housing (which can be regarded as capital fixed in place). Thus the crisis affected some places more severely than others, and the impact was most devastating where housing values had risen unrealistically in the years preceding 2008. In those real estate markets, there had seemed no limit to the escalation of home prices. Buyers were betting on continued appreciation, and many bought for speculative purposes with the intention of selling in the near future for a tidy profit. The banks propelled everything along with easy-to-obtain home loans, sometimes with variable interest rates they knew would prove fatal to buyers at a later stage. When the bubble finally burst, housing prices nosedived and myriad homeowners went under water as their home now became worth less than the value of their mortgage. This situation is referred to as ***negative equity*** (equity being the difference between market value and mortgage balance), a problem because it renders homeowners less affluent. In

these circumstances, they cannot afford to sell because to pay off the bank would result in a significant loss.

The scale of this housing crisis was enormous, and its duration has been especially painful. The first peak was reached in early 2009, when a staggering 28 percent of all mortgaged residential properties in the United States— almost 14 million homes—were affected. But worse was yet to come. After a dip in 2010, a second peak was reached in early 2011 (31 percent/just over 15 million homes). The level has fluctuated since then, and the newest data at press time (late 2012) indicated a return to 28 percent, possibly the beginning of a downward trend in response to improving national economic conditions.

Figure 3A-12 shows that negative-equity conditions vary considerably by State. Hardest hit were Nevada, Florida, Arizona, Georgia, and Michigan (in that order)— where the housing bubble had been at its greatest during the 2000s. It should also be noted that the crisis was particularly severe in what were until recently fast-growing metropolitan areas. In Nevada, worst off were Las Vegas and its suburbs as well as Reno; in Florida, topping the list were Miami, Orlando, and Tampa; and in Arizona, most affected were Phoenix and especially its suburb of Glendale. Michigan's high ranking, however, reflected a different situation because this State's economic problems were deeply rooted in the job losses associated with the long-term decline of the automobile industry. This is yet another reminder that

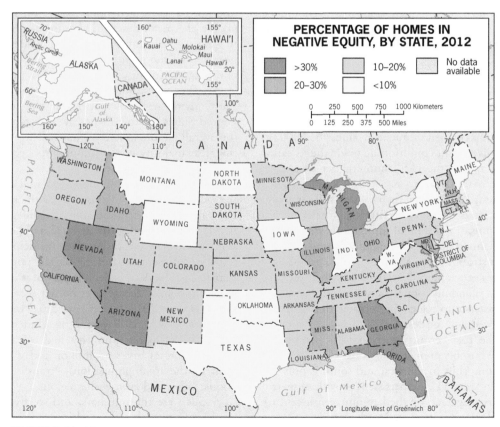

FIGURE 3A-12   © H. J. de Blij, P. O. Muller, J. Nijman, and John Wiley & Sons, Inc.

deindustrialization in the American Manufacturing Belt has forged a widening economic gap between Rustbelt cities like Detroit and such booming Sunbelt counterparts as Atlanta and Dallas-Fort Worth.

As the U.S. economy spiraled downward during the prolonged Great Recession, unemployment rose, stock markets experienced major jolts, and more and more people had difficulty maintaining homes financed by negative-equity-plagued mortgages. This swiftly led to an alarming rise in foreclosures, led by the States with the highest negative-equity percentages. Nevada has topped all the others since 2008, and even in 2012 an astonishing 1 out of 56 mortgaged properties in that State were foreclosed.

The effects of the economic crisis on Canada's housing market were less severe. Canadian banks had been more conservative than their U.S. counterparts in their mortgage lending, and the housing sector remained relatively healthy. Nonetheless, the crisis quickly became global in scope and Canada was not spared some of its harmful effects.

THE MAKING OF A MULTICULTURAL REALM

The Virtues of Mobility and Immigration

Given the mobility of North America's population, the immigrant streams that continue to diversify it, the economic changes affecting it, and the forces acting upon it, the population distribution map (Fig. 3A-2) should be viewed as the latest still in a motion picture, one that has been unreeling for four centuries. Slowly at first, then with accelerating speed after 1800, North Americans pushed their settlement frontier westward to the Pacific. Even today, such shifts continue. Not only does the "center of gravity" of population continue to move westward, but within the United States it is also shifting southward—the latter a drift that has gained momentum since the 1960s as the advent of universal air conditioning made the so-called Sunbelt [10] States of the U.S. southern tier ever more attractive to internal migrants.

The current population map is the still-changing product of numerous forces. For centuries, North America has attracted a pulsating influx of immigrants who, in the faster-growing United States, were rapidly assimilated into the societal mainstream. Throughout the realm, people have sorted themselves geographically to maximize their proximity to evolving economic opportunities, and they have shown little resistance to relocating as these opportunities successively favored new locales.

During the past century, such transforming forces have generated a number of major migrations [11] of which the still-continuing shift to the west and south is only the latest. Five others were: (1) the persistent growth of metropolitan areas, first triggered by the late-nineteenth-century Industrial Revolution's impact in North America; (2) the large-scale movement of African Americans from the rural South to the urban North during the latter stages of the industrial era; (3) the shift of tens of millions of urban residents from central cities to suburbs and subsequently to exurbs even farther away from the urban core; (4) the return migration of millions of African Americans from the deindustrializing North back to the growing opportunities in the South (in metropolises such as Atlanta and Charlotte); and (5) the strong and steady influx of immigrants from outside North America including, in recent times, Mexicans, Cubans, and other Latinos; South Asians from India and Pakistan; and East and Southeast Asians from Hong Kong, Vietnam, and the Philippines.

Several of the migration streams affecting North America rank among the largest in world history, creating the pair of plural societies that characterize this realm (see the box titled "The Migration Process"). North America functions, in some ways, as a global magnet for human resources, and its persistent prosperity hinges at least in part on wave after wave of ambitious immigrants, be they engineers from China, physicians from India, nurses from Jamaica, or farm workers from Mexico.

The Challenge of Multiculturalism

But growing diversity, especially at a time of globalization and *transnationalism*, comes with challenges. The sheer dimensions of immigration into the United States, from virtually all corners of the world, creates an increasingly complex ethnic and cultural mosaic that tests melting pot [12] assertions at every geographic scale. Today there are more people of African descent living in the United States than in Kenya. The number of Hispanic residents in America is nearing half the population of Mexico. Miami is the second-biggest Cuban city after Havana, and Montreal the largest French-speaking city in the world after Paris. In short, there are sufficient immigrant numbers in the United States for them to create durable societies within the overall national society. The challenge is to ensure that the great majority of the immigrants become full participants in that larger society.

The issue is compounded as well as politicized by the fact that never in its history has the realm received so large an infusion of undocumented (illegal) immigration in addition to the legitimate stream. The ongoing influx from Middle to North America, principally from or via Mexico, represents one of the biggest population shifts in human history. A considerable part of it is illegal, producing acrimonious debate over border security and law enforcement. In 2013, an estimated 6.7 million illegal immigrants from Mexico were in the United States at a time when the Hispanic minority had already become the country's largest (over 55 million today, more than one-sixth of the total population)—transforming neighborhoods, cities, and even entire regions.

Such are the numbers, and so diverse are the cultural traditions, that the melting pot that America once was is today morphing into something else. Spatially, the

The Migration Process

BOTH CANADA AND the United States are products of international migration. Europeans first crossed the Atlantic with the intent of establishing permanent colonies in the early 1600s, and from these colonies evolved the two countries of North America. The Europeanization of North America doomed the realm's indigenous societies, but this was only one of many areas around the world where local cultures and foreign invaders came face to face. Between 1835 and 1935, perhaps as many as 75 million Europeans departed for distant shores—most of them bound for the Americas (Fig. 3A-13). Some sought religious freedom, others escaped poverty and famine, still others simply hoped for a better life. A comparative few were transported against their will to penal colonies, and then there was of course forced movement related to slavery (mapped in Chapter 6A).

Studies of the **migration decision** show that migration flows vary in size with (1) the perceived difference between home (source) and destination; (2) the effectiveness of information flow, that is, the news about the destination that emigrants send back to those left behind waiting to decide; and (3) the distance between source and destination (shorter moves attract many more migrants than longer ones).

Every migration stream produces a counter-stream of returning migrants who cannot adjust, are unsuccessful, or are otherwise persuaded or compelled to return home. Migration studies also conclude that several discrete factors are at work in the process. **Push factors** motivate people to move away from an undesirable locale that may be afflicted by famine, armed conflict, religious persecution, or some other adversity. **Pull factors** attract them to destinations perceived to hold a promise of security, opportunity, or another desired goal.

To the early (and later) European immigrants, North America was a new frontier, a place to escape persecution and acquire a piece of land. Opportunities were reported to be unlimited. That perception of opportunity has never changed. Immigration continues to significantly shape the human-geographic complexion of the United States as well as Canada. Today's immigrants account for 43 percent of the annual population growth of the United States (and will surpass 50 percent by 2030). Never in its history, however, has the U.S. received so large an undocumented (illegal) immigration flow in addition to the legitimate stream, and the ongoing influx from Middle to North America is one of the largest population shifts in human history.

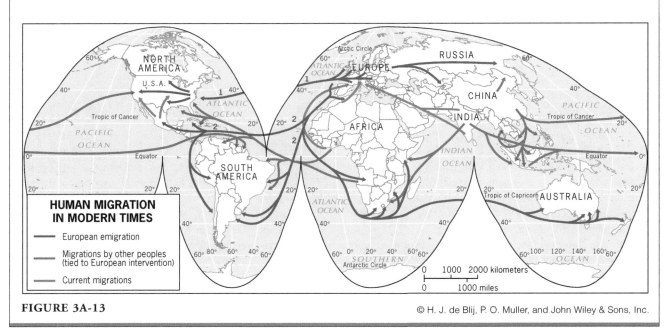

FIGURE 3A-13

© H. J. de Blij, P. O. Muller, and John Wiley & Sons, Inc.

United States is now completing its transformation into a ***mosaic culture***, an increasingly heterogeneous complex of separate, more or less uniform "tiles" whose residents spend less time than ever interacting and "melting." This applies not only to new immigrant groups but also to existing communities, underscored by the proliferation of walled-off, gated housing complexes in metropolitan areas across the realm. There is a serious downside to all this, as Bill Bishop writes in his landmark book, *The Big*

Sort: Why the Clustering of Like-Minded America Is Tearing Us Apart. As is the case in the world at large, balkanization fueled by people wanting to interact only with those closely resembling themselves leads to misunderstanding of others, miscalculations when it comes to decisions and policies, and widening fissures between communities. This could even threaten the very survival of the democratic values that have underpinned the evolution of American society.

Regional ISSUE | Immigration

IMMIGRATION BRINGS BENEFITS— THE MORE THE MERRIER!

"The United States and Canada are nations of immigrants. What would have happened if our forebears had closed the door to America after they arrived and stopped the Irish, the Italians, the eastern Europeans, and so many other nationalities from entering this country? Now we're arguing over Latinos, Asians, Russians, Muslims, you name it. Fact is, newcomers have always been viewed negatively by most of those who came before them. When Irish Catholics began arriving in the 1830s, the Protestants already here accused them of assigning their loyalty to some Italian pope rather than to their new country, but Irish Catholics soon proved to be pretty good Americans. Sound familiar? Muslims can be very good Americans too. It just takes time, longer for some immigrant groups than others. But don't you see that America's immigrants have always been the engine of growth? They become part of the world's most dynamic economy and make it more dynamic still.

"My ancestors came from Holland in the 1800s, and the head of the family was an architect from Rotterdam. I work here in western Michigan as an urban planner. People who want to limit immigration seem to think that only the least educated workers flood into the United States and Canada, depriving the less-skilled among us of jobs and causing hardship for citizens. But in fact America attracts skilled and highly educated as well as unskilled immigrants, and they all make contributions. The highly educated foreigners, including doctors and technologically skilled workers, are quickly absorbed into the workforce; you're very likely to have been treated by a physician from India or a dentist from South Africa. The unskilled workers take jobs we're not willing to perform at the wages offered. Things have changed! A few decades ago, American youngsters on summer break flooded the job market in search of temporary employment in hotels, department stores, and restaurants. Now they're vacationing in Europe or trekking in Costa Rica, and the managers of those establishments bring in temporary workers from Jamaica and Romania.

"And our own population is aging, which is why we need the infusion of younger people immigration brings with it. We don't want to become like Japan or some European countries, where they won't have the younger working people to pay the taxes needed to support the social security system. I agree with opponents of immigration on only one point: what we need is legal immigration, so that the new arrivals will get housed and schooled, and illegal immigration must be curbed. Otherwise, we need more, not fewer, immigrants."

LIMIT IMMIGRATION NOW!

"The percentage of recent immigrants in the U.S. population is the highest it has been in 70 years, and in Canada in 60 years. America is adding the population of San Diego every year, over and above the natural increase, and not counting illegal immigration. This can't go on. By 2020, more than one-sixth of the U.S. population will consist of recent immigrants. At least one-third of them will not have a high school diploma. They will need housing, education, medical treatment, and other social services that put a huge strain on the budgets of the States they enter. The jobs they're looking for often aren't there, and then they start displacing working Americans by accepting lower wages. It's easy for the elite to pontificate about how great immigration is for the American melting pot, but they're not the ones affected on a daily basis. Immigration is a problem for the working people. We see company jobs disappearing across the border to Mexico, and at the same time we have Mexicans arriving here by the hundreds of thousands, legally and illegally, and more jobs are taken away.

"And don't talk to me about how immigration now will pay social security bills later. I know a thing or two about this because I'm an accountant here in Los Angeles, and I can calculate as well as the next guy in Washington. Those fiscal planners seem to forget that immigrants grow older and will need social security too. And as for that supposed slowdown in the aging of our population because immigrants are so young and have so many children, over the past 20 years the average age in the United States has dropped by four months. So much for that nonsense. What's needed is a revamping of the tax structure, so those fat cats who rob corporations and then let them go under will at least have paid their fair share into the national kitty. There'll be plenty of money to fund social services for the aged. We don't need unskilled immigrants to pay those bills.

"And I'm against this notion of amnesty for illegal immigrants being talked about these days. All that would do is to attract more people to try to make it across our borders. I heard the president of Mexico propose opening the U.S.-Mexican border the way they're opening borders in the European Union. Can you imagine what would happen? What our two countries really need is a policy that deters illegal movement across that border, which will save lives as well as jobs, and a system that will confine immigration to legal channels. These days, that's not just a social or economic issue; it's a security matter as well."

Vote your opinion at www.wiley.com/go/deblijpolling

In Canada, the melting-pot notion was put to the test during the 1990s when East Asian immigrants from Hong Kong arrived during and following the 1997 takeover of the British crown colony by Beijing's communist government. Affluent Chinese families arriving in Vancouver proceeded to purchase and renovate (or frequently replace) traditional homes in long-stable Vancouver neighborhoods, arousing the ire of numerous locals. But in general, Canadian views on immigration differ from those in the United States. Canada has long faced critical labor shortages, especially in its western provinces including energy-booming Alberta and Asian-trade-burgeoning British Columbia. In need not only of professionals but also truck drivers and dock workers, Canada tries to balance its legal immigration process to keep it compatible with the country's employment as well as demographic needs. Across the realm, multicultural tendencies now vary on a regional basis depending on the subtle interplay of economics, existing cultural patterns, immigration, and local politics.

POINTS TO PONDER

- Whereas more than 70 percent of Canada's population lives within 200 kilometers (125 mi) of the northern U.S. border, only about 12 percent of the Mexican population lives that close to the southern U.S. border.

- There are only two states in the world that share the same country code for international telephone traffic: the United States and Canada.

- The United States does not have an official language. Should it?

- The North American rail freight system is unique among the world's realms in terms of its transport capacity and low cost.

- The U.S. and Canada are still each other's biggest overall trading partners, despite the rapid economic rise of China.

120°

Channel Is.
SAN DIEGO
TIJUANA
Ensenada
Mexicali
Salton Sea
SONORAN
DESERT
PHOENIX
Tucson
Las Cruces
Amarillo 100°
Oklahoma City
Little Rock
Memp

UNITED STAT

Cape San Quintin
30°
Nogales
El Paso
CIUDAD
JUÁREZ
Lubbock
Fort Worth
DALLAS
Jackson

Guadalupe
(MEXICO)
Archangel Island
Tiburón Island
Hermosillo
Chihuahua
Ciudad Acuña
Del Rio
EDWARDS PLATEAU
Austin
Baton Rouge
Beaumont

Cedros Island
Eugenia Point
SAN ANTONIO
HOUSTON
Galveston
New Orlea

Tropic of Cancer
Los Mochis
Culiacán
Torreón
Saltillo
Nuevo Laredo
Monclova
McAllen
Reynosa
MONTERREY
Guadalupe
Laredo
Corpus Christi
Brownsville
Matamoros

MISSISS
RIVER DE

Gulf
Mex

La Paz
Durango
Mazatlán
Zacatecas
Ciudad Victoria
Tampico

False Cape
Cabo San Lucas
MEXICO
20°
San Luis Potosí
Aguascalientes
Tepic
GUADALAJARA
LEÓN
Guanajuato
Querétaro
Poza Rica
Bay of
Campeche
Campeche
YUC

Marias Islands
Cape Corrientes
Puerto Vallarta
Colima
Morelia
MEXICO CITY
PUEBLA
Pachuca
Xalapa
Veracruz
Ciudad del Carmen
Chetu

Revillagigedo Islands
(MEXICO)
Toluca
Popocatépetl (Vol.)
5,465 m, 17,930 ft.)
Pico de Orizaba (Vol.)
(5,747 m, 18,855 ft.)
Villahermosa
Ciudad Pemex
Monclova

Chilpancingo
Juxtepec
Oaxaca
Coatzacoalcos
PETÉN

SIERRA MADRE DEL SUR
Acapulco
ISTHMUS OF
TEHUANTEPEC
Tuxtla Gutiérrez
Belmo
GUATEMALA
Puerto Bar

Salina Cruz
Gulf of
Tehuantepec
Tapachula
Quetzaltenango
Guatemala City
Santa Ana
San Salvador
EL SALVADOR

PACIFIC OCEAN

10°

Elevation (m)

3000
1500
600
300
150
0
below sea level
0
-150
-1500
-3000
-6000

Roads
Railroads

0 km   200   400   600   800
0 miles   100   200   300   400   500

Albers Equal-Area Projection
Scale 1:15,000,000

118

Archipiélago de Col
(Galápagos Islands
(ECUADOR)
Pinta I.
Marchena I.

119

IN THIS CHAPTER

- Building a wall between two realms
- Ciudad Juárez: The curse of cocaine
- Drug-related violence invades northern Central America
- The natural vulnerability of Hispaniola and other Caribbean islands
- Is small beautiful? The predicament of tiny island-nations

FIGURE 4A-1 © H. J. de Blij, P. O. Muller, and John Wiley & Sons, Inc.

CONCEPTS, IDEAS, AND TERMS

Indigenous 1
NAFTA 2
Maquiladoras 3
Land bridge 4
Archipelago 5
Hurricane Alley 6
Altitudinal zonation 7
Tierra caliente 8
Tierra templada 9
Tierra fría 10
Tierra helada 11
Tierra nevada 12
Tropical deforestation 13
Culture hearth 14
Mestizo 15
Hacienda 16
Plantation 17
Connectivity 18
Small-island developing economies 19

Look at a world map, and it is obvious that the Americas comprise two landmasses: North America extending from Alaska to Panama and South America from Colombia to Argentina. But here we are reminded that continents and geographic realms do not necessarily coincide. In Chapters 3A and 3B we discussed a North American realm whose southern boundary is the U.S.-Mexican border and the Gulf of Mexico. Between North America and South America lies the small but important geographic realm known as Middle America. Consisting of a mainland corridor and myriad Caribbean islands, Middle America is a highly fragmented realm.

DEFINING THE REALM

From Figure 4A-1 it is clear that Middle America is much wider than it is long. The distance from Baja California to Barbados is about 6000 kilometers (3800 mi), but from the latitude of Tijuana to Panama City is only half that distance. In terms of total area, Middle America is the second-smallest of the world's geographic realms. As the map shows, the dominant state of this realm is Mexico, larger than all its other countries and territories combined.

Middle America may be a small geographic realm by global standards, but comparatively it is densely peopled. Its population passed the 200-million milestone in 2011, more than half of it residing in Mexico alone, and the rate of natural increase (at 1.5 percent) remains above the world average. Figure 4A-2 shows Mexico's populous interior core area quite clearly, but note that the population in Guatemala and Nicaragua tends to cluster toward the Pacific rather than the

major geographic qualities of
MIDDLE AMERICA

1. Middle America is a relatively small realm consisting of the mainland countries from Mexico to Panama and all the islands of the Caribbean Basin to the east.

2. Middle America's mainland constitutes a crucial barrier between Atlantic and Pacific waters. In physiographic terms, this is a land bridge connecting the continental landmasses of North and South America.

3. Middle America is a realm of intense cultural and political fragmentation. The presence of many small, insular, and remote countries poses major challenges to economic development.

4. Middle America's cultural geography is complex. Various African and European influences dominate the Caribbean, whereas Spanish and indigenous traditions survive on the mainland.

5. The realm contains the Americas' least-developed territories and a substantial number of so-called small-island developing economies.

6. In terms of area, population, and economic potential, Mexico leads the realm.

7. Mexico and Panama are uniquely connected beyond the realm, the former because of its border with the United States and the latter because of the Panama Canal; the rest of the realm is relatively isolated.

Caribbean coast. Among the islands, this map reveals how crowded Hispaniola (containing Haiti and the Dominican Republic) is, but at this scale we cannot clearly discern the pattern on the smaller islands of the eastern Caribbean and the Bahamas, some of which are also densely populated.

What Middle America lacks in size it makes up in physiographic and cultural diversity. This is a realm of soaring volcanoes and spectacular shorelines, of tropical forests and barren deserts, of windswept plateaus and scenic islands. It holds the architectural and technological legacies of ancient indigenous [1] civilizations. Today it is a mosaic of immigrant cultures from Africa, Europe, and elsewhere,

richly reflected in music and the visual arts. Material poverty, however, is endemic: island Haiti is the poorest country in the Americas; Nicaragua, on the mainland, is almost as badly off. As we will discover, a combination of factors has produced a distinctive but challenged realm between North and South America.

GEOGRAPHICAL FEATURES

Sometimes you will see Middle and South America referred to in combination as "Latin" America, alluding to their prevailing Spanish-Portuguese heritage. This is an imperfect regional designation, just as "Anglo America," a term once commonly used for North America, was also improper. Such culturally based terminologies reflect historic power and dominance, and they tend to make outsiders out of those people they do not represent.

In North America, the term *Anglo* (as a geographic appellation) was offensive to many Native Americans, African Americans, Hispanics, Quebecers, and others. In Middle (and South) America, millions of people of indigenous-American, African, Asian, and European ancestries do not fit under the "Latin" rubric. You will not find the cultural landscape particularly "Latin" in the Bahamas, Barbados, Jamaica, Belize, or lengthy stretches of Guatemala and Mexico. So let us adopt the geographic neutrality of North, Middle, and South.

But is Middle America sufficiently different from either North or South America to merit distinction as a realm? Certainly, in this age of globalization and migration, many border areas are becoming transition zones, as is happening along the U.S.-Mexican

The setting of central Mexico City, which lies at the heart of the world's largest urban population agglomeration (estimated to have surpassed 30 million in 2013).

© David R. Frazier/Danita Delimont

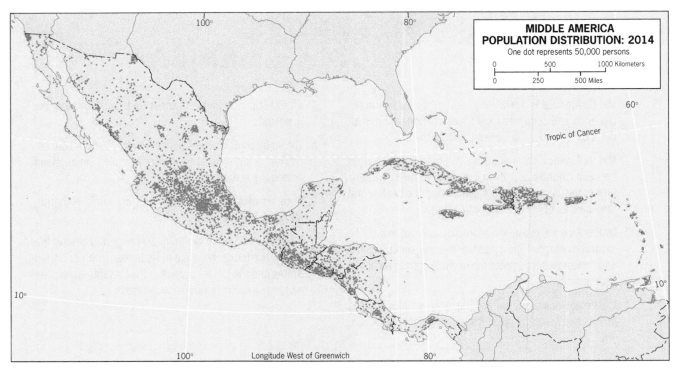

FIGURE 4A-2

© H. J. de Blij, P. O. Muller, and John Wiley & Sons, Inc.

boundary. Yet consider this: North America encompasses just a pair of states, and the entire continent of South America only 12 (plus France's dependency on the northeast coast). But far smaller Middle America, as we define it, incorporates more than three-dozen political entities, including several dependencies (or quasi-dependencies) of the Netherlands, the United Kingdom, and France as well as a few constituent territories of the United States. Therefore, unlike South America, Middle America is a multilingual patchwork of independent states, territories in political transition, and residual colonial dependencies, with strong continuing ties to the United States and non-Iberian Europe. Middle America is defined in large measure by its vivid multicultural geographiy.

The Realm's Northern Land Boundary

The 3169-kilometer (1969-mi) land border between North America and Middle America is the longest in the world separating a rich realm from a poor one. The U.S.-Mexican boundary crosses half the continent from the Pacific to the Gulf, but Mexican cultural influences penetrate deeply into the southwestern States and American impacts reach far into Mexico. To Mexicans the border is a reminder of territory lost to the United States in historic conflicts; to Americans it is a symbol of economic contrasts and illegal immigration. Along the Mexican side, the effects of NAFTA [2] (the North American Free Trade Agreement between Canada, the United

States, and Mexico that went into effect in 1994) have transformed Mexico's economic geography.

The implementation of NAFTA led to an economic boom as Mexico became part of a free-trade zone and

Automobiles wait at the border to enter the United States from Mexico at the Tijuana-San Ysidro port of entry just south of San Diego—the busiest land border crossing in the world. Here, in 2011, some 50,000 northbound vehicles and 25,000 pedestrians entered the U.S. every day. A major expansion of this California facility, located at the southern terminus of Interstate-5, is underway to increase its capacity and reduce vehicle waiting times. The number of Mexico-bound inspection lanes doubled from 11 to 22 in 2012; the U.S.-bound lanes will similarly expand from 34 to 63 by 2016.

© David R. Frazier Photolibrary, Inc./Alamy

market encompassing almost 475 million people. A major beneficiary was the strip of land that ran along the boundary with the United States. The resulting boom changed urban landscapes all along the emerging border zone—but it could not, of course, close the massive economic gap between the two sides.

Under NAFTA, factories based in Mexico could assemble imported, duty-free raw materials and components into finished products, which were then exported back into the U.S. market. Logically, most of these factories, called maquiladoras [3], are located as close to the U.S. border as possible. Thus manufacturing employment in the cities and towns along that border, from Tijuana on the Pacific to Matamoros at the mouth of the Rio Grande, expanded rapidly. By 2001, after only seven years of NAFTA's existence, there were some 3000 factories with more than 1.2 million workers in the border zone and in northern Yucatán (where Mérida was part of the process). Since then, these numbers have roughly stayed the same.

Mexico's growing economic linkages with its mighty northern neighbor have had a positive overall effect on the national economy, but they have increased regional inequalities and also made Mexico more vulnerable to economic crises in the United States. In 2008, Mexico entered a deep slump as exports to the recession-plagued U.S. declined sharply; by 2012, a slow recovery began to take hold. Mexico now provides about 12 percent of all U.S. imports annually, the third-largest source of foreign trade after China (18 percent) and Canada (14 percent). China

has been increasing its share more rapidly, even though it faces tariffs that NAFTA-member Mexico does not. This puts pressure on Mexico to improve its competitiveness in order to build an even closer economic relationship with the United States.

A Troubled Border Zone

Despite the recent economic development of the borderlands, the boundary itself has become increasingly troubled, with many in the United States crusading to reinforce it to deter illegal immigration and the smuggling of drugs. Although the flow of illegal crossings from Mexico into the U.S. has slowed, during the first eight years of this century American authorities annually apprehended up to a million would-be, illegal migrants, many of them repeat offenders. Some were so desperate to make it across that they risked their lives: the number of deaths in the border zone since 2000 has varied between 200 and 500 yearly—a painful reminder of the enormous gap in living standards and life opportunities between the two realms.

As the Great Recession took hold in the U.S. and reduced the demand for labor, illegal crossings and border apprehensions declined commensurately. Nonetheless, even if this traffic flow swings upward again as economic recovery proceeds, it appears that migrants in Middle America increasingly prefer to remain *within* their realm rather than head north. In Mexico, urbanization is proceeding apace, from 66 percent in 1980 to 77 percent in 2014, and it is the mid-sized and smaller cities with lower costs of living that are growing fastest today. If Mexico is able to develop and modernize its economy in a more regionally balanced manner (a topic discussed in greater detail in Chapter 4B), this internal population shift may well be sustainable in the years ahead.

Another huge concern in the border zone is the burgeoning cocaine trade, and to a lesser extent the smuggling of marijuana. Most cocaine is produced in northwestern South America, and almost all of what is destined for the U.S. market passes through Mexico (see Fig. 4B-6). Much of the marijuana consumed within the U.S. is grown in western Mexico and finds its way across the border as well. The contraband is mostly carried in trucks or cars, often disguised as regular cargo in myriad ways (e.g., stuffed in teddy bears, inside hollowed out furniture, or simply in boxes labeled anything from candy to engine parts). It is the sheer volume of this unlawful cross-border traffic that makes it virtually impossible for authorities to conduct sufficient

© Jim Wark/AirPhoto

The boundary between Mexico and the United States displays some stunning cross-border contrasts. In this scene, the crowded Mexican town of San Luis Colorado ends at a tall metal fence, where the Arizona desert takes over. This photo, therefore, looks eastward; south is to the right. Like other Mexican towns pressed against the border, San Luis Rio Colorado (locals simply call it San Luis) grew rapidly and chaotically in response to the opening of several maquiladoras, assembly plants making products for export to the United States.

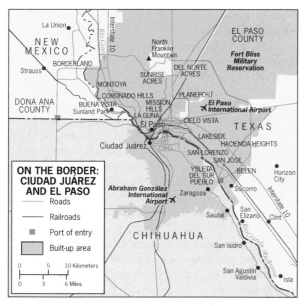

FIGURE 4A-3

© H. J. de Blij, P. O. Muller, J. Nijman, and
John Wiley & Sons, Inc.

increase in violence throughout northern Mexico (these drug wars are detailed in Chapter 4B).

In 2006, the U.S. government, responding both to homeland security concerns (potential terrorists are thought to enter the country via Mexico) and the tidal wave of cocaine smuggling, initiated the construction of a fortified fence along the entire length of the Mexican border. The very idea seems at odds with the ideals of closer economic and political cooperation, and many security experts questioned its efficacy. At any rate, in 2011, with about one-third of the border (ca. 1000 kilometers [650 mi]) hardened by fences and walls, the project to build a "virtual fence" to fill the remaining gaps had become such a boondoggle that it was canceled. However, formidable physical barriers are now concentrated around all the main crossing points, and it remains unclear how the longer-term economic health of the border zone they divide will be affected.

The Regions

As Figure 4A-1 suggests, Middle America can be divided into four distinct regions. Dominant **Mexico** occupies the largest part of the collective territory, with much of its northern border defined by the Rio Bravo (Rio Grande) from El Paso to the Gulf of Mexico. To the southeast, Mexico yields to the region named **Central America**, consisting of the seven republics of Guatemala, Belize, Honduras, El Salvador, Nicaragua, Costa Rica, and Panama. (Sometimes the entire mainland portion of the realm is incorrectly referred to as Central America, but only these seven countries constitute this region.) The **Greater Antilles** is the regional

inspections; and it is the infrastructure of the cities and industrial areas on the Mexican side of the border that facilitates the operation of the narcotics trade.

The city of Ciudad Juárez, probably the largest node in the hemispheric drug trade, is ideally located to handle this clandestine illicit activity. It is situated directly on the international boundary and forms a single built-up urban area with El Paso, Texas on the U.S. side—though the two are separated by a continuous artificial barrier running northwest-southeast across the entire metropolis (Fig. 4A-3). This map also shows the four ports of entry, which together account for about 25 million border crossings every year. Juárez has grown quite rapidly in the (post–1993) NAFTA era, and today exhibits numerous manufacturing districts as well as a sprawling mosaic of neighborhoods, ranging from clusters of upper-income *colonias* to the teeming slums that house the poorest of the new migrants from the south. With a plentiful supply of poor people willing to take the risk of driving or carrying drugs across the border, Juarez also has dozens of maquiladoras that can be bribed to store, conceal, and transport the contraband north. With Mexican authorities having little or no control over the area, it is hardly surprising that local law enforcement personnel are often implicated in the drug business. Once the prohibited substances cross over to El Paso, Interstate-10 is the designated east-west expressway in the United States. As the power of Mexican organized crime syndicates has grown enormously since 2000, the narcotics trade has triggered a concomitant, frightening

In 2010, groups of students in Mexico City staged this protest against the drug trafficking violence in Ciudad Juárez. An estimated 2738 people were murdered that year in Juárez, making it the most violent city on Earth. Since then, a declining murder rate has seen it fall into second place as a surge of drug-related violence during 2012 bestowed upon the Honduran city of San Pedro Sula the dubious distinction of being the "murder capital of the world."

© ALEX CRUZ/epa/Corbis

name that refers to the four large islands in the northern sector of the Caribbean Sea: Cuba, Jamaica, Hispaniola, and Puerto Rico; two countries, Haiti and the Dominican Republic, share the island of Hispaniola. And the ***Lesser Antilles*** form an extensive crescent of smaller islands from the Virgin Islands off Puerto Rico to Aruba near the northwestern coast of Venezuela; they also include the Bahamas island chain north of the Greater Antilles. In the Caribbean islands large and small, moist winds sweep in from the east, watering windward (wind-facing) coasts while leaving leeward (wind-protected) areas dry. On the map, the "Leeward" and "Windward" Islands actually are not "dry" and "wet," these terms having navigational rather than environmental implications.

PHYSICAL GEOGRAPHY

A Land Bridge

The funnel-shaped mainland, a 4800-kilometer (3000-mi) connection between North and South America, is wide enough in the north to contain two major mountain chains and a vast interior plateau, but narrows to a slim 65-kilometer (40-mi) ribbon of land in Panama. Here this strip of land—or *isthmus*—bends eastward so that Panama's orientation is east-west. Thus mainland Middle America is what physical geographers call a land bridge [4], an isthmian link between continents.

If you examine a globe, you can see some other present and former land bridges: Egypt's Sinai Peninsula between Asia and Africa, the (now-broken) Bering land bridge between northeasternmost Asia and Alaska, and the shallow waters between New Guinea and Australia. Such land bridges, though temporary features in geologic time, have played crucial roles in the dispersal of animals and humans across the planet. But even though mainland Middle America forms a land bridge, its internal fragmentation has always inhibited movement. Mountain ranges, swampy coastlands, and dense rainforests make contact and interaction difficult.

Island Chains

As shown in Figure 4A-1, the approximately 7000 islands of the Caribbean Sea stretch in a lengthy arc from Cuba and the Bahamas eastward and then southward to Trinidad, with numerous outliers outside (such as Barbados) and inside (e.g., the Cayman Islands) the main chain. As we noted above, the four large islands—Cuba, Hispaniola (containing Haiti and the Dominican Republic), Puerto Rico, and Jamaica—are called the Greater Antilles, and all the remaining smaller islands constitute the Lesser Antilles. The entire Antillean archipelago [5] (island chain) consists of the crests and tops of mountain chains that rise from the

floor of the Caribbean, the result of collisions between the Caribbean Plate and its neighbors (Fig. G-4). Some of these crests are relatively stable, but elsewhere they contain active volcanoes, and almost everywhere in this realm earthquakes are an ever-present danger—in the islands as well as on the mainland (Fig. G-5). Add to this the realm's seasonal exposure to Atlantic/Caribbean hurricanes, and it amounts to some of the highest-risk real estate on Earth.

Dangerous Landscapes

The danger from below is dramatically illustrated in the Haitian, western half of Hispaniola, which is laced with geologic fault lines associated with the nearby boundary that separates the North American and Caribbean plates (refer to Fig. 4B-10, inset map). On January 12, 2010, Haiti was hit by a massive earthquake; the epicenter of that 7.0 temblor was located just outside Port-au-Prince and virtually destroyed this teeming, impoverished capital city of over 2 million (see photo). At least 300,000 people died, and within a week more than a million had fled to the countryside. It was the worst natural disaster in Haiti's history, but certainly not the first.

The environmental hazard from above comes in the form of hurricanes, powerful tropical cyclones that annually

---

This shocking street scene in central Port-au-Prince is typical of the widespread devastation resulting from the 2010 earthquake that struck the Haitian capital. The human casualty toll was enormous, thousands of buildings were made uninhabitable, debris clogged the streets, and the economy was wrecked. Survivors depended almost exclusively on assistance from foreign governments and international relief agencies. But life somehow found a way to go on, as these resourceful people proved. All too soon, though, Haiti's plight disappeared from the headlines even as the human drama continued. The hemisphere's poorest country and weakest economy continues to face a colossal struggle to rebuild, its infrastructure still in shambles. In 2013, more than 350,000 people still lived in the hundreds of dirty and unsafe encampments where they sought refuge three years earlier.

© Craig Ruttle/Alamy

threaten the Caribbean Basin and its surrounding coast-lines. The eastern half of Middle America is one of the most hurricane-prone areas in the world. One of the key condi-tions for the formation of hurricanes is very warm ocean water, because it further heats the hot moist air rising above it to "fuel" the evolving storm. The prolonged Atlantic/Caribbean hurricane season extends from June 1 to Decem-ber 1, with the greatest number of tropical cyclones occur-ring in August and September when seawater reaches its highest temperatures. Most storms travel in a westerly direc-tion from their low-latitude spawning ground off the coast of West Africa, steered across the Atlantic by the trade winds to reach the Caribbean Sea. Once there, many of these cy-clones follow similar routes within Hurricane Alley [6] whose wide axis lies along all of the Greater Antilles and then broadens to include southern Florida, Mexico's Yuca-tán Peninsula, and all of the Gulf of Mexico. On average, every season sees the development of four to eight major hurricanes and rarely does a year go by without a destructive landfall on at least one of these densely populated areas.

Altitudinal Zonation of Environments

Continental Middle America and the western margin of South America are areas of high relief and strong environ-mental contrasts. Even though settlers have always favored temperate intermontane basins and valleys, people also cluster in hot tropical lowlands as well as high plateaus just below the snow line in South America's Andes Mountains. In each of these zones, distinct local climates, soils, vegeta-tion, crops, domestic animals, and modes of life prevail. Such altitudinal zones [7] (diagrammed in Fig. 4A-4) are known by specific names as if they were regions with dis-tinguishing properties—as in reality they are.

The lowest of these vertical zones, from sea level to 750 meters (2500 ft), is known as the *tierra caliente* [8], the

"hot land" of the coastal plains and low-lying interior basins where tropical agriculture predominates. Above this zone lie the tropical highlands containing Middle and South Amer-ica's largest population clusters, the *tierra templada* [9] of temperate land reaching up to about 1800 meters (6000 ft). Temperatures here are cooler; prominent among the com-mercial crops is coffee, while corn (maize) and wheat are the staple grains. Still higher, from about 1800 to 3600 meters (6000 to nearly 12,000 ft), is the *tierra fría* [10], the cold country of the higher Andes where hardy crops such as po-tatoes and barley are mainstays. Above the tree line, which marks the upper limit of the *tierra fría*, lies the *tierra helada* [11]; this fourth altitudinal zone, extending from about 3600 to 4500 meters (12,000 to 15,000 ft), is so cold and barren that it can support only the grazing of sheep and other hardy livestock. The highest zone of all is the *tierra nevada* [12], a zone of permanent snow and ice associated with the loftiest Andean peaks. As we will see, the varied human geography of mainland Middle and western South America closely reflects these diverse environments.

Tropical Deforestation

Before the Europeans arrived, two-thirds of continental Middle America (at lower altitudes) was covered by tropi-cal rainforests. It is estimated that at present only about 10 percent of this vegetation remains. Between 2000 and 2010, Central America lost almost 12 percent of its wood-lands, a deforestation rate close to ten times the global average. El Salvador today has lost virtually all of its forests, and most of the six other republics in its region will soon approach that stage. As for bedeviled Haiti, its ravaged woodlands have already reached the stage of complete de-nudation (as revealed in the aerial photo in Chapter 4B).

The causes of tropical deforestation [13] are related to the persistent economic and demographic problems of

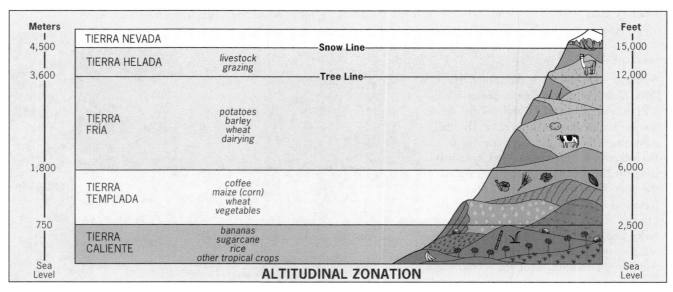

FIGURE 4A-4

© H. J. de Blij, P. O. Muller, and John Wiley & Sons, Inc.

© Humberto Olarte Cupas/Alamy

Despite scattered attempts to reverse this landscape scourge, deforestation continues to afflict Central America. Its worst effects plague the steeper slopes of interior highlands, as here in western Panama. In the wake of recent deforestation, the land near the top of this hill has already begun to erode, because in the absence of binding tree roots the copious tropical rains are making short work of the unprotected topsoil.

world's true culture hearths [14], a source area from which new ideas radiated outward and whose population could expand and make significant material as well as intellectual progress. Agricultural specialization, urbanization, trade, and transportation networks developed, and writing, science, art, and other spheres of achievement saw major advances. Anthropologists refer to the Middle American culture hearth as ***Mesoamerica***, which extended southeast from the vicinity of present-day Mexico City to central Nicaragua. Its development is particularly remarkable because it occurred in highly different geographic environments, each presenting obstacles that had to be overcome in order to unify and integrate large territories. First, in the low-lying tropical plains of what is now northern Guatemala, Belize, and Mexico's Yucatán Peninsula, and perhaps simultaneously in Guatemala's highlands to the south, the Maya civilization arose more than 3000 years ago. Later, far to the northwest on the high plateau in central Mexico, the Aztecs founded a major civilization centered on the largest city ever to exist in pre-Columbian times.

disadvantaged countries. In Central America, the leading cause has been the need to clear rural lands for cattle pasture as many countries, especially Costa Rica, became meat producers and exporters. Because tropical soils are so nutrient-poor, newly deforested areas are able to function as pastures for only a few years at most. These fields are then abandoned for other freshly cut lands and quickly become a ravaged landscape (see photo). Without the protection of tree roots, local soil erosion and flooding immediately become problems, affecting still-productive areas nearby. A second cause of deforestation is the rapid logging of tropical woodlands as the timber industry increasingly turns from the exhausted forests of the midlatitudes to harvest the rich tree resources of the equatorial zones, responding to accelerating global demands for housing, paper, and furniture. The third major contributing factor is related to the region's population explosion: as more and more peasants are required to extract a subsistence from inferior lands, they have no choice but to cut down the remaining forest for both firewood and additional crop-raising space, and their intrusion prevents the trees from regenerating.

CULTURAL GEOGRAPHY

Mesoamerican Legacy

Mainland Middle America was the scene of the emergence of a major ancient civilization. Here lay one of the

The Lowland Maya

The Maya civilization is the only major culture hearth in the world that arose in the lowland tropics. Its great cities, with their stone pyramids and massive temples, still yield archeological information today. Maya culture reached its zenith from the third to the tenth centuries AD. The Maya civilization, anchored by a network of city-states, unified an area larger than any of the present-day Middle American countries except Mexico. Its population probably totaled between 2 and 3 million; certain Maya languages are still used in the area to this day. The Maya city-states were marked by dynastic rule that functioned alongside a powerful religious hierarchy, and the great cities that now lie in ruins were primarily ceremonial centers. We also know that this culture produced skilled artists and scientists, and the Maya achieved a great deal in agriculture and trade as well.

The Highland Aztecs

In what is today the intermontane highland zone of Mexico, significant cultural developments were also taking place. Here, just north of present-day Mexico City, lay Teotihuacán, the first true urban center in the Western Hemisphere, which prospered for nearly seven centuries after its founding around the beginning of the Christian era.

The Aztec state, the pinnacle of organization and power in pre-Columbian Middle America, is thought to

From the Field Notes . . .

"We spent Monday and Tuesday upriver at Lamanai, a huge, still mostly overgrown Maya site deep in the forest of Belize. On Wednesday we drove from Belize City to Altun Ha, which

© H.J. de Blij

represents a very different picture. Settled around 200 BC, Altun Ha flourished as a Classic Period center between AD 300 and 900, when it was a thriving trade and redistribution center for the Caribbean merchant canoe traffic and served as an entrepôt for the interior land trails, some of them leading all the way to Teotihuacán. Altun Ha has an area of about 6.5 square kilometers (2.5 sq mi), with the main structures, one of which is shown here, arranged around two plazas at its core. I climbed to the top of this one to get a perspective, and sat down to have my sandwich lunch, imagining what this place must have looked like as a bustling trade and ceremonial center when the Roman Empire still thrived, but a more urgent matter intruded. A five-inch tarantula emerged from a wide crack in the sun-baked platform, and I noticed it only when it was about two feet away, apparently attracted by the crumbs and a small piece of salami. A somewhat hurried departure put an end to my historical-geographical ruminations."

www.conceptcaching.com

have originated in the early fourteenth century with the founding of a settlement on an island in a lake that lay in the *Valley of Mexico* (the area surrounding what is now Mexico City). This urban complex, a functioning city as well as a ceremonial center, named Tenochtitlán, was shortly to become the greatest city in the Americas and the capital of a large powerful state.

The Aztecs produced a wide range of impressive accomplishments, although they were better borrowers and refiners than they were innovators. They developed irrigation systems, and they constructed elaborate walls to terrace slopes where soil erosion threatened. Indeed, the greatest contributions of Mesoamerica's indigenous peoples surely came from the agricultural sphere and included the domestication of corn (maize), the sweet potato, cacao beans (the raw material of chocolate), and tobacco.

Spanish Conquest

Spain's defeat of the Aztecs in the early sixteenth century opened the door to Spanish penetration and supremacy. The Spaniards were ruthless colonizers but not more so than other European powers that subjugated other cultures. The Spaniards first enslaved the indigenous people and were determined to destroy the strength of their society. But biology accomplished what ruthlessness could not have achieved in so short a time: diseases introduced by the Spaniards and the slaves they imported from Africa killed millions of indigenous people.

Middle America's cultural landscape was drastically modified. Unlike the indigenous peoples, who had utilized stone as their main building material, the Spaniards employed great quantities of wood and used charcoal for heating, cooking, and smelting metal. The onslaught on the forests was immediate, and rings of deforestation swiftly expanded around the colonizers' towns. The Spaniards also introduced large numbers of cattle and sheep, and people and livestock now had to compete for available food (requiring the opening of vast areas of marginal land that further disrupted the region's food-producing balance). Moreover, the Spaniards introduced their own crops (notably wheat) and farming equipment, and soon large wheatfields began to encroach upon the small plots of corn that the indigenous people cultivated.

The Spaniards' most far-reaching cultural changes derived from their traditions as town dwellers. The indigenous people were moved off their land into nucleated villages and towns that the Spaniards established and laid out. In these settlements, the Spaniards could exercise the kind of rule and administration to which they were accustomed (Fig. 4A-5). The internal focus of each Spanish town was the central *plaza* or market square, around which both the local church and government buildings were located. The surrounding street pattern was deliberately laid out in gridiron form, so that any insurrections could be contained by having a small military force seal off the affected blocks and then root out the troublemakers. Each town was located near what was thought to be good agricultural land

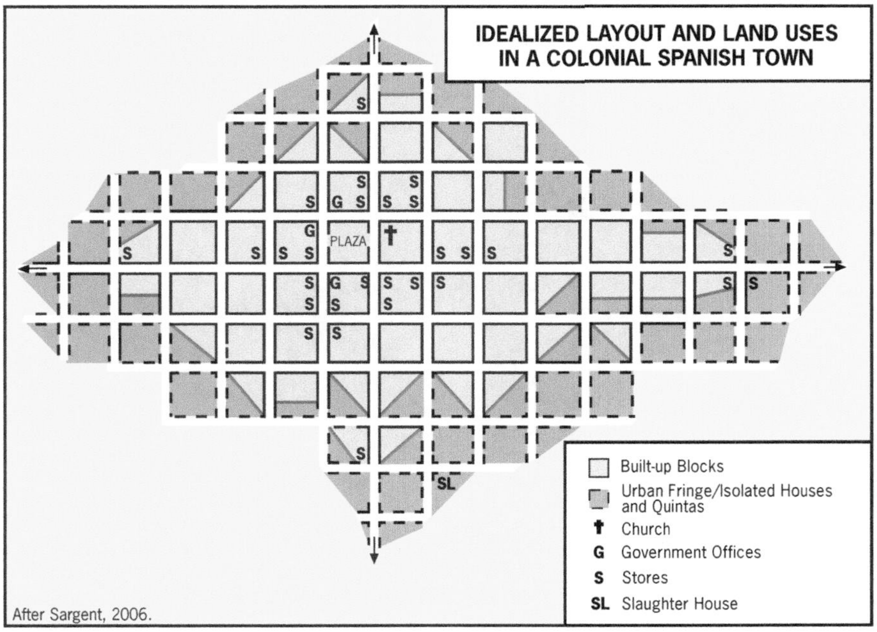

IDEALIZED LAYOUT AND LAND USES IN A COLONIAL SPANISH TOWN

Built-up Blocks
Urban Fringe/Isolated Houses and Quintas
† Church
G Government Offices
S Stores
SL Slaughter House

After Sargent, 2006.

FIGURE 4A-5   © H. J. de Blij, P. O. Muller, and John Wiley & Sons, Inc.

(which often was not so good), so that the indigenous people could venture out each day and work in the fields. Packed tightly into these towns and villages, they came face to face with Spanish culture. Here they (forcibly) learned the Europeans' Roman Catholic religion and Spanish language, and they paid their taxes and tribute to a new master. Many of Middle America's leading cities still bear this Spanish imprint.

Collision of Cultures

But Middle America is not Spain. The cultural fabric of Middle America reflects the collision of indigenous, Spanish, and other European influences. Indeed, in more remote areas in southeastern Mexico and interior Guatemala, the nucleated indigenous village survived and to this day native languages prevail over Spanish (see Fig. 4B-4).

In Middle America outside Mexico, only Panama, with its twin attractions of interoceanic transit and gold deposits, became an early focus of Spanish activity. From there, following the Pacific-fronting side of the isthmus, Spanish influence radiated northwestward through Central America and into Mexico. The major arena of international competition in Middle America, however, lay not on the Pacific side but on the islands and coasts of the Caribbean Sea. Here the British gained a foothold on the mainland, controlling a narrow coastal strip that extended southeast from Yucatán to what is now Costa Rica. As the colonial-era map (Fig. 4A-6) shows, in the Caribbean the Spaniards faced not only the British but also the French and the Dutch, all interested in the lucrative sugar trade,

all searching for instant wealth, and all seeking to expand their empires.

Much later, after centuries of European colonial rivalry in the Caribbean Basin, the United States entered the picture and made its influence felt in the coastal areas of the mainland, not through colonial conquest but through the introduction of widespread, large-scale, banana plantation agriculture. The effects of these plantations were as far-reaching as the impact of colonialism on the Caribbean islands. Because the diseases the Europeans had introduced were most rampant in these hot humid lowlands (as well as the Caribbean islands to the east), the indigenous population that survived was too small to provide a sufficient workforce. This labor shortage was quickly remedied through the trans-Atlantic slave trade from Africa that transformed the population composition of the Caribbean Basin.

The cultural variety of the Caribbean Basin is especially striking, and it is hardly an arena of exclusive Hispanic cultural heritage. For example, Cuba's southern neighbor, Jamaica (population 2.7 million, mostly of African ancestry), has a legacy of British involvement, while to the east in Haiti (10.7 million, overwhelmingly of African ancestry) the strongest imprints have been African and French. The Lesser Antilles also exhibit great cultural diversity. There are the (once Danish) U.S. Virgin Islands; French Guadeloupe and Martinique; a group of British-influenced islands, including Barbados, St. Lucia, and Trinidad and Tobago; and the Dutch St. Maarten (shared with the French) as well as the now-autonomous islands of the former Netherlands Antilles—Aruba, Curaçao, and Bonaire—off the northwestern Venezuelan coast.

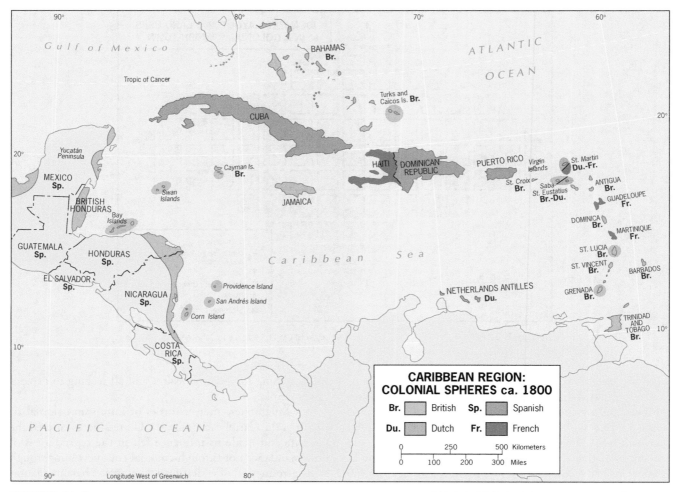

FIGURE 4A-6

© H. J. de Blij, P. O. Muller, and John Wiley & Sons, Inc.

POLITICAL AND ECONOMIC FRAGMENTATION

Independence

Independence movements stirred Middle America at an early stage. On the mainland, insurrections against Spanish authority (beginning in 1810) achieved independence for Mexico by 1821 and for the Central American republics by the end of the 1820s, resulting in the creation of eight different countries. The United States, concerned over European designs in the realm, proclaimed the Monroe Doctrine in 1823 to deter any European power from reasserting its authority in the newly independent republics or from further expanding its existing domains.

By the end of the nineteenth century, the United States itself had become a major force in Middle America. The Spanish-American War of 1898 made Cuba independent and placed Puerto Rico under the U.S. flag; soon thereafter, the Americans were in Panama constructing the Panama Canal. Meanwhile, with U.S. corporations propelling a boom based on massive banana plantations, the Central American republics had become colonies of the United States in all but name.

Independence came to the Caribbean Basin in fits and starts. Afro-Caribbean Jamaica as well as Trinidad and Tobago, where the British had brought in a large South Asian population, attained full sovereignty from the United Kingdom in 1962; other British islands (among them Barbados, St. Vincent, and Dominica) became independent later on. France, however, retains Martinique and Guadeloupe as *Overseas Départements* of the French Republic, and the Dutch islands are at various stages of autonomy. No less than 33 states are found on the political map of the Caribbean Basin today.

Regional Contrasts

There are some striking contrasts, socially and economically, between the Middle American uplands on the one hand and the Caribbean coasts and islands on the other (Fig. 4A-7). These were conceptualized by cultural geographer John Augelli into the **Mainland-Rimland framework**. The Euro-Indigenous **Mainland**, from Mexico southeast to Panama, is dominated by European (Spanish) as well as indigenous influences and also includes mestizo [15] sectors where the two ancestries mixed. As

From the Field Notes . . .

© Jan Nijman

"Driving around the small Caribbean island of Bonaire and coming face to face with this surreal landscape, I first thought I had experienced a mirage. These glistening white, perfectly cone-shaped hills are actually salt piles. This small (formerly Dutch) island off the coast of Venezuela possesses the perfect geographic conditions for salt production: it has a series of salt water inlets, it is very hot and dry, and lies in the zone of persistent trade winds. Remember that salt, nowadays taken for granted in every household, has long been one of the world's most precious spices, and was widely used for the preservation of meat and fish. The Dutch began large-scale production of salt in the 1620s; today this local industry is in the hands of the Antilles International Salt Company and continues to be an important source of Bonaire's foreign revenues."

www.conceptcaching.com

Figure 4A-7 shows, the Mainland is subdivided into several areas based on the strength of the indigenous legacy. The Mainland's Caribbean coastal strip and all of the Basin's islands to the east constitute the **Rimland**, which for the most part possesses a very different cultural heritage, based on a fusion of European and African influences.

Supplementing these contrasts are regional differences in outlook and orientation. The Caribbean Rimland was an area of sugar and banana plantations, of high accessibility, of seaward exposure, and of maximum cultural contact and mixture. The Middle American Mainland, being farther removed from these contacts, was an area of greater isolation. The Rimland was the domain of the great *plantation*, and its commercial economy was therefore susceptible to fluctuating world markets and tied to overseas investment capital. The Mainland was dominated by the *hacienda*, which was far more self-sufficient and less dependent on external markets.

This contrast between plantation and hacienda land tenure in itself constitutes strong evidence for the Rimland-Mainland dichotomy. The hacienda [16] was a Spanish institution, whereas the modern plantation was the concept of northwestern Europeans. On their haciendas, Spanish landowners possessed a domain whose productivity they might never push to its limits: the very possession of such a vast estate brought with it social prestige and a comfortable lifestyle. Native workers lived on the land—which may once have been their land—and had plots where they could grow their own subsistence crops. All this is written as though it is mostly in the past, but the legacy of the hacienda system, with its inefficient use of land and labor, still exists throughout mainland Middle America.

The plantation [17], in contrast, is all about efficiency and profit. Foreign ownership and investment is the norm, as is production for export. Most plantations grow only a single crop, be it sugar, bananas, or coffee. Much of

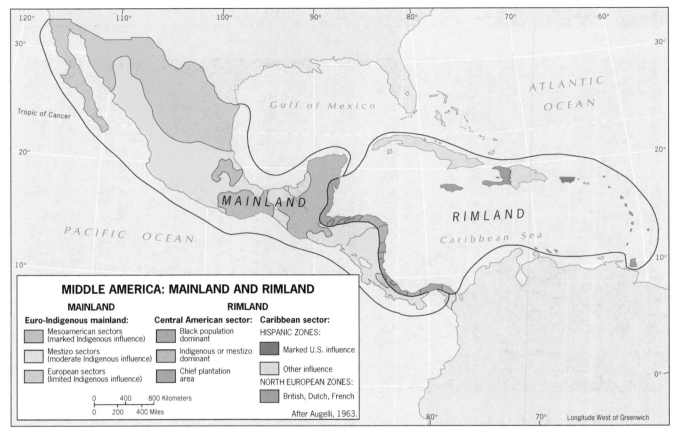

FIGURE 4A-7

© H. J. de Blij, P. O. Muller, and John Wiley & Sons, Inc.

the labor is seasonal—needed in large numbers mainly during the harvest period and such labor has been imported because of the scarcity of indigenous workers. With its "factory-in-the-field" operations (left photo), the plantation is far more efficient in its use of land and labor than the hacienda. Profit and wealth, rather than social prestige, are the dominant motives for the plantation's establishment and operation.

Contrasting land uses in the Middle American Rimland and Mainland give rise to some very different rural cultural landscapes. Huge stretches of the realm's best land continue to be controlled by (often absentee) landowners whose haciendas yield export or luxury crops, or foreign corporations that raise fruits for transport and sale on their home markets. The banana plantation shown here (left) lies near the Caribbean coast of Costa Rica. The vast fields of banana plants stand in stark contrast to the lone peasant who ekes out a bare subsistence from small cultivable plots of land, often in high-relief countryside where grazing some goats or other livestock is the only way to use most of the land.

John Coletti/Getty Images, Inc.

J. Gerard Sidaner/Science Source

Connections Matter

The unusual layout of the Middle American realm offers an opportunity to speculate about the role of spatial factors in (economic) development. Geographic fragmentation and magnitude undoubtedly play a part, and so does accessibility versus remoteness in the form of connectivity [18]. This is true for both the Caribbean and mainland components of the realm. As noted earlier, Mexico's northern margin is strongly connected to the United States, and this provides an impulse for the entire Mexican economy even if it tends to accentuate regional differences (discussed in Chapter 4B). Among Central American countries, there is no question that Panama is by far the best connected to the world economy; indeed, the Panama Canal provides an enormous range of global linkages in trade, finance, producer services, and other sectors of international business.

Now take a look at Figure 4A-8 and note how connectivity correlates with economic development. Of the eight mainland countries, Mexico and Panama have the highest GDP per capita; moreover, as we move away from the realm boundaries with North and South America toward the increasingly remote central interior of the Mexico-Panama land corridor, GDP per capita declines substantially. Nicaragua

© Liane Cary/Age Fotostock America, Inc.

Hundreds of thousands of North American retirees, and many affluent purchasers of second homes, have sought the sun and low-cost residential opportunities of Middle America, converting some areas into virtual exclaves of the North. From Mexico to Panama, waterfront real estate is among the attractions for these permanent and seasonal migrants, as here in Cabo San Lucas at the southern tip of Mexico's Baja California peninsula. This is yet another example of international connections that matter.

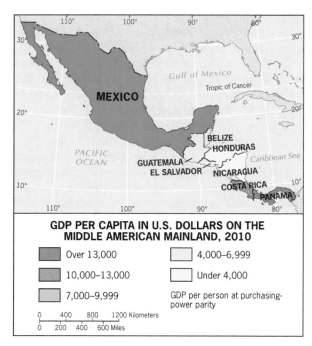

GDP PER CAPITA IN U.S. DOLLARS ON THE MIDDLE AMERICAN MAINLAND, 2010

- Over 13,000
- 10,000–13,000
- 7,000–9,999
- 4,000–6,999
- Under 4,000
- GDP per person at purchasing-power parity

FIGURE 4A-8   © H. J. de Blij, P. O. Muller, J. Nijman, and John Wiley & Sons, Inc.

and Honduras, tucked away in the middle of that narrowing land bridge, are the most distant from the bigger and more vibrant economies of the neighboring realms and decidedly lack the expanding external connections of Panama or even the historical connections of Belize (to the UK, its former colonial ruler) or Costa Rica (to the United States, triggered well over a century ago by the banana trade).

Ironically, the isolation of parts of the land bridge has in recent years made it a preferred route for narco-trafficking, particularly cocaine from Colombia on its way to Mexico where powerful drug cartels control its shipment into the United States. The inaccessible interior stretches and the many waterways surrounding the land bridge combine to thwart the ability of fiscally challenged governments to adequately patrol the region and enforce laws. The rise of drug trafficking also plays a huge role in the alarming increase of organized criminal activity and violence, especially in Honduras, El Salvador, and Guatemala. In 2011, the head of the U.S. Southern Military

Regional ISSUE   The Role of the Tourist Industry in Middle American Economies

IN SUPPORT OF THE TOURIST INDUSTRY

"As the general manager of a small hotel in St. Maarten, on the Dutch side of the island, I can tell you that without tourists, we would be in deep trouble economically. Mass tourism, plain and simple, has come to the rescue in the Caribbean and in other countries of Middle America. Look at the numbers. Here it's the only industry that is growing, and it already is the largest worldwide industry. For some of the smaller countries of the Caribbean, this is not just the leading industry but the only one producing external revenues. Whether it's hotel patrons or cruise-ship passengers, tourists spend money, create jobs, fill airplanes that give us a link to the outside world, require infrastructure that's good not just for them but for locals too. We've got better roads, better telephone service, more items in our stores. All this comes from tourism. I employ 24 people, most of whom would be looking for nonexistent jobs if it weren't for the tourist industry.

"And it isn't just us here in the Caribbean. Look at Belize. I just read that tourism there, based on their coral reefs, Mayan ruins, and inland waterways, brought in U.S. $100 million last year, in a country with a total population of only about 300,000! That sure beats sugar and bananas. In Jamaica, they tell me, one in every four workers has a job in tourism. And the truth is, there's still plenty of room for the tourist industry to expand in Middle America. Those Americans and Europeans can close off their markets against our products, but they can't stop their citizens from getting away from their awful weather by coming to this tropical paradise.

"Here's another good thing about tourism. It's a clean industry. It digs no mine shafts, doesn't pollute the atmosphere, doesn't cause diseases, doesn't poison villagers, isn't subject to graft and corruption the way some other industries are.

"Last but not least, tourism is educational. Travel heightens knowledge and awareness. There's always a minority of tourists who just come to lie on the beach or spend all their time in some cruise-ship bar, but most of the travelers we see in my hotel are interested in the place they're visiting. They want to know why this island is divided between the Dutch and the French, they ask about coral reefs and volcanoes, and some even want to practice their French on the other side of the border (don't worry, no formalities, just drive across and start talking). Tourism's the best thing that happened to this part of the world, and other parts too, and I hope we'll never see a slowdown."

CRITICAL OF THE TOURIST INDUSTRY

"You won't get much support for tourism from some of us teaching at this college in Puerto Rico, no matter how important some economists say tourism is for the Caribbean. Yes, tourism is an important source of income for some countries, like Kenya with its wildlife and Nepal with its mountains, but for many countries that income from tourism does not constitute a real and fundamental benefit to the local economies. Much of it may in fact result from the diversion to tourist consumption of scarce commodities such as food, clean water, and electricity. More of it has to be reinvested in the construction of airport, cruise-port, overland transport, and other tourist-serving amenities. And as for items in demand by tourists, have you noticed that places with many tourists are also places where prices are high?

"Sure, our government people like tourism. Some of them have a stake in those gleaming hotels where they can share the pleasures of the wealthy. But what those glass-enclosed towers represent is globalization, powerful multinational corporations colluding with the government to limit the opportunities of local entrepreneurs. Planeloads and busloads of tourists come through on prearranged (and prepaid) tour promotions that isolate those visitors from local society.

"Picture this: luxury liners sailing past poverty-stricken villages, luxury hotels towering over muddy slums, restaurants serving caviar when, down the street, children suffer from malnutrition. If the tourist industry offered real prospects for economic progress in poorer countries, such circumstances might be viewed as the temporary, unfortunate byproducts of the upward struggle. Unfortunately, the evidence indicates otherwise. Name me a tourism-dependent economy where the gap between the rich and poor has narrowed.

"As for the educational effect of tourism, spare me the argument. Have you sat through any of those 'culture' shows staged by the big hotels? What you see there is the debasing of local culture as it adapts to visitors' tastes. Ask hotel workers how they really feel about their jobs, and you'll hear many say that they find their work dehumanizing because expatriate managers demand displays of friendliness and servitude that locals find insulting to sustain.

"I've heard it said that tourism doesn't pollute. Well, the Alaskans certainly don't agree—they sued a major cruise line on that issue and won. Not very long ago, cruise-ship crews routinely threw garbage-filled plastic bags overboard. That seems to have stopped, but I'm sure you've heard of the trash left by mountain-climbers in Nepal, the damage done by off-road vehicles in the wildlife parks of Kenya, the coral reefs injured by divers off Bonaire or the Virgin Islands. Tourism is here to stay, but it is no panacea."

Vote your opinion at www.wiley.com/go/deblijpolling

Command warned that this part of Central America had become the "deadliest zone in the world." Not surprisingly, national murder rates in El Salvador and Honduras for that year turned out to be the highest and second-highest on Earth, respectively, with fourth-ranked Guatemala close behind (by 2012, Honduras had moved up to first place).

Is Small Beautiful?

As noted, the Middle American realm is exceptional in the modest size of its territorial extent and population. But the number of constituent countries is considerable, and they tend to be quite small. Caribbean islands often invoke images of beautiful scenery, tropical cocktails, and shiny blue waters, yet their economic realities are almost invariably harsh.

The limited land areas of the Lesser Antilles each average well below half a million people, and that, combined with insularity, remoteness, and low connectivity, poses formidable challenges that are common to small-island developing economies [19]. First, natural resources are frequently limited, which requires a heavy reliance on imports made more expensive by added transport costs. Second, the cost of government is relatively high on a per capita basis: even the smallest population will require services such as schools, hospitals, and waste disposal. Third, these specialized services must often be brought in from elsewhere. And fourth, local production cannot really benefit from economies of scale, which means that local producers can be put out of business by cheaper imports, thereby driving up unemployment.

Given the Caribbean Basin's limited economic options, does the tourist industry offer better opportunities? Opinions on this question are divided. The resort areas, scenic treasures, and historic locales of Caribbean America attract between 20 and 25 million visitors annually, with about half of them traveling on Florida-based cruise ships. Certainly, Caribbean tourism is a prospective money-maker for many islands. In Jamaica alone, this industry accounts for about one-fifth of the gross domestic product and employs more than one-fourth of the labor force.

But Caribbean tourism also has serious drawbacks. The invasion of poor communities by affluent tourists contributes to rising local resentment, which is further fueled by the glaring contrasts of shiny new hotels towering over substandard housing and luxury liners gliding past poverty-stricken villages. At the same time, tourism can have the effect of debasing local culture, which often is adapted to suit the visitors' tastes at hotel-staged "culture" shows. In addition, the cruise industry tends to monopolize revenues (accommodations, meals, entertainment) with relatively few dollars flowing into the local economy. Finally, even though tourism does generate income in the Caribbean, the intervention of island governments and multinational corporations can remove opportunities from local entrepreneurs in favor of large operators and major resorts.

The Push for Regional Integration

Another challenge for the Middle American realm is to foster greater economic integration. Many of the countries on the mainland as well as in the Caribbean are poorly connected within the realm and are heavily dependent on major outside countries, particularly the United States. For the large majority of these countries, the United States is their primary trading partner. Consider this: of all the trade involving Middle American countries, less than 10 percent occurs within the realm. And less than 1 percent takes place between the Caribbean Basin and the Middle American mainland.

Over the years, efforts have been made to advance economic integration and convert this realm into more of a *functional region*. The mainland saw the creation of the Central American Common Market in 1960, but it became moribund within a decade because of the 1969 war between El Salvador and Honduras that was followed by wider intraregional conflict throughout the 1970s and 1980s (some with U.S. involvement). The organization was resuscitated in the 1990s, but since 2005 it has been strongly overshadowed by **CAFTA**, the Central American Free Trade Agreement with the United States. CAFTA seems a mixed blessing: it may increase access to U.S. markets and lead to cheaper imports, but it may also galvanize the dominant position of the United States at the cost of greater intraregional integration.

Within the Caribbean Basin itself, **CARICOM** (Caribbean Community) was established in 1989 and today consists of 15 full members, including nearby Guyana and Suriname in South America. To a certain extent, CARICOM follows the model of the European Union and in 2009 even introduced a common passport. But economic change has been painfully slow, a reminder that the geography of the Middle American realm poses many formidable challenges. Clearly, these cannot be easily overcome even with the best political and economic intentions.

> **◖ POINTS TO PONDER**
>
> - The 3169-kilometer (1969-mi) land border between North America and Middle America is the longest in the world that separates a rich realm from a poor one.
> - The United States is the single most important economic partner of just about every country and territory in this realm—is that a positive or a negative for Middle America?
> - "Poor Mexico . . . so far from God and so close to the United States"—former Mexican President Porfirio Diaz.
> - Most of the small Caribbean island-nations contain less than half a million people—is that enough to sustain a viable economy?

DEFINING the Realm

IN THIS CHAPTER

- South America's commodities boom
- The growing assertiveness of indigenous peoples
- Inequality and violence: A hallmark of South America?
- Brazil on the move
- The Chinese are coming . . .

CONCEPTS, IDEAS, AND TERMS

Unity of place 1
Indigenous 2
Altiplano 3
Land alienation 4
Liberation theology 5
Cultural pluralism 6
Commercial agriculture 7
Subsistence agriculture 8
Uneven development 9
Rural-to-urban migration 10
Megacity 11
"Latin" American City model 12
Informal sector 13
Barrio (favela) 14
Dependencia theory 15

FIGURE 5A-1 © H. J. de Blij, P. O. Muller, and John Wiley & Sons, Inc.

O f all the continents, South America has the most familiar shape—a gigantic triangle connected by mainland Middle America's tenuous land bridge to its neighbor in the north. South America also lies not only south but mostly east of its northern counterpart. Lima, the capital of Peru—one of the continent's westernmost cities—lies farther east than Miami, Florida. Thus South America juts out much more prominently into the Atlantic Ocean toward southern Europe and Africa than does North America. But lying so far eastward means that South America's western flank faces a much wider Pacific Ocean, with the distance from Peru to Australia nearly twice that from California to Japan.

DEFINING THE REALM

As if to reaffirm South America's northward and eastward orientation, the western margins of the continent are rimmed by one of the world's longest and highest mountain ranges, the Andes, a giant wall that extends unbroken from Tierra del Fuego near the continent's southern tip in Chile to northeastern Venezuela in the far north (Fig. 5A-1). The other major physiographic feature of South America dominates its central north—the Amazon Basin; this vast humid-tropical amphitheater is drained by the mighty Amazon River, which is fed by several major tributaries. Much of the remainder of the continent can be classified as plateau, with the most important components being the Brazilian Highlands that cover most of Brazil southeast of the Amazon Basin, the Guiana Highlands located north of the lower Amazon Basin, and the cold Patagonian Plateau that blankets the southern third of Argentina. Figure 5A-1 also reveals two other noteworthy river basins beyond Amazonia: the Paraná-Paraguay Basin of south-central South

America, and the Orinoco Basin in the far north that drains interior Colombia and Venezuela.

PHYSIOGRAPHY

Explorers' Continent

It was here in northern South America that the great German explorer and scientist Alexander von Humboldt, one of the founders of the modern discipline of geography, embarked on his legendary expeditions in the early nineteenth century. After landing on the coast of Venezuela and trekking across the continent's northern interior, the 30-year-old Humboldt was struck by the area's biodiversity, its majestic natural beauty, and the adaptive abilities of the human populations. He discovered and named many species of flora and fauna, traversed tropical grasslands and jungles, met with indigenous peoples, crossed dangerous rivers, and reached the summit of the highest mountain in the Americas climbed by Europeans at the time (Ecuador's Chimborazo). He compiled large numbers of maps and was one of the first scientists to note how the coastlines of eastern South America and western Africa fitted together like pieces of a jigsaw puzzle, speculating about the continents' geologic movements.

Humboldt was most important in the rise of the modern discipline of geography because of his many discoveries as well as his views on the unity of place [1]: that in a particular locale or region intricate connections exist between climate, geology, biology, and human cultures. As such, he laid the foundation for modern geography as an *integrative discipline* with a spatial perspective. It took him four decades after his arrival in South America to produce his magnum opus that articulated this holistic perspective, the highly ambitious and appropriately titled *Cosmos* (published in five volumes in 1845).

Almost three centuries earlier, the opposite end of South America was the scene of a crucial stage in the first circumnavigation of the globe and expedition led by Ferdinand Magellan. Once it became clear that Columbus

Symbol of the ongoing development thrust into South America's interior, the new Ponte Rio Negro, the first major bridge in the Amazon Basin and Brazil's longest, links the city of Manaus to its satellite, Iranduba.

© Ian Trower/Robert Harding Imagery/Corbis

major geographic qualities of
SOUTH AMERICA

1. South America's physiography is dominated by the Andes Mountains in the west and the Amazon Basin in the central north. Much of the remainder is plateau country.

2. Almost half of the realm's area and just under half of its total population are concentrated in one country—Brazil.

3. South America's population remains concentrated along the continent's periphery. Most of the interior is sparsely peopled, but sections of it are now undergoing significant development.

4. Interconnections among the states of the realm are improving rapidly. Economic integration has become a growing force, but is still at an early stage.

5. Regional economic contrasts and disparities, both in the realm as a whole and within individual countries, remain strong.

6. Cultural pluralism prevails in almost all of the realm's countries and is often expressed regionally.

7. Rapid urban growth continues to mark much of the South American realm, and urbanization overall is today on a par with the levels of the United States and western Europe.

8. This realm contains abundant natural riches, and it has benefited in recent years from increased global demand for raw materials.

---

had stumbled upon America, not India, Spanish and Portuguese explorers continued their efforts to discover a westward passage from the Atlantic to the Pacific. This took them to the far south along what is now the Argentinean coast. Magellan and his crew spent some five months in Patagonia, named by Magellan for "big-foot people" (official, but never-verified, reports of the voyage told of the crew's mysterious encounters with 8-foot giants). With the onset of spring in 1520, Magellan's five ships set sail for the treacherous waters of what he named the *Estrecho de Todos los Santos*—now called the Strait of Magellan (Fig. 5A-1). Of the five ships in Magellan's fleet, only three survived the daring, 600-kilometer (375-mile)-long passage; the other two crashed on the rocks in the icy waters of the Southern Ocean.

Myriad Climates and Habitats

If the Russian realm is the widest in east-west extent, the South American realm is the longest measured from north to south. Within South America, no other country is more emblematic of this elongated geography than Chile, averaging only about 150 kilometers (90 mi) in width but 4000 kilometers (2500 mi) in length. As a consequence of this latitudinal span, fully one-tenth of our planet's circumference, the realm contains an enormous variety of climates and vegetation. Combine this with substantial variation in elevation from west to east, and it is clear why South America has such an impressive range of natural habitats.

Take another look at the map showing the global distribution of climates (Fig. G-7) and note the variation in climatic types, particularly in the realm's northwest and southern half. Travel northeast from Lima, Peru for about 600 kilometers (375 mi) and you encounter no less than four different climate zones: arid, highland, and two varieties of

humid tropical. A transect of similar length from Santiago, Chile eastward across the continent to Buenos Aires, Argentina will take you through five climate zones: interior highland, arid, and semiarid environments bracketed by a different humid temperate climate along each coast. Vegetation in South America varies accordingly, from lush tropical rainforests to rocky and barren snow-covered mountaintops to grasslands, fertile as well as parched. This natural diversity also makes for considerable cultural differences, as we shall soon see.

STATES ANCIENT AND MODERN

Thousands of years before the first European invaders appeared on the shores of South America, peoples now referred to as indigenous [2] had migrated into the continent via North and Middle America and founded societies in coastal valleys, in river basins, on plateaus, and in mountainous locales. These societies achieved different and remarkable adaptations to their diverse natural environments, and by about 1000 years ago, a number of regional cultures thrived in the elongated valleys between mountain ranges of the Andes from present-day Colombia southward to Bolivia and Chile. These high-altitude valleys, called *altiplanos* [3], provided fertile soils, reliable water supplies, building materials, and natural protection to their inhabitants.

The Inca State

One of these *altiplanos*, at Cuzco in what is now Peru, became the core area of South America's greatest indigenous empire, that of the **Inca**. The Inca were expert builders whose stone structures (among which Machu Picchu near Cuzco is the most famous), roads, and bridges helped to

From the Field Notes . . .

"Traveling on Peru's Cuzco *altiplano*, it was easy to get a sense of the advantages of this highland environment to the Incas of

the past. The soils are fertile, temperatures are moderate, and the surrounding snowcapped ranges of the Andes feed the Urubamba River and many other streams. The Urubamba Range in the background, partially hidden behind the clouds, rises up to nearly 6000 meters (19,000 ft) and the city of Cuzco itself lies at 3350 meters (11,000 ft). For centuries, this area has produced abundant corn (seen in the foreground), potatoes, and other *tierra fría* crops. But the retreating glaciers in the higher elevations are now a cause of concern. Global warming may jeopardize what has been nature's gift to this *altiplano* for many centuries: a reliable water supply."

© Jan Nijman   **www.conceptcaching.com**

unify their vast empire; they also proved themselves to be efficient administrators, successful farmers and herders, and skilled manufacturers; their scholars studied the heavens, and physicians even experimented with brain surgery. Great military strategists, the Inca integrated the peoples they vanquished into a stable and well-functioning state, an amazing accomplishment given the high-relief terrain they had to contend with (see photo).

As a minority ruling elite in their far-flung empire, the Inca were at the pinnacle in their rigidly class-structured, highly centralized society. So centralized and authoritarian was their state that a takeover at the top was enough to gain immediate power over all of it—as a small army of Spanish invaders discovered in the 1530s. The European invasion brought a quick end to thousands of years of indigenous cultural development and changed the map forever.

The Iberian Invaders

The modern map of South America started to take shape when the Iberian colonizers began to understand the location and economies of the indigenous societies. The Inca, like Mexico's Maya and Aztec peoples, had accumulated gold and silver at their headquarters, possessed productive farmlands, and constituted a ready labor force. Not long after the defeat of the Aztecs in 1521, Francisco Pizarro sailed southward along the continent's northwestern coast, learned of the existence of the Inca Empire, and withdrew to Spain to organize its overthrow. He returned to the Peruvian coast in 1531 with 183 men and two dozen horses, and the events that followed are well known. In 1533, his party rode victorious into Cuzco.

At first, the Spaniards kept the Incan imperial structure intact by permitting the crowning of an emperor who

was under their control. But soon the breakdown of the old order began. The new order that gradually emerged in western South America placed the indigenous peoples in serfdom to the Spaniards. Great haciendas were formed by land alienation [4] (the takeover of indigenously held land by foreigners), taxes were instituted, and a forced-labor system was introduced to maximize the profits of exploitation.

Lima, the west-coast headquarters of the Spanish conquerors, soon became one of the richest cities in the world, its wealth based on the exploitation of vast Andean silver deposits. The city also served as the capital of the Viceroyalty of Peru, as the Spanish authorities quickly integrated the new possession into their colonial empire (Fig. 5A-2). Subsequently, when Colombia and Venezuela came under Spanish control and, later, when Spanish settlement expanded into what is now Argentina and Uruguay, two additional viceroyalties were added to the map: New Granada and La Plata.

Meanwhile, another vanguard of the Iberian invasion was penetrating the east-central part of the continent, the coastlands of present-day Brazil. This area had become a Portuguese sphere of influence because Spain and Portugal had signed a treaty in 1494 to recognize a north-south line 370 leagues west of the Cape Verde Islands as the boundary between their New World spheres of influence. This border ran approximately along the meridian of 50°W longitude, thereby cutting off a substantial triangle of eastern South America for Portugal's exploitation (Fig. 5A-2). But a brief look at the political boundaries of South America (Fig. 5A-1) shows that this treaty did not limit Portuguese colonial territory to lands east of the 50th meridian. Instead, Brazil's boundaries were bent far inland to include almost the entire Amazon Basin, and the country came to be only slightly smaller in territorial size than all the other South American countries combined. This westward thrust was the result of

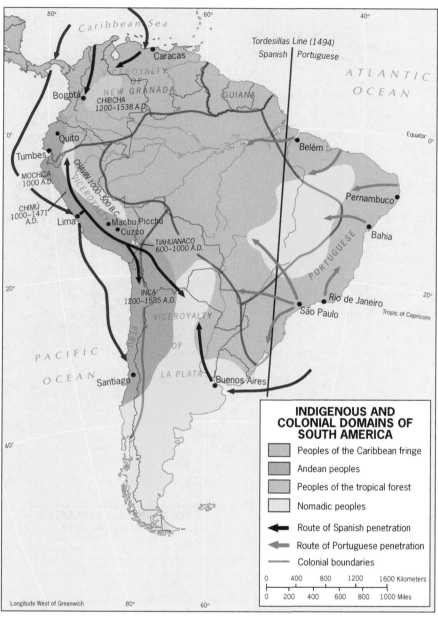

FIGURE 5A-2

© H. J. de Blij, P. O. Muller, and John Wiley & Sons, Inc.

Portuguese and Brazilian penetration, particularly by the *Paulistas*, the settlers of São Paulo who needed indigenous slave labor to run their plantations.

Independence and Isolation

Despite their adjacent location on the same continent, their common language and cultural heritage, and their shared national problems, the countries that arose out of South America's Spanish viceroyalties (together with Brazil) until quite recently existed in a considerable degree of isolation from one another. Distance as well as physiographic barriers reinforced this separation, and the realm's major population agglomerations still adjoin the coast, mainly the eastern and

northern coasts (Fig. 5A-3). The viceroyalties existed primarily to extract riches and fill Spanish coffers. In Iberia, there was little interest in developing the American lands for their own sake. Only after those who had made Spanish and Portuguese America their new home and who had a stake there rebelled against Iberian authority did things begin to change, and then very slowly. Thus South America was saddled with the values, economic outlook, and social attitudes of eighteenth-century Iberia—not the best tradition from which to begin the task of forging modern nation-states.

Certain isolating factors had their effect even during the wars for independence. Spanish military strength was always concentrated at Lima, and those territories that lay farthest from their center of power—Argentina as well as

FIGURE 5A-3   © H. J. de Blij, P. O. Muller, and John Wiley & Sons, Inc.

Chile—were the first to gain independence from Spain (in 1816 and 1818, respectively). In the north, Simón Bolívar led the burgeoning independence movement, and in 1824 two decisive military defeats there spelled the end of Spanish power in South America.

This joint struggle, however, did not produce unity because no fewer than nine countries emerged from the three former viceroyalties. It is not difficult to understand why this fragmentation took place. With the Andes intervening between Argentina and Chile and the Atacama Desert between Chile and Peru, overland distances seemed even greater than they really were, and these obstacles to contact proved quite effective. Hence, from their outset the new countries of South America began to grow apart amid friction and even wars. Only within the past two decades have the countries of this realm finally begun to

recognize the mutual advantages of increasing cooperation and to make lasting efforts to steer their relationships in this direction.

THE CULTURAL MOSAIC

When we speak of the interaction of South American countries, it is important to keep in mind just who does the interacting. The fragmentation of colonial South America into ten individual republics, and the subsequent postures of each of these states, was the work of a small minority that constituted the landholding, upper-class elite. Therefore, in every country a vast majority—be they indigenous people in Peru or those of African descent in Brazil—could only watch as their European masters struggled with one another for supremacy.

From the Field Notes . . .

© H.J. de Blij

"Near the waterfront in Belém lie the now-deteriorating, once-elegant streets of the colonial city built at the mouth of the Amazon. Narrow, cobblestoned, flanked by tiled frontages and arched entrances, this area evinces the time of Dutch and Portuguese hegemony here. Mapping the functions and services here, we recorded the enormous diversity of activities ranging from carpentry shops to storefront restaurants and from bakeries to clothing stores. Dilapidated sidewalks were crowded with shoppers, workers, and people looking for jobs (some newly arrived, attracted by perceived employment opportunities in this growing city of 2.2 million). The diversity of population in this and other tropical South American cities reflects the varied background of the region's peoples and the wide hinterland from which these urban magnets have drawn their inhabitants."

www.conceptcaching.com

The Population Map—Then and Now

If we were able to reconstruct a map of South America's population before the arrival of the Europeans (a "pre-Columbian" map, as it would be called), it would look quite different from the current one in Figure 5A-3. Indigenous societies inhabited not only the Andes and adjacent lowlands but also riverbanks in the Amazon Basin, where settlements numbering in the thousands subsisted on fishing and farming. They did not shy away from harsh environments such as those of the island of Tierra del Fuego in the far south, where the fires they kept going against the bitter cold led the Europeans to name the place "land of fire."

Today the map looks quite different. Many of the indigenous societies succumbed to the European invaders, not just through warfare but also because of the diseases the Iberian conquerors brought with them. Geographers estimate that 90 percent of native Amazonians died within a few years of contact, and the peoples of Tierra del Fuego also are no longer there to build their fires. From one end of South America to the other, the European arrival spelled disaster.

Spanish and Portuguese colonists penetrated the interior of South America, but the great majority of the settlers stayed on or near the coast, a pattern still visible today. Almost all of the realm's major cities have coastal or near-coastal locations, and the current population distribution map gives you the impression of a continent yet to be penetrated and inhabited. But look carefully at Figure 5A-3, and you will see a swath of population located well inland from the settlements along the northwest coast, most clearly in Peru but also extending northward into Ecuador and southward into

Bolivia. That is the legacy of the Inca Empire and its incorporated peoples, surviving in their mountainous redoubt and still numbering in the tens of millions.

Indigenous Reawakening

Today, South America's long-downtrodden indigenous peoples are staging a social, political, and economic reawakening. In several of the realm's countries, where their numbers are large enough to translate into political strength, they have begun to realize their potential. The indigenous peoples in Peru constitute 45 percent of the national population, and in Bolivia they are in the majority at 55 percent.

Newly empowered indigenous political leaders are emerging and bringing the plight of the realm's aboriginal peoples to both local and international attention. South America's indigenous peoples were conquered, decimated by foreign diseases, robbed of their best lands, subjected to involuntary labor, denied the right to grow their traditional crops, socially discriminated against, and swindled out of their fair share of the revenues from resources in their traditional domains. They may still be the poorest of the realm's poor, but they are increasingly asserting themselves. For some South American states, the consequences of this movement will be far-reaching.

The indigenous reawakening is in part related to changing religious practices in South America. Officially, just over 80 percent of the population is Roman Catholic, and traditionally South Americans tend to be viewed as devout followers of the Vatican. But recent surveys show that many do not attend church regularly and that more than half of all Catholics describe themselves as believers of the doctrine, rather than adherents of the Church. Since the late nineteenth century, the Catholic Church has often been criticized for its conservative position on social issues and for siding with the establishment. During the 1950s, a powerful movement known as Liberation theology [5] emerged in South America and subsequently gained followers around the world. The movement was a blend of Christian religion and socialist philosophy that interpreted the teachings of Christ as a quest to liberate the impoverished masses from oppression. Although the Church has lately been trying to make amends, it could not avoid losing popular support, especially among indigenous peoples. In recent years, Protestant-evangelical faiths have also been gaining many new adherents, largely at the expense of Catholicism.

African Descendants

As Figure 5A-2 shows, the Spaniards initially got very much the better of the territorial partitioning of South America—not just in land quality but also in the size of the aboriginal labor force. When the Portuguese began to develop their territory, they turned to the same lucrative activity that their Spanish rivals had pursued in the Caribbean—the plantation cultivation of sugar for the European market. And they, too, found their workforce in the same source region, as millions of Africans (nearly half of all who came to the Americas) were brought in bondage to the tropical Brazilian coast north of Rio de Janeiro (see Fig. 6A-6). Not surprisingly, Brazil now has South America's largest black population, which is still heavily concentrated in the country's poverty-mired northeastern States. With Brazilians of direct or mixed African ancestry today accounting for just over half of the population of 198 million, the Africans decidedly constitute a major immigration of foreign peoples into South America.

Ethnic Landscapes

The cultural landscape of South America, similar to that of Middle America, is a layered one. Indigenous inhabitants cultivated and crafted diverse landscapes throughout the continent, some producing greater impacts than others. When the Europeans arrived, the cultural transformation that resulted from depopulation severely impacted the environment. Native peoples now became minorities in their own lands, and Europeans introduced crops, animals, and ideas about land ownership and land use that irreversibly changed South America. They also brought in Africans from various parts of Subsaharan Africa. Europeans from non-Iberian Europe also started immigrating to South America, especially during the first half of the twentieth century. Japanese settlers arrived in Brazil and Peru during the same era. All of these elements have contributed to the present-day ethnic complexion of this realm. Figure 5A-4 shows the distinct concentrations of indigenous and African cultural dominance, as well as areas where these groups are largely absent and people of European ancestry predominate.

FIGURE 5A-4

© H. J. de Blij, P. O. Muller, and John Wiley & Sons, Inc.

Of course, ethnic origins are not always so straightforward, and patterns can change as a result of internal migrations and ethnic mixing. In recent years, research on individual DNA and genetics has taught us a lot about the regional and group origins of people. On the map, Argentina is indicated as having predominantly European ancestry. More specifically, recent research shows that, for the average Argentine, nearly 80 percent of his or her genetic structure is European, 18 percent aboriginal, and 2 percent African. If nobody had any mixed ancestors, these percentages would translate perfectly into European, indigenous, and African shares of the population—but of course that is not the case. Many people do not have perfect knowledge about their ethnic ancestry, and while some may be strictly of one single origin, many others will have some degree of mixed ancestry. In the aggregate, however, there is no doubt that the population of cone-shaped southern South America is predominantly of European origin. South America, therefore, is a realm marked by cultural pluralism [6], where indigenous peoples of various cultures, Europeans from Iberia and elsewhere, Africans mainly from western tropical Africa, and even some Asians from Japan, India, and Indonesia cluster in adjacent areas but generally do not mix. The bottom line is a cultural mosaic of almost endless variety.

ECONOMIC GEOGRAPHY

Agricultural Land Use and Deforestation

The internal divisions of this cultural kaleidoscope are further reflected in the realm's economic landscape. In South America, larger-scale commercial [7] or market (for-profit) and smaller-scale subsistence agriculture [8] (primarily for household use) exist side by side to a greater degree than anywhere else in the world (Fig. 5A-5). The geography of plantations and other commercial agricultural systems was initially tied to the distribution of landholders of European background, whereas subsistence farming (such as highland mixed subsistence-market, agroforestry, and shifting

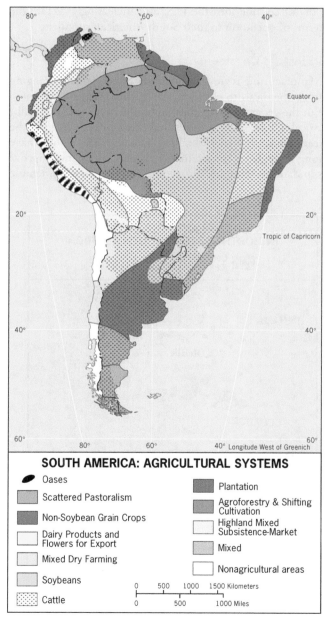

SOUTH AMERICA: AGRICULTURAL SYSTEMS

Oases
Scattered Pastoralism
Non-Soybean Grain Crops
Dairy Products and Flowers for Export
Mixed Dry Farming
Soybeans
Cattle

Plantation
Agroforestry & Shifting Cultivation
Highland Mixed Subsistence-Market
Mixed
Nonagricultural areas

0   500   1000   1500 Kilometers
0   500   1000 Miles

FIGURE 5A-5

© H. J. de Blij, P. O. Muller, and John Wiley & Sons, Inc.

cultivation) is historically associated with the spatial patterns of indigenous peoples as well as populations of African and Asian descent.

At a broader level of generalization, agricultural systems and land use in South America vary in close relationship to physiography, as one would expect. Forestry and agroforestry prevail in the Amazon Basin; ranching dominates in the grasslands of the Southern Cone; and different forms of agriculture, with or without irrigation, are found in an extensive zone from northeastern Brazil to northern Argentina, as well as scattered among pockets of moderate elevation in the Andean highlands. Land uses throughout South America are changing rapidly today, mainly due to ongoing deforestation and the introduction or expansion of new crops. The fastest-growing crop is soybeans, the cultivation of which now dominates much of east-central Brazil and spills over into adjacent areas of Paraguay, Uruguay, and Argentina (Fig. 5A-5).

Deforestation is a particularly acute problem in northern Brazil. In the past, deforestation was attributed mainly to small-scale landholders, colonists who had made their way into the Amazon rainforest to eke out a new living. The usual pattern of settlement often went like this. As main and branch highways were cut through the forest, settlers followed (frequently in response to government-sponsored land occupation schemes), moving out laterally to clear land for farming (see final photo in Chapter 5B). Subsistence crops were planted, but within a year or two, weed infestation and declining soil fertility made these plots unproductive. As soil fertility continued to decline, the settlers planted grasses and then sold their land to cattle ranchers. The peasant farmers then moved on to newly opened nearby areas, cleared more land for planting, and the cycle repeated itself.

Unfortunately, this activity not only entrenches low-grade land uses across widespread areas, but also entails the burning and clearing of vast stands of tropical woodland (in fact, since the 1980s, an area of rainforest about the size of Ohio has been lost *annually* in northern Brazil). To make matters even worse, the deforestation crisis continues to intensify as **agro-industrial** operations engaged in large-scale production for export markets increasingly penetrate Amazonia and transform its land cover.

As South American economies modernize, agriculture remains highly important. Almost one-fifth of this realm's workforce is still employed in the primary sector that includes farming, cattle raising, and fishing—a much greater share than in North America. The South American contribution to global trade in grains, soybeans, coffee, orange juice, sugar, and many other crops is significant and growing. And in addition to all these successful agricultural endeavors, illegal farming thrives in the form of narcotics production, particularly cocaine.

The Geography of Cocaine

All of the cocaine that enters the United States comes from South America, mainly Colombia, Peru, and Bolivia. Within these three countries, cocaine annually brings in billions of (U.S.) dollars and "employs" tens of thousands of workers, constituting a powerful industry. The first of the three stages of cocaine production involves the extraction of coca paste from the coca plant, a raw-material-oriented activity that is located near the areas where the plant is grown. The main zone of coca-plant cultivation is along the eastern slopes of the Andes and in adjacent tropical lowlands in Bolivia, Peru, and Colombia. Today, five areas dominate in the growing of coca leaves for narcotic production: Bolivia's Chaparé district in the marginal Amazon Lowlands northeast of the city of Cochabamba; the Yungas Highlands north of the Bolivian capital, La Paz; north-central Peru's Huallaga and neighboring valleys; south-central Peru's Apurimac Valley, southeast of Huancayo; and the areas around the guerrilla-controlled territories of southern Colombia (Fig. 5A-6).

Coca leaves harvested in the source areas of the Andes and nearby interior lowlands make their way to local collection centers, located at the convergence of rivers and trails, where coca paste is extracted and prepared. The second stage of production involves the refining of that coca paste (about 40 percent pure cocaine) into cocaine hydrochloride (more than 90 percent pure), a lethal concentrate that is diluted with substances such as sugar or flour before being sold on the streets to consumers. Cocaine refining requires sophisticated chemicals, carefully controlled processes, and a labor force skilled in their supervision. Most of this processing is dominated by Colombia and takes place in the rebel-held territory of the lowland central-south and east, beyond the reach of the Bogotá government (see Fig. 5B-3). Interior Colombia also possesses the geographic advantage of intermediate location, lying between the source areas to the south (as well as locally) and the U.S. market to the north.

The final stage of production entails the distribution of cocaine to the marketplace, which depends on an efficient, clandestine transportation network that leads into the United States. Private planes operating out of remote airstrips were the preferred "exporting" method until about a decade ago, and for some time Miami was at the center of cocaine distribution in the United States. But aggressive U.S. measures along the coasts of Florida as well as the Gulf of Mexico have effectively closed down trans-Caribbean flight paths and caused a shift. Much of the cocaine now travels overland to be smuggled by sea through northwestern South America's Pacific and Caribbean seaports. As noted in Chapter 4A, its main destination is Mexico (often via countries in northern Central America), which today supplies almost all the cocaine that enters the United States.

Since 2010, Venezuela has become an additional important link in northbound trafficking, and today about one-quarter of all U.S.-bound cocaine passes through that country. Colombia's FARC and other insurgent groups, originally based in the country's central south, have expanded to establish themselves in the Venezuelan border zone because the savanna on the other side—flat, remote, and beyond the effective control of distant Caracas—is

ideal for operating airstrips (Fig. 5A-6). Indeed, they can be fashioned in a matter of hours by dragging a log behind a pick up truck to smooth the ground, important whenever Venezuelan forces bomb the runways. Thus cocaine is increasingly smuggled across the border, particularly into Venezuela's Apure State from which small aircraft transport it to various cartel strongholds in Mexico for distribution in the United States (see Fig. 4B-6).

The rerouting of drugs through Mexico has been aided by the increased northward flow of goods into the United States under NAFTA—providing ever wider opportunities for smuggling via the millions of trucks that cross the border each year. It has also triggered the rapid rise of organized crime as several Mexican drug gangs evolved into sophisticated international cartels that now control the inflow of cocaine into the U.S. and increasingly dictate the terms of operation to their South American suppliers.

Industrial Development

Manufacturing is growing rapidly in South America, ranging from chemicals to electronics and from textiles to biofuels. But the geography of industrial production varies markedly. Brazil, Chile, and Argentina have traditionally been in the lead, while countries like Peru, Ecuador, and Bolivia have long struggled to modernize their economies and improve standards of living. Within countries, there is considerable

FIGURE 5A-6   © H. J. de Blij, P. O. Muller, J. Nijman, and John Wiley & Sons, Inc.

uneven development [9] as well. Most manufacturing is concentrated in and around major urban centers, leaving vast empty spaces in the interior of the realm.

Brazil, in particular, is increasingly drawing attention for its momentous growth and the rising sophistication of a number of economic sectors. In the past, typical Brazilian exports were foods and footwear. Today, the leading exports include oil (thanks to the fortuitous discovery of huge offshore reserves in the past few years), steel, and state-of-the-art Embraer aircraft. For almost a decade now, Brazil has been included as one of the four biggest emerging markets in the world, along with Russia, India, and China—the so-called **BRICs**.

Despite recent impressive economic growth across much of the realm, it is clear that the longstanding isolation of its individual countries remains a serious obstacle. Nonetheless, most governments agree that tighter integration, political as well as in terms of transportation infrastructure, would greatly enhance economic opportunities.

Economic Integration

The separatism that has long characterized international relations in this realm is finally giving way as South American countries discover the benefits of forging new partnerships with one another. But integration is only beginning and the realm continues to be fragmented: only about 25 percent of its exports stay within South America (a very low share when compared to Europe, where intrarealm exports total close to 70 percent). Nonetheless, things are moving in the right direction. With mutually advantageous trade the catalyst, a new continentwide spirit of cooperation is blossoming at every level. Periodic flare-ups of boundary disputes now rarely escalate into open conflict. Cross-border rail, road, and pipeline projects, stalled for years, are multiplying steadily. For example in southern South America, five formerly contentious nations are developing the *hidróvia* (water highway), a system of river locks that is opening most of the Paraná-Paraguay Basin to barge transport; similar proposals have been advanced to connect this basin to the Amazon River system. And importantly, investments today flow more freely than ever from one country to another, particularly in the agricultural sector.

Recognizing that free trade may well solve several of the realm's economic-geographic problems, governments are now pursuing multiple avenues of economic supranationalism. In 2014, South America's republics were affiliating with the following major trading blocs:

- *Mercosur/l* (*Mercosur* in Spanish; *Mercosul* in Portuguese)**:** Launched in 1995 by countries of the Southern Cone and Brazil, this Common Market established a free-trade zone and customs union linking Brazil, Argentina, Uruguay, and Paraguay. Venezuela joined in 2012 and Bolivia will fully accede by 2014. Meanwhile, founding member Paraguay was suspended in 2012 following the overthrow of its elected leader. With Colombia, Chile, Ecuador, and Peru participating as associate members, this organization aspires to become the dominant free-trade organization for all of South America.

- *Andean Community:* First formed as the Andean Pact in 1969 and then restarted in 1995 as a customs union with common tariffs for imports, this bloc consists of Colombia, Peru, Ecuador, and Bolivia. Venezuela was a member until it withdrew in 2006.

- *Union of South American Nations (UNASUR):* Founded in 2008 in the Brazilian capital of Brasília, the 12 independent countries of South America signed a treaty to create a union envisioned to be similar to the European Union (see Chapter 1A), whose proclaimed goals are a continental parliament, a coordinated defense effort, a single passport for all its citizens, and greater cooperation on infrastructure development. However, significant disagreement among member-states concerning specifics puts the completion of these efforts many years into the

An aerial image of one of South America's most spectacular raw-material sites: northern Brazil's Carajás Iron Ore Mine, located where the southeastern rim of the Amazon Basin meets the Brazilian Highlands in the center of Pará State. This is be the world's richest as well as largest proven deposit of iron ore, whose open-pit mines steadily deepen and sprawl outward as minerals are extracted from the surface—one stripped-away, environmentally degrading layer at a time. In 2012, 320 million metric tons were hauled away via a dedicated, 850-kilometer (535-mi) railroad to the Atlantic port of São Luis (see Fig. 5B-9).

NASA image created by Jesse Allen, using EO-1 ALI data provided courtesy of the NASA EO-1 team

future. UNASUR was preceded by the South American Community of Nations.

- *Pacific Alliance (PA):* Inaugurated in 2012, this newest bloc's founding members were Mexico, Colombia, Peru, and Chile. They swiftly formed a free-trade area among themselves and announced their commitment to further economic integration "with a clear orientation to Asia." In 2013, while the Mercosur/l countries squabbled with one another, the PA was advancing steadily with a collective economic growth rate almost twice as high. Candidates for new membership were lining up, led by Costa Rica, Panama, and Guatemala; other countries, led by Canada and the United States, expressed interest in acquiring *observer* status.

- *Free Trade Area of the Americas (FTAA):* The United States and other NAFTA proponents have tried to move this hemispheric free-trade idea forward, but it has been resisted by peasants and workers in South America, and formally opposed by Mercosur/l. As long as the terms of trade remain set by the North, the Southern partners will be reluctant to participate in this initiative.

The Commodities Boom

Since shortly after the turn of this century, the South American economy in the aggregate has grown robustly by about 5 percent annually. Much of this growth has occurred in Brazil, Chile, and Peru, but other parts of the continent also fared well. A leading reason has been the steadily rising demand for the realm's abundant raw materials in the global marketplace, in no small part resulting from the explosive growth (and voracious raw-material appetites) of China and India. These two Asian giants have been gobbling up Brazilian soybeans, Chilean copper, Peruvian silver, Venezuelan oil, and so much more. Over the past few years, commodity prices have skyrocketed and South America has reaped the benefits. Thus much of the realm was virtually unaffected by the global recession that arose during the late 2000s, which enabled South America to strengthen its position in the global economy. Even though growth has leveled off since 2011, partially in response to slowing Asian demand, in absolute terms the exporting of raw materials remains at a high level.

Heavy reliance on the production of raw materials (slightly more than 50 percent of the realm's exports today) is not always beneficial. As the saying goes, what goes up must come down: world commodity prices—and therefore the foreign revenues of countries overly tied to them—can be notoriously unstable. A second cautionary note is that high demands for commodities can drive up the value of a producing country's currency, which can limit sales of other exports because the latter become more expensive for foreign trading partners. Third, natural resource management, because of complex ownership issues and exploitation rights, invites corruption and complacency (note, for instance, that discoveries of major oil reserves do not often result in a society's advancement). Finally, and most importantly, many resources (especially minerals and energy deposits) are finite, and it is important for producing countries to plan for a future without them. That, of course, is a major challenge to political leaders who tend to think no further than the next election. But if governments engage in wise resource management and development strategies, the commodities boom can only contribute to their nation's overall economic growth.

From the Field Notes . . .

© H.J. de Blij

© H.J. de Blij

"Two unusual perspectives of Rio de Janeiro form a reminder that here the wealthy live near the water in luxury high-rises, such as these overlooking Ipanema Beach—while the poor have million-dollar views from their hillslope *favelas*, such as Rocinho."

www.conceptcaching.com

URBANIZATION

Rural-Urban Migration

As in most other realms, South Americans are leaving the land and migrating to towns and cities. South America's modern urbanization process got an early start and has been intensifying since 1950 as the growth of urban settlements averaged 5 percent a year. Meanwhile, rural areas have grown by less than 2 percent annually over those same six-plus decades. As a result, the realm's urban population has climbed to its current level of 82 percent, ranking it with those of western Europe and the United States. These numbers underscore not only the dimensions but also the durability of the rural-to-urban migration [10] from the countryside to the cities.

In South America, as in Middle America, Africa, and Asia, people are attracted to the cities and driven from the poverty of the rural areas. Both **push** and **pull** factors are at work. Rural land reform has been very slow in coming, and for this and other reasons every year tens of thousands of farmers simply give up and leave, seeing little or no possibility for economic advancement. The urban centers lure them because they are perceived to provide opportunity—the chance to earn a regular wage; visions of education for their children, better medical care, upward social mobility, and the excitement of life in a big city draw hordes to places such as São Paulo and Lima.

But the actual move can be traumatic. Cities in developing countries are surrounded and often invaded by squalid slums, and this is where the urban immigrant most often finds a first—and sometimes permanent—abode in a makeshift shack without even the most basic amenities and sanitary facilities (see photo). Unemployment remains persistently high, often exceeding 25 percent of the available labor force. But still the people come, hopeful for a better life, the overcrowding in the shantytowns worsens, and the threat of regional-scale disease and other disasters rises.

Regional Patterns

The generalized spatial pattern of South America's urban transformation is displayed in Figure 5A-7, which shows a **cartogram** of the continent's population. Here we see not only the realm's countries in population space relative to each other, but also the proportionate sizes of individual large cities within their total national populations.

Regionally, the Southern Cone (countries colored green) is the most highly urbanized. Today in Argentina, Chile, and Uruguay, almost all of the population resides in cities. Ranking after them in urbanization is Brazil (tan). The next highest group of countries (beige) borders the Caribbean Sea in the north. Not surprisingly,

the Andean countries (brown) constitute the realm's least urbanized zone. Figure 5A-7 tells us a great deal about the relative positions of major metropolises in their countries. Three of them—Brazil's São Paulo and Rio de Janeiro, and Argentina's Buenos Aires—rank among the world's megacities [11] (cities whose populations exceed 10 million). But today even the population of the Amazon Basin is more than 70 percent urbanized.

The "Latin" American City Model

The urban experience in the South and Middle American realms varies because of diverse historical, cultural, and economic influences. Nevertheless, there are a number of common threads that have prompted geographers to search for useful generalizations. One is the model of the intraurban spatial structure of the "Latin" American City model [12] proposed by Ernst Griffin and Larry Ford (Fig. 5A-8).

The idea behind a **model** is to create an idealized representation of reality, displaying as many key real-world elements as possible. In the case of South America's cities, the

A 2012 satellite image of Manaus, the fastest-growing large Brazilian metropolis, now with a population of 2 million. Located at the confluence of the Rio Negro and the coffee-colored, sediment-rich Rio Solimões (the local Brazilian name for the Amazon River), this used to be one of Brazil's most remote places. But today it has become a leading hub in the ongoing colonization and urbanization of the Amazon Basin—symbolized by its Ponte Rio Negro Bridge (thin white line at the central left edge of the image), which opened in 2011 (see chapter-opening photo).

© NASA/Corbis

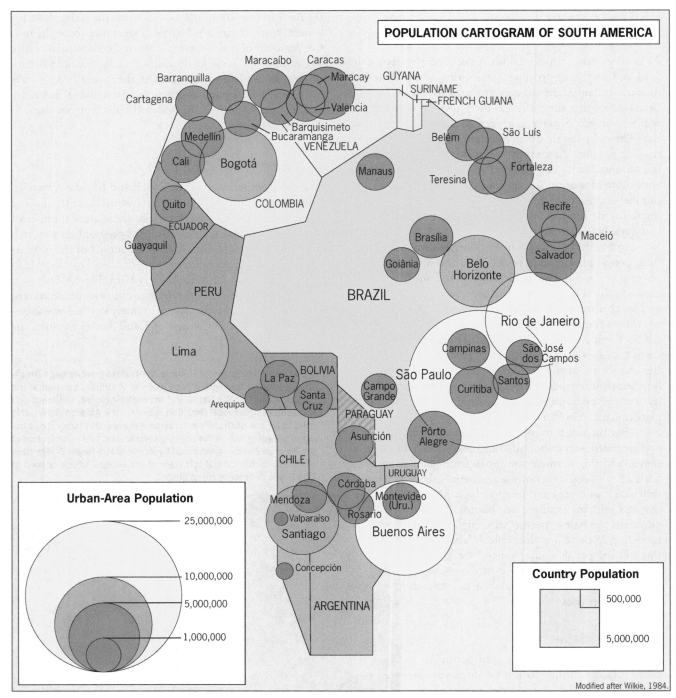

FIGURE 5A-7

© H. J. de Blij, P. O. Muller, and John Wiley & Sons, Inc.

basic spatial framework of city structure, which blends traditional elements of South and Middle American culture with modernization forces now reshaping the urban scene, is a composite of radial sectors and concentric zones. Anchoring the model is the ***central business district (CBD)***, the primary business, employment, and entertainment focus of the surrounding metropolis. The CBD contains many modern high-rise buildings but also mirrors its colonial beginnings. As shown in Figure 4A-5, by colonial law

Spanish colonizers were required to lay out their cities around a central square, or plaza, dominated by a church and government buildings. Santiago's *Plaza de Armas*, Bogotá's *Plaza Bolívar*, and Buenos Aires's *Plaza de Mayo* are classic examples (see photo in *From the Field Notes*). The plaza was the hub of the city, which later outgrew its old core as new commercial districts formed nearby; but to this day the plaza remains a ceremonial center and an important link with the past.

A GENERALIZED MODEL OF LATIN AMERICAN CITY STRUCTURE
After Griffin and Ford, 1980.

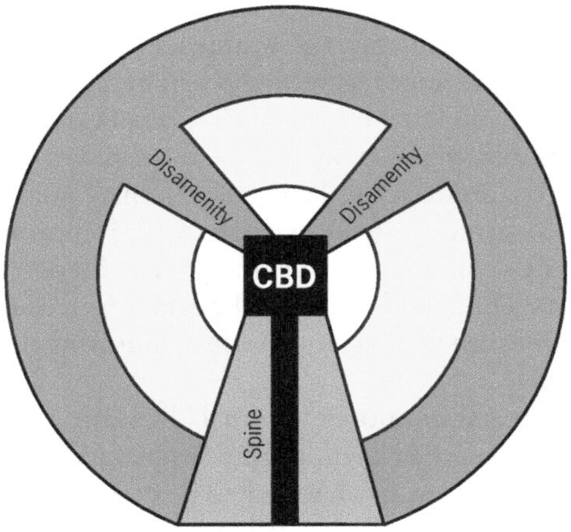

Disamenity · Disamenity · CBD · Spine

Commercial/Industrial

Elite Residential Sector

Zone of Maturity

Zone of *In Situ* Accretion

Zone of Peripheral Squatter Settlements

CBD Central Business District

FIGURE 5A-8

© H. J. de Blij, P. O. Muller, and John Wiley & Sons, Inc.

Radiating outward from the urban core along the city's most prestigious axis is the commercial *spine*, which is adjoined by the *elite residential sector* (shown in green in Fig. 5A-8). This widening corridor is essentially an extension of the CBD, featuring offices, retail facilities, and housing for the upper and upper-middle classes.

The three remaining concentric zones are home to the less fortunate residents of the city, with income level and housing quality decreasing as the distance from the CBD increases. The *zone of maturity* in the inner city contains housing for the middle class, who invest sufficiently to keep their aging dwellings from deteriorating. The adjacent *zone of* in situ *accretion* is one of much more modest housing interspersed with unkempt areas, representing a transition from inner-ring affluence to outer-ring poverty and taking on slum characteristics.

The outermost *zone of peripheral squatter settlements* is home to the millions of comparatively poor and unskilled workers who have recently migrated to the city. Here many newcomers earn their first cash income by becoming part of the informal sector [13], in which workers are undocumented and money transactions are beyond the control of government. The settlements consist mostly of self-help housing, vast shantytowns known as *barrios* [14] in Spanish-speaking South America and *favelas* in Brazil. Some of their entrepreneurial inhabitants succeed more

From the Field Notes . . .

"Cuzco is the historic capital of the Inca Empire, located in the Andes of southeastern Peru. The city center is a UNESCO-designated World Heritage Site and attracts well over a million tourists each year. I drove out of the valley up the hillside to get a good view of the layout of the center, so typical of Spanish colonial cities. The *Plaza de Armas* with its parks and benches is surrounded by the Cathedral of Santo Domingo and other religious and municipal buildings, and adjacent areas around them are used for commerce and retailing. Located farther away from the *Plaza* are newer residential areas. This historic Inca capital was sacked in the early sixteenth century by Pizarro, and only some Inca ruins remain in the center; outside the city lies the impressive Sacsayhuaman fortress, with most of its walls still intact. This is not a very large city—it is too remote for that—but the population has tripled over the past quarter-century to more than 500,000."

© Jan Nijman   www.conceptcaching.com

than others, transforming parts of these shantytowns into beehives of activity that can propel resourceful workers toward a middle-class existence.

A final structural element of many South American cities forms an inward, narrowing sectoral extension of the zone of peripheral squatter settlements and is known as the *zone of disamenity*. It consists of undesirable land along highways, rail corridors, riverbanks, and other low-lying areas; people here are so poor that they are forced to live in the open. Thus the realm's cities present enormous contrasts between poverty and wealth, squalor and comfort—harsh contrasts all too frequently observed in the urban landscape.

FUTURE PROSPECTS

The Need for Stability

As this decade opened, a number of South American countries were celebrating two centuries of independence. What mattered most, for nationalistic purposes, was the date when independence was declared, even if it took additional years for Spain to recognize that new political status. The wars with Spain lasted from 1808 (not coincidentally, soon after Spain had been weakened by Napoleon's invasion of Iberia) to 1838. Brazil's independence from Portugal was achieved during that same period, in 1822.

But the first two centuries of freedom have not seen the evolution of the kind of stable, mature political climates and institutions that one might have expected. South American countries have been in frequent political turmoil. Dictatorial regimes ruled from one end of the realm to the other; unstable governments fell with damaging frequency. Widespread poverty, harsh regional disparities, poor internal surface connections, limited international contact, and economic stagnation prevailed.

Today all that is being cast aside as South America enters a new era of dramatic transition. Well into the second decade of the twenty-first century, formal democracy seems to have taken hold almost everywhere. Long-isolated countries are becoming more interconnected through new transportation routes and trade agreements. New settlement frontiers are being opened. Energy resources, some long exploited and others newly discovered, are boosting national economies as world prices have risen. Foreign states and corporations have appeared on the scene to buy commodities and invest in infrastructure. The pace of globalization is accelerating from Bogotá to Buenos Aires.

Yet progress still varies enormously across the realm (as detailed in Chapter 5B), and these exciting developments need to be viewed against a backdrop of persistent problems of deep inequality and persistent class divisions, ethnic tension, and political malfeasance.

Problems of Inequality and Violence

An important indicator of South America's economic growth since 2000 has been the steady expansion of its middle class:

in fact, the World Bank recently reported that this social stratum had increased its presence within the realm's income-earning population from 20 to 29 percent during the first decade of this century. Nonetheless, deep divisions persist, and many South American governments will need to address these inequalities more aggressively than in the past. By most measures, the disparity between rich and poor is still wider in this realm than in any other, and wealth remains disproportionately concentrated in the hands of a small minority (the richest 20 percent of the people control approximately 70 percent of all wealth, while the poorest 20 percent own 2 percent). Thus South America's leaders are forced to walk a fine line between fueling growth while improving the lives of the masses.

In several countries, internal divisions are complicated by the resurgence of indigenous peoples, and the resulting polarization has harmed civil society, undermined social cohesion, and abetted rising violence. In Colombia, internal strife since the late 1940s has claimed more than a million lives as it divided the country, drew countless peasants into the production of cocaine, and deeply politicized the population. Venezuela now has a murder rate nearly ten times higher than that of the United States. In Brazil's São Paulo and other metropolises, gated communities for higher-income residents have now become standard, armed with state-of-the-art security systems to wall off crimes committed by the poor; and in Rio de Janeiro relentless, grinding poverty in its teeming slums has made them ever more dangerous communities.

The Shadow of the United States

The United States has long played a key role in this realm, beginning with the Monroe Doctrine's 1823 assertion that European colonial powers had no rights to South America. During the Cold War (1945–1990), the United States became politically involved in a number of countries, mainly to keep Soviet influence out of the Western Hemisphere (as in Chile during the early 1970s). This did not always enhance its local standing; in fact, anti-Americanism never seems far from the surface in South America, based heavily on past U.S. support for right-wing dictatorships and continuing perceptions of imperialistic behavior.

To be sure, relations with the United States have never been smooth and were always asymmetrical. For instance, South America today attracts only about 4 percent of all U.S. foreign trade. But the United States remains the biggest trading partner for the realm as a whole, accounting for almost one-fifth of the exports and imports of all South American countries. Thus it was hardly a coincidence that *dependencia* theory [15] originated here in South America during the 1960s. It was a new way of thinking about economic development and underdevelopment that explained the persistent poverty of some countries in terms of their unequal relations with the world's more affluent countries. Whatever the current validity of *dependencia* theory, the asymmetry remains, and U.S. foreign policy,

Photo by Fabio Rossi/Globo/Getty Images, Inc.

Nothing symbolizes China's new economic drive in South America more than its growing interest in its burgeoning fellow BRIC. In 2011, the two countries concluded a (U.S.) $7 billion deal in which Chinese investors helped finance a major expansion of Brazil's already-booming soybean production. Billions of additional dollars of Chinese investment contributed to the new *Superporto do Açu* that opened for business in late 2012. The photo shows a Chinese delegation visiting the construction site in 2010. Açu is located about 400 kilometers (250 mi) northeast of Rio de Janeiro, and its massive 3-kilometer (2-mi)-long concrete pier jutting out into the Atlantic contains ten berths capable of accommodating the largest ships afloat (which are also Chinese). Brazilian investors have called this facility the "Highway to China," and today it claims to be the world's largest port for handling bulk cargoes.

to becoming the most important world power in the South American realm.

Nearly invisible just ten years ago, China has made its presence felt across South America in a variety of ways that include establishing new embassies and consulates, buying up companies, partnering joint ventures, financing infrastructure projects and development assistance, and sending as well as inviting high-level trade delegations. Their motives are clear: the Chinese need key raw materials such as oil, copper, and a plethora of minerals to fuel the enormous economic growth of their country (see photo). At the same time, they are seeking to expand markets for Chinese exports, and the steadily expanding middle classes of Brazil and other countries make enticing targets.

Whether it is the United States or China, South Americans will need to carefully consider how and where to focus their economic attention. Within the realm itself, there is still much to be done in terms of building political accord and economic integration. Undoubtedly, those Chinese investments mentioned above will help to build the bridges so badly needed to bring this realm more closely together.

as viewed from South America, is not always credible. Interestingly, America's special interests in the realm are now under increased pressure from another major power that would have been furthest from President Monroe's mind back in 1823: China.

China Calling

By 2010, China had displaced the United States as the leading trading partner of Brazil and Chile, and in 2011 Peru joined that list. Argentina and Colombia may soon be next because in both China is already a close second. These remarkable developments have yet to fully register in the United States; meanwhile, China is well on its way

POINTS TO PONDER

- The Amazonian rainforest is mainly located within Brazil but sometimes is referred to as "the lungs of the Earth." Should its preservation be a global responsibility?

- Is it a coincidence that both Liberation theology and *dependencia* theory originated in this realm?

- The map of South America's religions is changing. Brazil is still nominally the world's largest Roman Catholic country, but the number of adherents is declining and now accounts for barely 60 percent of the national population (down from 90 percent as recently as 1970).

- Should China's rapidly growing involvement in South America be a cause for concern in the United States?

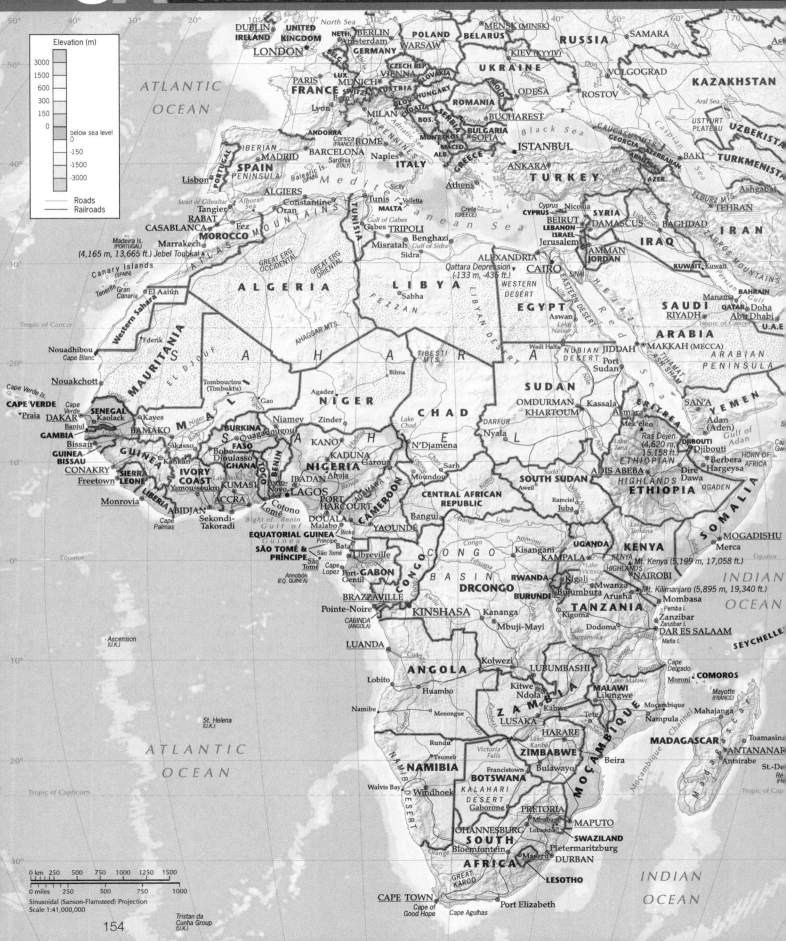

Elevation (m)

3000
1500
600
300
150
0

below sea level
0
-150
-1500
-3000

Roads
Railroads

0 km 250 500 750 1000 1250 1500

0 miles 250 500 750 1000

Sinusoidal (Sanson-Flamsteed) Projection
Scale 1:41,000,000

Tristan da
Cunha Group
(U.K.)

DEFINING the Realm

IN THIS CHAPTER

- Emerging Africa
- The cradle of humankind
- Wildlife conservation and sustainable development
- Neocolonial land grabs?
- Africa's ethnic mosaic
- Beating the AIDS scourge

CONCEPTS, IDEAS, AND TERMS

FIGURE 6A-1   © H. J. de Blij, P. O. Muller, and John Wiley & Sons, Inc.

The African continent occupies a special place in the physical as well as the human world. This is where **human evolution [1]** began. In Africa we formed our first communities, spoke our first words, and created our first art. From Africa our ancestor hominins spread outward into Eurasia more than 2 million years ago. From Africa our species emigrated, beginning perhaps 95,000 years ago, northward into present-day Europe and eastward via southern Asia into Australia and, much later, farther afield into the Americas. Disperse our forebears did, but we should remember that, at the source, we are all Africans.

DEFINING THE REALM

For millions of years, therefore, Africa served as the cradle for the emergence of humankind. For tens of thousands of years, Africa was the source of human cultures. Yet in Chapters 6A and 6B we encounter an Africa that has been struck by human dislocation on a scale unmatched anywhere in the world. Africa's misfortunes, however, are of more recent making and cannot be separated from foreign involvements: from imperialism to colonialism to the geopolitical impact of the Cold War. Today, there are hopeful signs that this catastrophic interlude is ending and that for once global (economic) relations are helping to propel this realm forward.

The focus in these two chapters will be on Africa south of the Sahara, for which the unsatisfactory but convenient name **Subsaharan Africa** has come into use to signify not physically "under" the great desert but directionally south of it. The African continent contains two geographic realms: the African, extending from the southern margins of the Sahara to the Cape of Good Hope, and the western flank of the realm dominated by the Muslim faith and Islamic culture whose heartland lies in the Middle East and the Arabian Peninsula. The great desert forms a formidable barrier between the two, but the powerful influences of Islam crossed the Sahara centuries before the first Europeans set foot in West Africa. By that time, the African kingdoms in what is known today as the Sahel had been converted, creating an Islamic foothold all along the northern periphery of the African realm (see Fig. G-3). As we note later, this cultural and ideological penetration had momentous consequences for Subsaharan Africa.

The African continent may be partitioned into two human-geographic realms, but the landmass is indivisible. Before we investigate the human geography of Subsaharan Africa, therefore, we should take note of the entire continent's unique physical geography (Figs. 6A-1 and 6A-2). We have already noted Africa's situation at the center of the planet's land hemisphere; moreover, no other landmass is positioned so squarely astride the equator, reaching almost as far to the south as to the north. This location has much to do with the distribution of Africa's climates, soils, vegetation, agricultural potential, and human population.

AFRICA'S PHYSIOGRAPHY

Africa accounts for about one-fifth of the Earth's entire land surface. Territorially, it is as big as China, India, the United States, Mexico, and Europe combined. The north coast of Tunisia lies 7700 kilometers (4800 mi) from the southernmost coast of South Africa. Coastal Senegal, in West Africa, lies 7200 kilometers (4500 mi) from the tip of the *Horn* in easternmost Somalia. These distances have critical environmental implications. Much of Africa is far from maritime

Chinese construction crews at work on the new African Union Building in Adis Abeba, the capital of Ethiopia. Chinese companies are investing and working all over Subsaharan Africa, and make no secret of their voracious appetite for the realm's abundant, diverse natural resources.

© Per-Anders Pettersson/Corbis

major geographic qualities of
SUBSAHARAN AFRICA

1. Physiographically, Africa is a huge plateau continent without a major "spinal" mountain range but with a set of Great Lakes, several major river basins, variable rainfall, soils of generally inferior fertility, and mainly savanna and steppe vegetation.

2. Hundreds of distinct ethnic groups make up Subsaharan Africa's culturally rich and varied population. They far outnumber the states in this realm, and only rarely do state and ethnic boundaries coincide.

3. Most of Subsaharan Africa's peoples depend on farming for their livelihood.

4. The realm is rich in raw materials vital to industrialized countries, but many economies continue to rely on primary activities—the extraction of resources—and not the greater income-generating activities of manufacturing and assembly.

5. The realm is famous for its wildlife, but many species are threatened. Combining bioconservation and sustainable development is a major challenge when the outside world covets elephant tusks and rhinoceros horns.

6. Severe dislocation still affects a number of Subsaharan African countries, from the Sudans to Zimbabwe. This realm has by far the largest refugee population in the world today.

7. Foreign interest in the realm's natural resources, from commodities to agricultural land, has been expanding rapidly in recent years.

8. Subsaharan Africa has recently experienced swift economic growth, with a half-dozen countries among the fastest growing in the world today.

sources of moisture. In addition, as Figure G-7 shows, large parts of the landmass lie in latitudes where global atmospheric circulation systems produce arid conditions. The Sahara in the north and the Kalahari in the south form parts of these globe-girdling desert zones. Water supply is one of Africa's foremost problems.

Rifts and Rivers

Africa's topography reveals several properties that are not replicated on other landmasses. Alone among the continents, Africa does not have a mountain backbone; neither the northwestern Atlas nor the far southern Cape Ranges are in the same league as the Andes or Himalayas. Where Africa does have high mountains, as in Ethiopia and South Africa, these are deeply eroded plateaus or, as in East Africa, high snowcapped volcanoes. Furthermore, Africa is one of only two continents containing a cluster of Great Lakes, and the only one whose lakes result from powerful tectonic forces in the Earth's crust. These lakes (with the exception of Lake Victoria) lie in deep trenches called **rift valleys [2]**, which form when huge parallel fractures or faults appear in the Earth's crust and the strips of crust between them sink, or are pushed down, to form great, steep-sided, linear valleys. In Figure 6A-2 these rift valleys, which stretch more than 9600 kilometers (6000 mi) from the Red Sea to Swaziland, are marked by red lines.

Africa's rivers, too, are unusual: their upper courses frequently bear landward, seemingly unrelated to the coast toward which they eventually flow. Several rivers, such as

Farms along the fertile, terraced wall of Kenya's Eastern Rift Valley—a key corridor in the evolution of our human species.

© H.J. de Blij

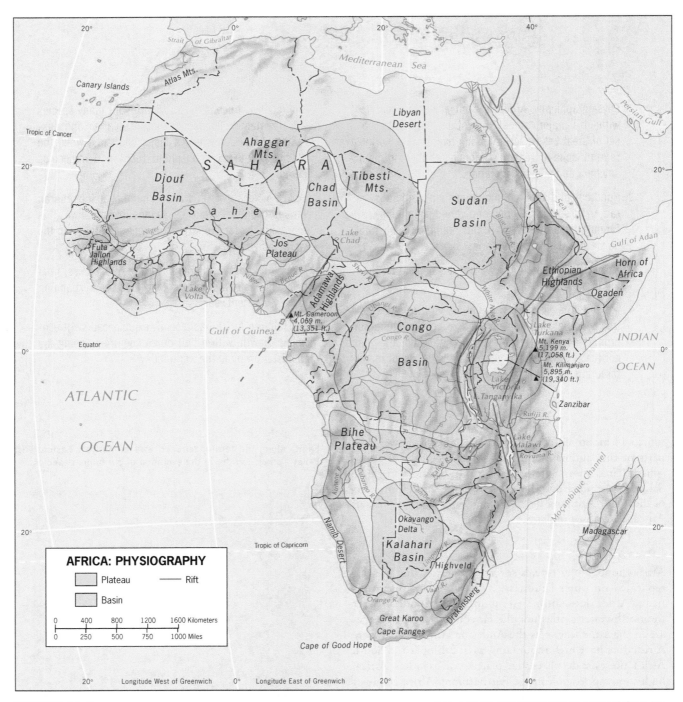

FIGURE 6A-2

© H. J. de Blij, P. O. Muller, and John Wiley & Sons, Inc.

the Nile and the Niger, have inland as well as coastal deltas. Major waterfalls, notably Victoria Falls on the Zambezi, or lengthy systems of cataracts, separate the upper from the lower river courses.

Finally, Africa may be described as the plateau continent. Except for some comparatively limited coastal plains, almost the entire continent lies above 300 meters (1000 ft) in elevation, and fully half of it lies over 800 meters (2500 ft) high. As Figure 6A-2 indicates, the plateau surface has sagged under the weight of accumulating sediments into a

half-dozen major basins (three of them in the Sahara). The margins of Africa's plateau are marked by escarpments, often steep and step-like. Most notable among these is the Great Escarpment of southeastern South Africa, marking the eastern edge of the Drakensberg Mountains.

Continental Drift and Plate Tectonics

Africa's remarkable and unusual physiography was a key piece of evidence that geographer Alfred Wegener used to

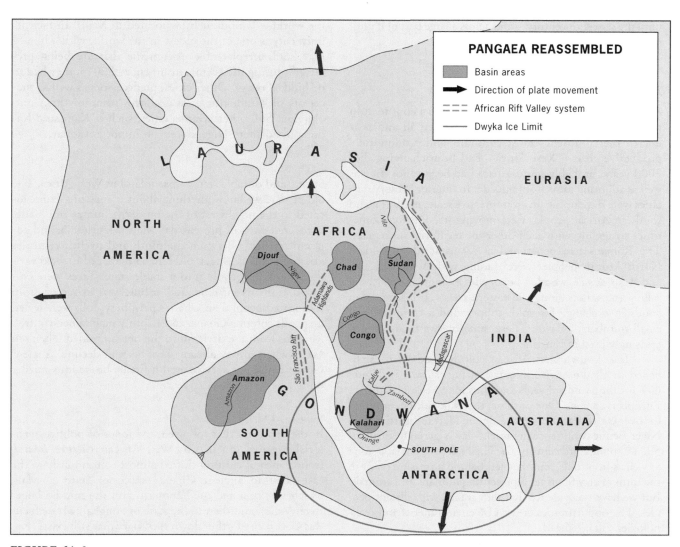

FIGURE 6A-3

© H. J. de Blij, P. O. Muller, and John Wiley & Sons, Inc.

construct his hypothesis of continental drift [3]. All of the present-day continents, Wegener reasoned, lay assembled into one giant landmass called **Pangaea** not very long ago (220 million years) in geologic time. The southern part of this supercontinent was *Gondwana*, of which Africa formed the core (Fig. 6A-3). When, roughly about 200 million years ago, tectonic forces began to split Pangaea apart, Africa (and the other landmasses) acquired its present configurations. That process, now known as ***plate tectonics***, continues and is marked by earthquakes and volcanic eruptions. By the time it started, however, Africa's land surface had begun to acquire some of the features that mark it today—and make it unique. The rift valleys, for example, demarcate the zones where plate movement continues—hence the linear shape of the Red Sea, where the Arabian Plate is separating from the African Plate (Fig. G-4). And yes, the rift valleys of East Africa probably mark the further fragmentation of the African Plate (some geophysicists have already referred to a Somali Plate, which they predict will separate, Madagascar-like, from the rest of Africa).

Africa's ring of escarpments, its rifts, its river systems, its interior basins, and its lack of significant mountains all relate to the continent's central position within Pangaea—all pieces of the puzzle that led to an explanation based on plate tectonics theory.

AFRICA'S HISTORICAL GEOGRAPHY

Africa is the cradle of humankind. Archeological research has chronicled 7 million years of transition from Australopithecenes to hominins to *homo sapiens*. It is therefore ironic that we know comparatively little about Subsaharan Africa from 5000 to 500 years ago—that is, before the onset of European colonialism. This is partly due to the colonial period itself, during which African history was neglected, numerous African traditions and artifacts were destroyed, and many misconceptions about African cultures and institutions became entrenched. It is also a result of the absence of a written history over most of Africa south of the Sahara until the sixteenth century—and across a large part of it until much later than that.

African Genesis

Africa on the eve of the colonial period was a continent in transition. For several centuries, the habitat in and near one of the continent's most culturally and economically productive areas—West Africa—had been changing. For 2000 years, probably more, Africa had been innovating as well as adopting ideas from outside. In interior West Africa, cities were developing on an impressive scale; in central and southern Africa, peoples were moving, readjusting, sometimes struggling with each other for territorial supremacy. The Romans had penetrated as far as southern Sudan, North African peoples were trading with West Africans, and Arab *dhows* (wooden boats with triangular sails) were sailing the waters along the eastern coasts, bringing Asian goods in exchange for gold, copper, and a comparatively small number of slaves. These same dhows today are increasingly used in tourism.

It is known that African cultures had been established in all the environmental settings shown in Figure G-7 for thousands of years and thus long before Islamic or European contact. One of these, the Nok culture, endured for over eight centuries on the Benue Plateau (north of the Niger-Benue confluence in present-day Nigeria) from about 500 BC to the third century AD. The Nok people made stone as well as iron tools, and they left behind a treasure of art in the form of clay figurines representing humans and animals. But we have no evidence that they traded with distant peoples. The opportunities created by environments and technologies still lay ahead.

Early Trade

West Africa, over a north-south span of a few hundred kilometers, displayed an enormous contrast in environments, economic opportunities, modes of life, and products. The peoples of the tropical forest produced and needed goods that were different from the products and requirements of the peoples of the dry, distant north. For example, salt is a prized commodity in the forest, where humidity precludes its formation, but it is plentiful in the desert and semiarid steppe. This enabled the desert peoples to sell salt to the forest peoples in exchange for ivory, spices, and dried foods. Thus there evolved a degree of *regional complementarity* between the peoples of the forest and those of the drylands. And the savanna peoples—those located in between—found themselves in a position to channel and handle the trade (which is always economically profitable).

The markets in which these goods were exchanged prospered and grew, and urban centers arose in the savanna belt of West Africa. One of these old cities, now an epitome of isolation, was once a thriving center of commerce and learning and one of the leading urban places in the world—Timbuktu (now located in Mali). In fact, its university is one of the oldest in the world, with a library that holds irreplaceable documents that are being preserved (during the Islamic insurgency of 2013, they had to be hidden away). Other cities, predecessors as well as successors of Timbuktu, have declined, some of them into oblivion. Still other savanna cities, such as Kano and Kaduna in northern Nigeria, remain important today.

Early States

Strong and durable states arose inland in West Africa. The oldest state we know anything about is ancient Ghana, located to the northwest of the modern country of Ghana. It covered parts of present-day Mali, Mauritania, and adjacent territory. Between the ninth and twelfth centuries AD, and perhaps longer, old Ghana managed to weld various groups of people into a stable state. Taxes were collected from its citizens, and tribute was extracted from subjugated peoples on Ghana's periphery; tolls were levied on goods entering Ghana, and an army maintained control. Muslims from the drylands to the north invaded Ghana in 1067, when it may already have been in decline. Ancient Ghana could not survive, and it finally broke into smaller units.

Eastward Shift

In the centuries that followed, the focus of politico-territorial organization in this West African **culture hearth** (source area of culture) shifted almost continuously to the east—first to ancient Ghana's successor state of Mali, which was centered on Timbuktu and the middle Niger River Valley, and then to the state of Songhai, whose focus was Gao, a city farther down the Niger that still exists (Fig. 6A-4). This eastward movement may have been the result of the growing influence and power of Islam. Traditional animist religions prevailed in ancient Ghana, but Mali and its successor states sent massive, gold-laden pilgrimages to Mecca along the savanna corridor south of the Sahara, passing through present-day Khartoum and Cairo. Of the tens of thousands who participated in these pilgrimages to Islam's holiest city (located in western Arabia), some remained behind. Today, many Sudanese trace their ancestry to the West African savanna kingdoms.

Beyond the West

West Africa's savanna zone undoubtedly experienced momentous cultural, technological, and economic developments, but other parts of Africa made progress as well. Early states emerged in present-day Sudan, Eritrea, and Ethiopia. Influenced by key innovations from the Egyptian culture hearth to the north, these kingdoms were stable and durable: the oldest, Kush, lasted 23 centuries (Fig. 6A-4). The Kushites built elaborate irrigation systems, forged iron tools, and created impressive structures as the ruins of their long-term capital and industrial center, Meroe, reveal. Nubia, to the southeast of Kush, became Christianized until

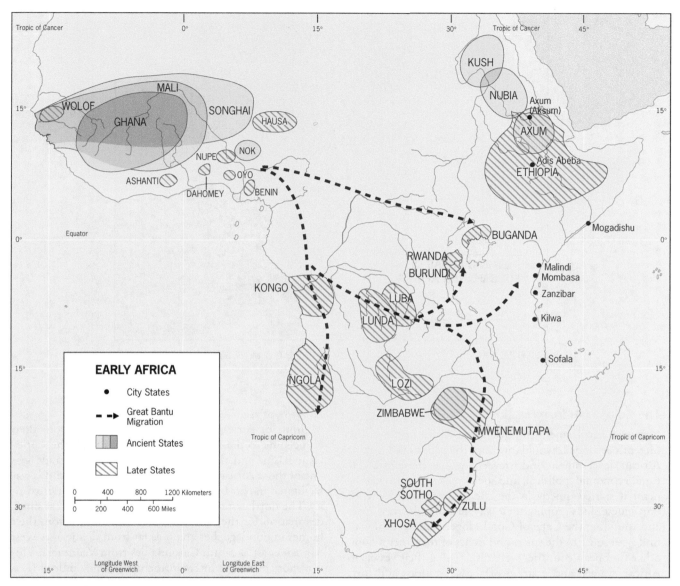

FIGURE 6A-4

© H. J. de Blij, P. O. Muller, and John Wiley & Sons, Inc.

the Muslim wave overtook it in the eighth century. And Axum was the richest market in northeastern Africa, a powerful kingdom that controlled Red Sea trade and endured for six centuries. Axum, too, was a Christian state facing the Islamic surge, but Axum's rulers deflected the Muslim advance and gave rise to the Christian dynasty that eventually shaped modern Ethiopia.

The process of **state formation** [4] spread throughout Africa and was still in progress when the first European contacts occurred in the late fifteenth century. Large and effectively organized states developed on the equatorial west coast (notably Kongo) and on the southern plateau from the southern part of the Congo River Basin southeastward to Zimbabwe. East Africa had several city-states, including Mogadishu, Kilwa, Mombasa, and Sofala.

Bantu Migration

A crucial event commencing about 5000 years ago affected virtually all of Equatorial, West, and Southern Africa: the Great Bantu Migration from present-day Nigeria and Cameroon southward and eastward across the continent. This epic advance appears to have occurred in waves that populated the Great Lakes area and ultimately penetrated South Africa, where it resulted in the formation of the powerful Zulu Empire in the nineteenth century (Fig. 6A-4).

All this reminds us that, before European colonization, Africa was a realm of rich and varied cultures, diverse lifestyles, technological progress, and external trade. It was, however, also a highly fragmented realm, its cultural mosaic (Fig. 6A-5) spelling weakness when European intervention came to change the social and political map forever.

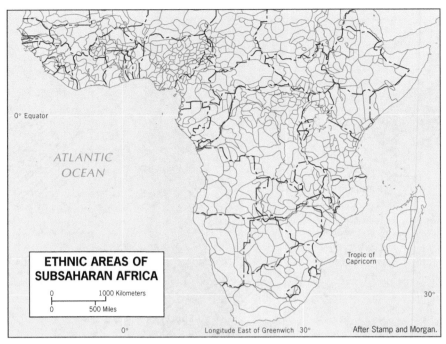

FIGURE 6A-5

© H. J. de Blij, P. O. Muller, and John Wiley & Sons, Inc.

The Colonial Transformation

European involvement in Subsaharan Africa began in the fifteenth century. It would interrupt the path of indigenous African development and irreversibly alter the entire cultural, economic, political, and social makeup of the continent. It started quietly in the late fifteenth century, with Portuguese ships groping their way all along the west coast and rounding the Cape of Good Hope. Their goal was to find a sea route to the spices and riches of the Orient. Soon other European countries were dispatching their vessels to African waters, and a string of coastal stations and forts sprang up. In West Africa, the nearest part of the continent to European spheres in Middle and South America, the initial impact was strongest. At their coastal control points, the Europeans traded with African intermediaries for the slaves who were destined to work New World plantations, for the gold that had been flowing northward across the desert, and for highly prized ivory and spices.

Coastward Reorientation

Suddenly, the centers of activity lay not with the inland cities of the savanna belt but with the foreign stations on the Atlantic coast. As the interior declined, the coastal peoples thrived. Small forest states gained unprecedented wealth, transferring and selling slaves captured in the interior to the European traders on the coast. Dahomey (now called Benin) and Benin (now part of neighboring Nigeria) were states built on the slave trade. When slavery was eventually abolished in Europe, those who had inherited the power and riches it had brought vigorously opposed abolition on both continents.

Horrors of the Slave Trade

Millions of Africans were forced to migrate from their homelands to the Americas, especially Brazil, the Caribbean Basin, and the United States. The slave trade was one of those African disasters alluded to earlier, and it was facilitated in part by what we may call the peril of proximity. The northeastern tip of Brazil, by far the largest single destination for the millions of Africans forced from their homes in bondage, lies about as far from the nearest West African coast as South Carolina lies from Venezuela. This is a short maritime intercontinental journey indeed (it is more than twice as far from West Africa to South Carolina). That proximity facilitated the forced migration of millions of West Africans to Brazil, which in turn contributed to the emergence of an African cultural diaspora in Brazil that is without equal in the New World (see Chapter 5B).

Although slavery was not new to West Africa, the *kind* of slave raiding and trading the Europeans introduced certainly was. In the interior of Africa and within city-states, kings, chiefs, and prominent families traditionally took a few slaves, but the status of those slaves was unlike anything that lay in store for those who were shipped across the Atlantic. In fact, large-scale slave trading had been introduced in East Africa long before the Europeans brought it to West Africa. African intermediaries from the coast raided the interior for able-bodied men and women and marched them in chains to the Arab markets on the coast (the island of Zanzibar was one such slave trading market). There, packed in specially built dhows, they were carried off to Arabia, Persia, and India. When the European slave

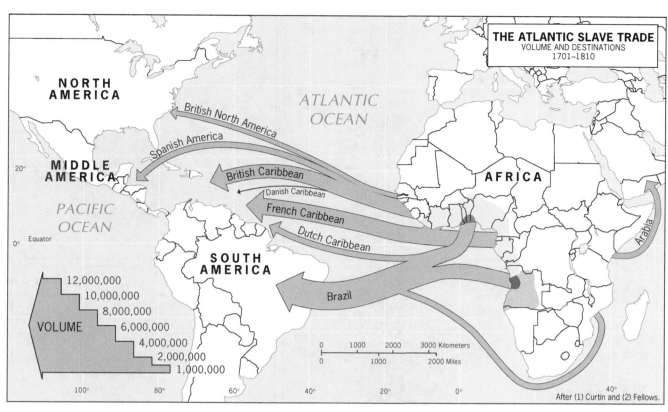

FIGURE 6A-6

© H. J. de Blij, P. O. Muller, and John Wiley & Sons, Inc.

trade took hold in West Africa, however, its volume was far greater. Europeans, Arabs, and collaborating Africans ravaged the continent, forcing perhaps as many as 30 million persons away from their homelands in captivity (Fig. 6A-6). Families were destroyed, as were entire communities and cultures; those who survived their exile suffered unfathomable misery.

The European presence on the West African coast completely reoriented its trade routes, for it initiated the decline of the interior savanna states discussed earlier and strengthened the coastal forest states. Moreover, the Europeans' insatiable demand for slaves ravaged the population of the interior. But it did not lead to any major European thrust toward the interior or produce colonies overnight. The African intermediaries were well organized and strong, and they held off their European competitors, not just for decades but for centuries. Although the Europeans first appeared in the fifteenth century, they did not carve up West Africa until nearly 400 years later, and they did not conquer many other areas until after the beginning of the twentieth century.

Colonization

In the second half of the nineteenth century, whether or not they had control, the European powers finally laid claim to virtually all of Africa. Colonial competition was intense, and spheres of influence began to overlap. It was time for negotiation among the powerful, and in 1884 a conference was convened in Berlin to carve up the African map (see box titled "The Berlin Conference"). The major colonial contestants were Britain, France, Portugal, Belgium, and Germany itself. On maps spread across a large table, representatives from these powers drew boundaries, exchanged real estate, and forged a new map that would become a liability in Africa decades later. As Figure 6A-7 indicates, when the three-month conference was in progress, most of Africa remained under traditional African rule. Not until after 1900 did the colonial powers manage to control all the areas they had marked off and acquired on their new maps.

It is important to examine Figure 6A-7 carefully because the colonial powers governed their new dependencies in very different ways, and their contrasting legacies are still in evidence to this day in the countries their colonies spawned. Some colonial powers were democracies at home (Great Britain and France); others were dictatorships (Portugal and Spain). The British established a system of **indirect rule [5]** over much of their domain, leaving indigenous power structures in place and making local rulers representatives of the British Crown. This was unthinkable in the Portuguese colonies, where harsh, direct control predominated. The French sought to create culturally assimilated elites that would represent French ideals in the colonies.

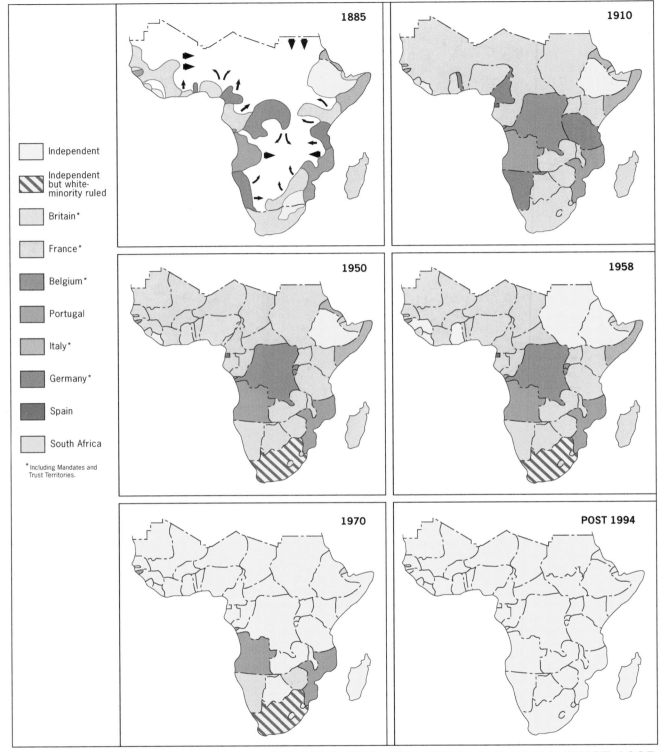

Independent

Independent but white-minority ruled

Britain*

France*

Belgium*

Portugal

Italy*

Germany*

Spain

South Africa

*Including Mandates and Trust Territories.

1885

1910

1950

1958

1970

POST 1994

COLONIZATION AND DECOLONIZATION SINCE 1885

FIGURE 6A-7

© H. J. de Blij, P. O. Muller, and John Wiley & Sons, Inc.

The Berlin Conference

IN NOVEMBER 1884, the imperial chancellor and architect of the German Empire, Otto von Bismarck, convened a conference of 14 states (including the United States, which had no African claims) to settle the political partitioning of Africa. Bismarck wanted not only to expand German spheres of influence in Africa but also to play off Germany's colonial rivals against one another to the Germans' advantage. The major colonial contestants in Africa were: (1) the British, who held beachheads along the West, South, and East African coasts; (2) the French, whose main sphere of activity was in the area of the Senegal River as well as north and northwest of the Congo Basin; (3) the Portuguese, who now desired to extend their coastal stations in Angola and Moçambique deep into the interior; (4) King Leopold II of Belgium, who was amassing a personal domain in the Congo Basin; and (5) Germany itself, active in areas where the designs of other colonial powers might be obstructed, as in Togo (between British holdings), Cameroon (a wedge into French spheres), South West Africa (taken from under British noses in a swift strategic move), and East Africa (where German Tanganyika broke the British design to assemble a solid block of territory stretching northward from the Cape to Cairo).

When the conference convened in Berlin, more than 80 percent of Africa was still under traditional African rule.

Nonetheless, the colonial powers' representatives drew their boundary lines across the entire map. These lines were drawn through known as well as unknown areas, pieces of territory were haggled over, boundaries were erased and redrawn, and African real estate was exchanged among European governments. In the process, African peoples were divided, unified regions were ripped apart, hostile societies were thrown together, hinterlands were disrupted, and migration routes were closed off (for an idea, see Fig. 6A-5). Not all of this was felt immediately, of course, but these were some of the effects when the colonial powers began to consolidate their holdings and the boundaries on paper became barriers on the African landscape (Fig. 6A-7).

The Berlin Conference was Africa's undoing in more ways than one. The colonial powers superimposed their domains on the African continent. By the time Africa regained its independence after the late 1950s, the realm had acquired a legacy of political fragmentation that could neither be eliminated nor made to operate satisfactorily. The African politico-geographical map is therefore a permanent liability that resulted from three months of ignorant, greedy acquisitiveness during a period when Europe's search for minerals and markets had become insatiable.

King Leopold II of Belgium sought to claim Congo Free State as his own personal fiefdom. After financing the expeditions that staked Belgium's claim in Berlin, he embarked on a campaign of exploitation and genocide of such ruthlessness that, after the impact of the slave trade, Leopold's reign of terror was Africa's most severe demographic disaster, with an estimated 10 million murdered (chronicled unforgettably in Joseph Conrad's classic novella, *Heart of Darkness*). By 1909, the Belgian government had taken over following Leopold's death and began to mirror Belgium's own internal divisions: corporations, government administrators, and the Roman Catholic Church each pursued their sometimes competing interests. But no one thought to change the name of the colonial capital: it remained Leopoldville until the Belgian Congo achieved independence in 1960.

Colonialism did transform Africa, but in its post-Berlin form it lasted less than a century. In Ghana (then named the Gold Coast), for example, the Ashanti (Asante) Kingdom was still fighting the British in the early years of the twentieth century; by 1957, Ghana was independent again. These days, most of Subsaharan Africa has already marked half a century of independence, and, in retrospect, the colonial period should be seen as an interlude rather than a paramount chapter in modern African history—although it did leave a deep and lasting geographic imprint, especially on the realm's cultural landscape.

POSTCOLONIAL AFRICA

In Subsaharan Africa, more than in any other realm, there is a huge discrepancy between the geography of territorial states (imposed by the former colonial powers) and the geography of national and ethnic identities (look again at Fig. 6A-5). The political map of Subsaharan Africa has 45 states but no nation-states (apart from some microstates and ministates in the islands and the far south). Centrifugal forces are powerful, cultural pluralism prevails, and outside interventions during the Cold War, when communist and anticommunist foreigners took sides in local civil wars, worsened conflict within many African states.

Clearly, the failings of democracy across the realm in past decades cannot be understood without considering this precarious legacy. Corruption and incompetence have seemed rampant, but at a deeper level it was often the (political exploitation of) ethnic fragmentation and tribal tensions that impeded or undermined enlightened governance.

Colonialism's economic legacy was not much better. In Africa, capitals, core areas, port cities, and transport systems were laid out to maximize colonial profit and facilitate the exploitation of minerals and soils; the colonial mosaic inhibited interregional communications except where cooperation enhanced efficiency. Colonial Zambia and Zimbabwe, for instance (then respectively named Northern and Southern Rhodesia), were landlocked and needed outlets, so railroads were built to Portuguese-owned ports. But

From the Field Notes . . .

"Looking down on this enormous railroad complex northeast of Johannesburg, South Africa, we were reminded of the fact that almost an entire continent was turned into a wellspring of raw materials carried from interior to coast and shipped to Europe and other parts of the world. This complex lies near Witbank in the eastern Rand, a huge inventory of freight trains ready to transport ores from the plateau to Durban and Maputo. But at least South Africa acquired a true transportation network in the process, ensuring regional interconnections; in most African countries, railroads serve almost entirely to link resources to coastal outlets."

www.conceptcaching.com

© H.J. de Blij

such routes did little to create internal African linkages. The modern map reveals the results: in West Africa you can travel from the coast into the interior of all the coastal states along railways or adequate roads. But no modern routeways were ever built to connect these coastal neighbors to each other.

A Realm in Need of Infrastructure

In Chapters 6A and 6B you will encounter numerous references to African countries with fast-growing economies, rising revenues, and newly opened resource reserves. But you will read much less about intra-African trade and transportation, diversifying economies, and the kind of regional complementarity that made the old West African states so stable and successful. Africa needs infrastructure: a network of high-speed highways, a system of railroads, and a speedier way to traverse its few connecting rivers. Take a boat up the Congo River from Kinshasa, and get ready for about a week of slow going, stops, transfers, delays, and lost perishables. Try taking the surface route from Cairo via the Nile to Khartoum, and you will surely fly the next time.

That is one thing for visitors and tourists, but another for businesses. According to World Bank estimates, only 13 percent of Subsaharan African trade is internal, the lowest percentage of intra-realm trade in the world. Try to import goods from abroad or export your products overseas, and the cost of transport can add 50 percent or more to the retail price. About the only way to manufacture something in northern Nigeria and sell it in Senegal is to truck it via potholed roads to Port Harcourt or Lagos, load it onto a boat, ship it to Dakar, and then hope that your customer is in that port and not somewhere in the interior. No decent road links the eleven countries along the coast from Nigeria to Senegal, so forget about selling things along the way.

Africa needs north-south and east-west roads as well as railroads. It also needs more efficient border posts; fewer export and import restrictions, tariffs, and tolls to help farmers sell to their neighbors; and less corruption. On the roads, too much traffic crawls along at slow speeds, easily victimized at roadside checkpoints where bribes have to be paid. There is nothing like a 100-kph (63-mph) truck barreling along to market on a four-lane, hard-surfaced highway to discourage this.

NATURAL ENVIRONMENTS

Only the southernmost tip of Subsaharan Africa lies outside the tropics. Although African elevations are comparatively high, they are not high enough to ward off the heat that comes with a tropical location except in especially favored locales such as the Kenya Highlands and parts of Ethiopia. And, as we already noted, Africa's bulky shape means that much of the continent lies far from maritime moisture sources. Variable weather and frequent droughts, therefore, are among Africa's unrelenting environmental challenges.

It is useful at this point to refer back to Figure G-7. As that map shows, Africa's climatic regions are distributed almost symmetrically about the equator, though more so in the center of the landmass than in the east, where elevation changes the picture. The hot, rainy climate of the

Congo Basin merges gradually, both northward and southward, into climates with distinctly dry winter seasons. Winter, however, is marked more by drought than by cold. In parts of the area mapped ***Aw*** (tropical savanna), the annual seasonal cycle produces two rainy seasons, often referred to locally as the long rains and the short rains, separated by two winter dry periods. As you go farther north and south away from the moist Congo Basin, the dry season(s) grow longer and the rainfall diminishes and becomes less and less dependable.

Wildlife Under Threat

Africa's shrinking rainforests and vast savannas form the world's last refuges for wildlife ranging from primates to wildebeests. Gorillas and chimpanzees survive in dwindling numbers in threatened forest habitats, while millions of herbivores range in great herds across the savanna plains where people compete with them for space. European colonizers, who introduced hunting as a "sport" (a practice that did not exist within African cultural traditions) and who brought their capacities for mass destruction to animals as well as people in Africa, helped clear vast areas of wildlife and pushed species to near-extinction.

Later, colonial rulers and subsequent national governments laid out game reserves and other kinds of conservation areas, but these were not sufficiently large or well enough connected to allow herd animals to adhere to their seasonal and annual migration routes. The same climatic variability that affects farmers also affects wildlife, and when the rangelands wither, the animals seek better pastures. When the fences of a game reserve wall them off, they cannot survive. When there are no fences, the wildlife invades neighboring farmlands and destroys crops, and the farmers retaliate. After thousands of years of equilibrium, the competition between humans and animals in Africa has taken a new turn.

But it is not solely population pressure that is threatening African wildlife. The horn of the rhinoceros became a valued property for Arabs who fashion them into dagger handles and, in powdered form, a purported aphrodisiac for wealthy East Asians able to afford this as a luxury. As a result, the northern white rhinoceros is now nearing extinction; the number of all species of rhino has fallen from several hundred thousand to only about 20,000 today. A terrible tragedy is befalling the African elephant as the value of its ivory tusks has skyrocketed; the Chinese illicit market is likely to exterminate this species within the next decade. Note that it is external demand, not internal circumstance, that is hastening this calamity. Meanwhile, competition for land has more to do with the decline of Africa's lion population (from around 400,000 half a

From the Field Notes . . .

"Flying a small propeller plane over East Africa's semiarid grasslands, we had a good view of a Maasai village near the border between Kenya and Tanzania. The Maasai are a pastoral people whose main livelihood is herding cattle, sheep, and goats. I could clearly see the fenced 'kraals' where they keep their animals at night (during the day they are moved around) and the small dwellings that surround them. The more animals a man (!) has, the higher his status. But this way of life is under pressure: many have decided to settle in towns or cities because they offer more and better opportunities. And this area is also the northern extension of Tanzania's famous Serengeti National Park, and here wildlife preservation comes into direct conflict with the Maasai way of life. 'It is really impossible,' said the park guide on the 10-seater plane with us, pointing down at the settlement. 'Of course they want to protect their cattle, but they are killing lions and other animals that should be protected. And we must tell them all the time that they have to stay out of certain areas because the cattle compete for food with the wild animals.' Nodding agreeably, I thought to myself: yes, but isn't this their land? As with so many other places around the world where we want to protect nature, we must involve the local people. That is much easier said than done."

© Jan Nijman   www.conceptcaching.com

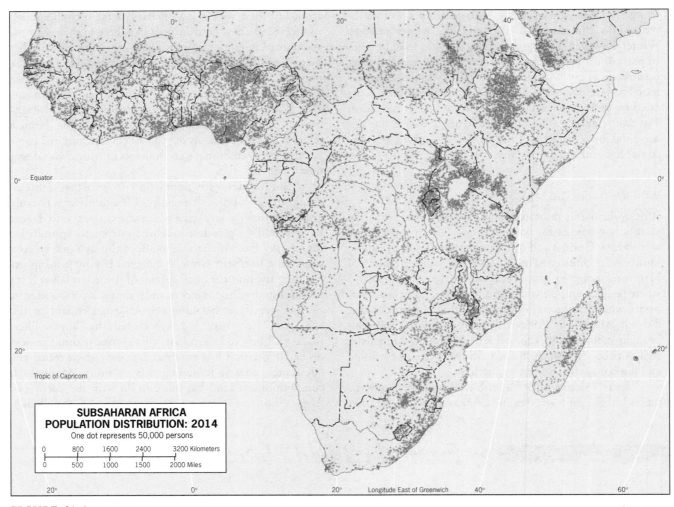

FIGURE 6A-8

© H. J. de Blij, P. O. Muller, and John Wiley & Sons, Inc.

century ago to barely more than 20,000 today) as well as the threat to other species. It is in some ways the end of the Cenozoic era, the last gasp of a fauna that emerged after the demise of the dinosaurs, survived ice ages and glaciations, and now falls victim to humankind's relentless rise.

People, Farmlands, and Environments

It would seem that there could be space for wildlife as well as humans in Subsaharan Africa. Figure 6A-8 does not present a picture of a densely-peopled realm: although there are major clusters of population in West Africa (where Nigeria is the realm's most populous country), East Africa (encircling Lake Victoria), and the African Horn (where Ethiopia's highlands sustain a large concentration), most of the rest of the realm seems relatively sparsely populated. Our Data Table in Appendix B bears out this impression: all the countries of Subsaharan Africa *combined* have a population only slightly above two-thirds of China's alone.

But much of this population continues to depend on farming for their livelihood, and we have already seen that African environments are difficult for millions of farmers. Not everywhere, of course: Africa has its areas of good soil, ample water, and robust farm productivity. However, these areas are not extensive. The major population concentration in the Great Lakes region reflects the volcanic soils of Mount Kilimanjaro as well as those of the Western Rift Valley zone. The Ethiopian Highlands were once known as the "breadbasket of northeastern Africa" and retain their capability for greater productivity than is presently the case. Higher-latitude, cooler, and moister areas of South Africa are exceptionally productive in a wide range of farm produce. And parts of West Africa sustain intensive farming. Taken together, however, these highly productive areas do not add up to the huge, fertile, alluvial basins of China or India—or even the (North African) Nile Valley and Delta. The great majority of African farmers face daunting challenges that include: (1) climatic variability, (2) the economic policies of national governments, and (3) the difficulties African

© AP/Wide World Photos

The cell phone revolution has made a dramatic impact on farmers in many parts of the developing world, especially in Subsaharan Africa where distances can be far, land lines absent, and market information scarce. Between 2005 and 2012, the number of cell phone subscriptions increased sixfold to encompass nearly 60 percent of the population. Now farmers and market women, such as the Kenyan woman pictured here, can stay in touch to better gauge when it is best to market crops and to better manage logistics.

farmers face in reaching world markets. Look again at Figure G-7, and you can see the relatively short distances involved as the moist tropics of the equatorial Congo Basin give way to the deserts of the north and south. Moreover, as the annual rainfall total declines, its variability increases, so that farmers in the drier zones cannot count on sufficient moisture in any given year.

Moreover, the economic policies of national governments frequently disadvantage farmers as the prices of their products are kept artificially low to please urban (and politically powerful) consumers. And in this era of globalization, African farmers often get a raw deal on world markets. For all the talk of free trade in the wealthy global core, many governments favor their local farmers over those of Africa (as well as other parts of the global periphery), from rice subsidies in Japan to "market support" in France.

AFRICANS AND THEIR LAND

Although rainfall is a critical physical criterion for farming, a number of political and economic factors are also influential. Among them are land tenure; commercial

(for-profit) versus subsistence (household-level) agriculture; type of farming system (rotational, shifting cultivation, intercropping, etc.); crop prices; government policies promoting the planting of one crop over another; indigenous agricultural knowledge of particular crops; and the degree of technology adoption and mechanization.

With nearly two-thirds of the realm's livelihoods dependent on farming, the issue of land tenure is crucial. Land tenure [6] refers to the way people own, occupy, and use land. African traditions of land tenure are different from those found in Europe or the Americas. In most of Subsaharan Africa, communities, not individuals, customarily hold land. Occupants of the land have temporary, custodial rights to it and cannot sell it. Land may be held by large (extended) families, a village community, or even a traditional chief who holds the land in trust for the people. His subjects may house themselves on it and farm it, but in return they must follow his rules.

Land Ownership Versus Land Alienation

At the onset of colonialism [7], colonial administrators intended to control the most fertile areas of the occupied colonies through eviction of indigenous peoples. In some cases this was done by physical force (mostly through military conquest), and in other areas by coercion. Prior to colonialism, many traditional African livelihood systems adhered to sustainable land management practices such as leaving the land fallow or rotational grazing. Viewing this land as unused, colonial planners initiated a process of land alienation [8] not unlike what happened in Middle and South America. Many of the most fertile and productive areas were placed under the direct control of colonial settlers and governments. As time went by, these lands were bought and sold and became private legal property. At the end of the colonial era, several newly independent African countries initiated programs whereby land would revert to traditional forms of ownership and management. However, the legacy of colonialism has been difficult to overcome, and some African governments have adopted policies on land management that continue to marginalize small farmers.

Rapid population growth, such as Africa has experienced since the end of the colonial era, makes access to land even more complicated. Traditional systems of land use, which involve subsistence farming in various forms ranging from shifting cultivation to pastoralism, work best when the population is fairly stable and tenure is communal. Land must be left fallow to recover from cultivation, and pastures must be kept free of livestock so that the grasses can revive. The African population explosion that began in the mid-twentieth century set into motion a cycle of land overuse. When soils cannot rest and pastures are overgrazed, the land becomes degraded and yields decline.

Subsistence Farming

Although there is commercial farming in parts of Africa, most African farmers remain subsistence farmers who grow grain crops (maize [corn], millet, sorghum) in drier areas and root crops (yams, manioc [cassava], sweet potatoes) where moisture is adequate. Others herd livestock, mostly cattle and goats, as they counter environmental and climatic variability. Farmers and pastoralists alike have been unable to secure access to regular markets and stable prices for their products because of government policies that often promote one particular type of export-oriented crop (for example, peanuts in Gambia; tea and coffee in Kenya; cacao [cocoa] in Ivory Coast) over other crops that do not fetch high prices on the world market.

Even though African farmers learned to adapt to these problems, farm yields in Africa have remained modest. Governments, in response to World Bank policies, paid greater attention to high-profile industrial projects and as a result have neglected agriculture. The decline of African agriculture has been disproportionally hard on Africa's women who, according to current estimates, produce 75 percent of all local food in Subsaharan Africa. Development policies frequently pay too little attention to this situation and its related household dynamics, thereby dooming many well-intentioned projects.

The Green Revolution [9] the development of more productive, drought-tolerant, pest-resistant, higher-yielding types of grain has had less impact in Africa than elsewhere (see box titled "A Green Revolution for Africa?"). Where people depend mainly on rice and wheat, the Green Revolution pushed back the prospect of increased hunger. But not enough research was done on this realm's dominant crops, mostly tubers, so the advances of the Green Revolution barely touched Africa. And, in any case, the Green Revolution is hardly an unqualified remedy: the poorest farmers, who need help the most, can least afford the more expensive, higher-yielding seeds or pesticides that are so often trequired.

Foreign Agribusiness in Africa

Low agricultural productivity resulting from inefficiency, coupled with governments' need for more revenues, have converged in some African countries to result in the selling or long-term leasing of huge tracts of public land to the big-time investors of multinational agro-industrial corporations. The idea is that if you do not have the means to develop your land, then large-scale agribusiness [10] is the best option to increase yields and simultaneously fill government coffers. Foreign investors, in turn, are motivated by steadily rising global food prices, brightening prospects for biofuels, and growing shortages of arable land in their own

---

A Green Revolution for Africa?

THE TERM *Green Revolution* refers to the development of higher-yielding varieties of grains through genetic manipulation. Since the 1970s, it has narrowed the worldwide gap between population and food production, and it was especially influential in regions where people depend mainly on rice and wheat for their staples. The Green Revolution has had less impact in Subsaharan Africa, however. In part, this relates to the realm's high rate of population growth (which is substantially higher than that of India or China). Other reasons have to do with Africa's staples: rice and wheat support only a small part of this realm's population. Corn (maize) supports many more, along with sorghum, millet, and other grains. In moister areas, root crops, such as the yam and cassava as well as the plantain (similar to the banana) supply most calories. These crops were not priorities in Green Revolution research.

Lately, there have been a few signs of improvement. Scientists have worked toward two goals: first, to develop strains of corn and other crops that would be more resistant to Africa's virulent crop diseases, and second, to increase the productivity of those strains. But these efforts faced serious problems. An average African hectare (2.5 acres) planted with corn, for instance, yields only about half a ton of corn, whereas the global average is 1.3 tons. When a virus-resistant variety was developed and distributed throughout Subsaharan Africa in the 1980s, yields rose significantly where farmers could afford to buy the new strain as well as the fertilizers it required. Nigeria saw a near-doubling of its production before it leveled off. Hardier varieties of root crops also raised yields in some areas.

Clearly, Africa needs more than this to reverse the trend toward food deficiency because food production has simply not kept pace with population growth. Lack of capital, inefficient farming methods, inadequate equipment, soil exhaustion, male dominance, apathy, and devastating droughts also contributed to this decline—not to mention affordability problems with more expensive higher-yielding seeds and pesticides. And the realm's seemingly endless series of civil conflicts have also reduced farm output. The Green Revolution may narrow the gap between production and need, but the battle for food sufficiency and security in Subsaharan Africa is far from won.

Regional
ISSUE Neocolonial Land Grabs?

THESE LAND DEALS ARE A SOLUTION TO OUR PROBLEMS

"When the dust of all this drama settles around so-called 'land grabs', it should be clear to anybody that our government has come up with a brilliant solution to the country's problems. As an accountant here in the capital of Adis Abeba, I know a few things about costs and benefits, and in these land deals Ethiopia comes out as a winner.

"We mustn't fool ourselves: decade after decade this country has been hit by famines and food shortages. It was not just people going hungry; hundreds of thousands have died as a result. Surely one reason for this has been that we have failed to produce enough food. The landholdings are too small to be efficient and most farmers don't have the means or the knowledge to improve yields.

"The way forward for us and several other countries in Africa is to use our abundant land and natural resources to our advantage, to allow foreign investors to come in and exploit these resources for us. It's not like we are giving it away. Not at all! In most cases it is not a permanent sale but a lease, and the agreements contain provisions that they must sell a minimum share of the harvest in Ethiopia so all of it cannot be exported. And they must hire Ethiopian workers.

"Food in this country will become cheaper, you will see, simply because there will be more of it. Foreign agri-businesses know their stuff. Government income will rise from these deals, and these revenues can be invested in education and infrastructure. That, in turn, will create more employment opportunities. I can understand the fears of people about these land deals but they are misplaced and old-fashioned. In the global economy today, you must be willing to deal with the outside world, use the resources you've got to your advantage. That is what we are doing."

AFRICA IS BEING ROBBED, ONCE AGAIN

"It is hard to believe this is really happening, but it's true and I've seen it with my own eyes here in Ethiopia. Families who have been farming for many years are forced off the land so the government can lease it to foreign investors. It is a disaster because we Ethiopians no longer control our own land and what we grow on it. I own a shop here in a small town in western part of the country and I have seen prices go up. Many of my customers are rural people who used to grow their own food but now they must pay in cash. The government promised them all kinds of things when they terminated the leases on these small farms, yet little has come of it.

"Where is a country going when it sells its land to outsiders? That is my question to you. How can you ever believe that big foreign companies will keep the interests of the Ethiopian people in mind? Of course they don't! Why do you think they come here in the first place? They grow just one or two crops to export back to their own country. Quite a few are said to be rich Arabs from the Gulf states, where fertile land is scarce. Many just grow rice, a food we Ethiopians don't eat much of. I even heard a story of one company growing sorghum for their camels in Arabia!

"And don't believe the argument that these lands were not being cultivated. Do you really think we Africans would let good land sit idle? We have millions of small farmers looking for every bit of fertile soil they can find on which to earn a living. Worst of all is when the outsiders buy up the land and don't do anything with it. Foreign investors get such good deals from our government that they just sit on the land as a speculative investment. They believe Africa is rising and that the land will increase in value, so they wait until they can sell it for a profit in the future. In the meantime, we can't touch our own natural resources. It is a scandalous situation."

Vote your opinion at www.wiley.com/go/deblijpolling

---

countries. For many, acquiring land in Africa is a long-term proposition based on expectations that natural resources will become ever more scarce in the future as demand increases while supply declines.

In 2009 alone, 44 million hectares (110 million acres) were involved in such land transactions—an area the size of California and West Virginia combined. Most of this land was in Sudan, Ethiopia, and Moçambique. Some of the investors were African, but many others were foreign (always a contentious issue). When the government of Madagascar in that same year declared its intention to sell half of all arable public lands to a South Korean corporation, protests ensued and quickly escalated to a

level that forced the government to cancel the transaction and resign.

The impact of these gigantic land deals is mixed. In some cases, output on the large commercial farms far exceeds previous levels of production. But in many others, investors seem to have had mainly speculative intentions and much farmland remains idle. In either situation, significant numbers of small farmers are uprooted and their villages destroyed. Understandably, there is now growing mistrust among grass-roots populations, and the success of these ventures increasingly depends on how they are handled by the government, especially regarding assistance provided to locals most directly affected. To date, the record of countries involved in such schemes has been highly variable: Sudan has performed miserably, but others (including Moçambique) have shown considerable economic growth.

ENVIRONMENT AND HEALTH

The study of human health in spatial context is the field of medical geography [11], and medical geographers employ modern methods of analysis (including geographic information systems) to track disease outbreaks, identify their sources, detect their carriers, and prevent their recurrence. Alliances between medical personnel, epidemiological researchers, and geographers have already yielded significant results. Doctors know how a disease ravages the body; geographers know how climatic conditions such as wind direction or variations in river flow can affect the distribution and effectiveness of disease carriers. This collaboration helps protect vulnerable populations.

Tropical Africa is the source area of many serious illnesses and has thereby become the focus of much research in medical geography. Investigators look at the carriers (*vectors*) of infectious diseases, the environmental conditions that give rise to them, and also the cultural and social geography of disease dispersion and transmission. Comparing medical, environmental, and social/cultural maps can integrate crucial evidence to help combat the scourge.

In Africa today, hundreds of millions of people carry one or more maladies, often without knowing exactly what ails them. A disease that infects many people (the *hosts*) in a kind of equilibrium, without causing rapid and widespread deaths, is said to be endemic [12] to that population. People affected may not die suddenly or dramatically, but their quality of life and productive capacity are hindered as their overall health is weakened and can deteriorate rapidly when a more acute illness strikes. In tropical Africa, hepatitis, venereal diseases, and hookworm are among many public-health threats in this category.

Epidemics and Pandemics

When a disease outbreak has local or regional dimensions, it is called an epidemic [13]. It may claim thousands, even tens of thousands, of lives, but it remains confined to a certain area, perhaps one defined by the range of its vector. In tropical Africa, trypanosomiasis, the disease known as sleeping sickness and vectored by the tsetse fly, has regional dimensions (Fig. 6A-9). The extensive herds of savanna wildlife form the *reservoir* of this disease, and the tsetse fly transmits it both to livestock and people. It is endemic to wildlife, but it also kills cattle, so Africa's herders try to keep their animals in tsetse-free zones. African sleeping sickness appears to have originated in a West African source area during the fifteenth century, and from there it spread throughout much of tropical Africa. Its

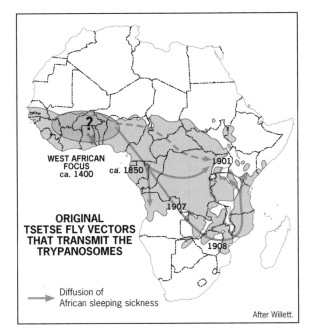

FIGURE 6A-9

© H. J. de Blij, P. O. Muller, and John Wiley & Sons, Inc.

epidemic range was limited by that of the tsetse fly: where there are no tsetse flies, there is no sleeping sickness. More than anything else, the tsetse fly has kept substantial parts of Subsaharan Africa's savannas free of livestock and open to wildlife.

When a disease spreads worldwide, it is described as a pandemic [14]. Africa's and the world's most deadly vectored disease is malaria, transmitted by a mosquito and the killer of at least 1 million people each year. Eradication campaigns against the mosquito vector have had some success, but always the carrier has come back with renewed vigor. At present, as many as 300 million people are affected by malaria globally. Although current efforts at combatting the disease through increased use of mosquito nets appears to be having good results, most of the million-plus annual deaths are African children under the age of five. Indeed, the short life expectancies for the realm's tropical countries listed in Appendix B partly reflect this mortality from malarial infection.

Despite these 'natural' challenges associated with the environment, there has been remarkable progress in battling various diseases in recent years. This is especially evident in the sharp decline of infant mortality rates across the realm, averaging 4 percent annually over the past decade. Yet even though one in ten African children still does not reach the age of five, these rates are now declining faster than any other realm has ever experienced. Three countries—Kenya, Senegal, and Rwanda—have seen their rates drop dramatically by more than 8 percent for several years in a row. This indicates that the spreading of infectious diseases is steadily coming under control—through vaccinations, education, and especially the widespread introduction of 'insecticide-treated bednets' (a simple, cheap, yet highly effective innovation that has found its way into even the most remote villages all across the realm).

The Battle Against AIDS

Malaria remains Africa's deadliest disease to this day, but since 1980 AIDS has dominated the medical news from this part of the world. AIDS first erupted in Subsaharan Africa and quickly became a global pandemic; no geographic realm has been spared.

AIDS stands for Acquired Immune Deficiency Syndrome, the body's failure to protect itself against a virus. That virus, for want of a better name at the time researchers were trying to identify it, is called the Human Immunodeficiency Virus (HIV). Thus the disease is properly called HIV/AIDS. Since it was first recognized in the early 1980s, more than 70 million people worldwide have contracted HIV/AIDS and about half that number have died of it, as many as 80 percent of them Africans.

By the early 1990s, HIV/AIDS had spread most virulently in Equatorial and East Africa, and medical geographers referred to an "AIDS Belt" from DRCongo* to Kenya. A decade later, however, the worst-afflicted countries lay in Southern Africa. In 2012, 23.5 million HIV-positive people were living in Subsaharan Africa, 69 percent of the world's total. The largest HIV-infected national populations were in South Africa (about 6 million) and Nigeria (almost 3 million); ranked next were Moçambique, Tanzania, and Zimbabwe, with each recording about 1.5 million victims. In certain other countries, such as DR-Congo, the outbreak of the disease is known to be severe: there, at least 1.3 million people are believed to be infected, but reliable estimates have not been available in recent years. When standardized for population size, the dire situation of several countries becomes even clearer: around 25 percent of the population aged 15–49 are HIV-positive in Lesotho, Swaziland, and Botswana; 18 percent in neighboring South Africa; and close to 14 percent in Zimbabwe, Zambia, and Namibia.

More than 60 percent of all those infected are women, reflecting cultural and social circumstances. Overall, no part of tropical Africa has been spared. Life expectancies plummeted. Children by the millions were orphaned. Companies lost workers and were unable to replace them. National economies contracted. Associated costs—benefits, treatment, medicines—skyrocketed.

Why is Africa suffering so disproportionately? First, HIV/AIDS originated in tropical African forest margins and rapidly spread through all segments of society. Second,

---

*Two countries in Africa have the same short-form name, *Congo*. In this book, we use **DRCongo** for the much larger Democratic Republic of the Congo, and **Congo** for the smaller Republic of the Congo just to its northwest.

the social stigma associated with HIV/AIDS, which is sexually transmitted, makes acknowledging and treating it especially problematic. Third, life-prolonging medications are expensive and particularly difficult to provide in remote rural areas. Fourth, governmental leadership during the AIDS crisis has varied from highly aggressive and effective (as in Uganda, where political and medical officials cooperated in a massive campaign to distribute free condoms and advocate their use) to catastrophically negligent, as in South Africa where government ministers for a time misled the public and unnecessarily delayed the mass medical intervention that was critically needed.

The situation remained serious in 2013, but some important progress in the battle against HIV/AIDS was being made. A new South African government continues to aggressively address the AIDS crisis. Public-health campaigns elsewhere are having a beneficial effect. Lower-cost, generic anti-HIV medicines are today becoming more widely available through international help. The number of new infections across the realm in 2012 dropped to 1.7 million, down from 2.4 million in 2001—a decline mainly due to better education and the growing use of condoms. Those who carry the disease also live longer as result of improved treatment and the wider availability of medication—even though many still do not have access to it. Most encouraging, more than 6 million Africans were receiving antiretroviral therapy in 2012, up from only 100,000 in 2003.

CULTURAL PATTERNS

We tend to think of Africa in terms of its prominent countries and well-known cities, its development problems and political dilemmas, but Africans themselves have another perspective. The colonial period created states and capitals, introduced foreign languages to serve as the *linguae francae*, and brought railways and roads. The colonizers stimulated labor movements to the mines they opened, and they disrupted many other migrations that had been part of African life for many centuries. But they did not change the ways of life of most of the people. Despite accelerating urbanization, 63 percent of the realm's population still live in, and work near, Africa's hundreds of thousands of villages. They speak one of well over a thousand languages in use in this realm. The villagers' concerns are local; their focus is on subsistence, health, and safety. They worry that the conflicts over regional power and/or political ideology will engulf them, as has happened to tens of millions in Liberia, Sierra Leone, Ethiopia, Rwanda, DRCongo, and Angola since the 1970s. Africa's (numerically) largest cultural groups form major nations, such as the Yoruba of Nigeria and the Zulu of South Africa. Africa's smallest groups of people number just a few thousand. As a geographic realm, Subsaharan Africa has the most complex and fragmented cultural mosaic on Earth (see Fig. 6A-5).

African Languages

Africa's linguistic geography is a key component of that cultural intricacy. Most of Subsaharan Africa's more than one thousand languages do not have a written tradition, making classification and mapping difficult. Scholars have attempted to delimit an African language map, and Figure 6A-10 is a composite of their efforts. One feature is common to all language maps of this continent: the geographic realm begins approximately where northern Africa's Afro-Asiatic language family (mapped in yellow in Fig. 6A-10) gives way, although the pattern is sharper in West Africa than to the east.

In Subsaharan Africa, the dominant language family is the Niger-Congo family, of which the Kordofanian subfamily is a small, historic, far northeastern outlier (Fig. 6A-10), and the Niger-Congo languages carry the other subfamily's name. This subfamily (mapped in purple) extends across the realm from West to East and Southern Africa. The Bantu language forms the largest branch of this subfamily, but Niger-Congo languages in West Africa, such as Yoruba and Akan, also have millions of speakers. Another important language family is the Nilo-Saharan family (mapped in orange), extending from Maasai in Kenya northwest to Teda in Chad. No other language families are of similar extent or importance: the Khoisan family, of ancient origins, now survives among the dwindling Khoi and San peoples of the Kalahari in the southwest; the small white minority in South Africa speak Indo-European languages; and Malay-Polynesian languages prevail in Madagascar, which was peopled from Southeast Asia before Africans reached it.

The Most Widely Used Languages

About 40 African languages are spoken by 1 million people or more, and a half-dozen by 10 million or more: Hausa (43 million), Yoruba (22 million), Ibo, Swahili, Lingala, and Zulu. Although English and French have become important *linguae francae* in multilingual countries

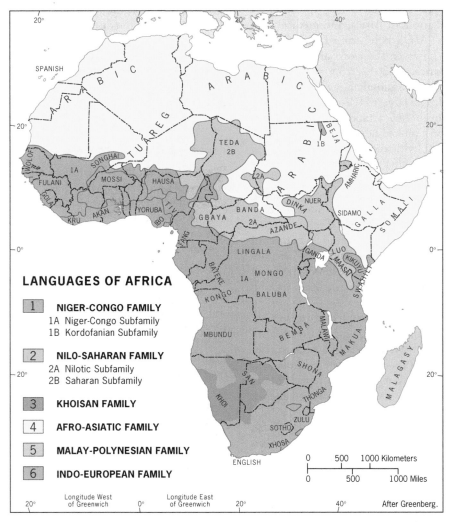

FIGURE 6A-10   © H. J. de Blij, P. O. Muller, and John Wiley & Sons, Inc.

© Pascal Maitre/Cosmos/Aurora Photos, Inc.

The faithful kneel during Friday prayers outside a mosque in Kano, northern Nigeria. The survival of Nigeria as a unified state is an African success story; the Nigerians have overcome strong centrifugal forces in a multiethnic country that is dominantly Muslim in the north, Christian-animist in the south. In the 1990s, some Muslim clerics began calling for an Islamic Republic in Nigeria, and after the death of the dictator Abacha and the election of a non-Muslim president, the Islamic drive intensified. A number of Nigeria's northern States adopted Sharia (strict Islamic) law, which led to destructive riots between the majority Muslims and minority Christians who felt threatened by this turn of events—a situation that continues to deteriorate (elaborated in Chapter 6B). Can Nigeria avoid the fate of Sudan?

such as Nigeria and Ivory Coast (where officials even insist on spelling the name of their country *Côte d'Ivoire* in the Francophone manner), African languages also serve this purpose. Hausa is a common language across the West African savanna; Swahili is widely used in East Africa. And pidgin languages—mixtures of African and European tongues—are found along West Africa's coast; millions of Pidgin English (called *Wes Kos*) speakers use this medium in Nigeria and Ghana. However, not all African languages are going to survive: Nigeria alone has 17 endangered (near-extinct) languages, and in the continent at large as many as 63 languages are on the verge of extinction.

Language and Culture

Multilingualism [15] can be a powerful centrifugal force in society, and African governments have tried with varying success to establish national alongside local languages. Nigeria, for instance, made English its official language because none of its 500-odd languages, not even Hausa, had sufficient internal interregional use. But using a European, colonial language as an official medium invites criticism, and Nigeria remains divided on this issue. On the other hand, making a dominant local language official would give rise to negative reactions from ethnic minorities. Language remains a potent force in Africa's cultural life.

Religion in Africa

Africans had their own belief systems long before Christians and Muslims arrived to convert them. And for all of Subsaharan Africa's cultural diversity, its people had a consistent view of their place in nature. Spiritual forces, according to African tradition, are manifest everywhere in the natural environment (a religious world view known as *animism*), not in a supreme deity that exists in some remote place. Thus gods and spirits affect people's daily lives, witnessing every move, rewarding the virtuous and punishing (through injury or crop failure, for example) those who misbehave. Ancestral spirits can inflict misfortune on the living. They are everywhere: in the forest, rivers, and mountains.

As with land tenure, the religious views of Africans clashed fundamentally with those held by the colonizers. Monotheistic *Christianity* first penetrated Africa in the northeast when Nubia and Axum were converted, and Ethiopia has been a Coptic Christian stronghold since the fourth century AD. But the Christian churches' real invasion did not commence until the onset of colonialism after the turn of the sixteenth century. Christianity's various denominations made inroads in different locales: Roman Catholicism in much of Equatorial Africa, mainly at the behest of the Belgians; the Anglican Church in British colonies; and Presbyterians and others elsewhere. And these days, as in South America, Evangelical churches continue to rapidly gain adherents.

Some of those churches are now far more conservative than their counterparts in Europe and North America, even those appealing to the most conservative congregations in the United States. A split in the U.S. Episcopal (Anglican) Church regarding the treatment of gays and lesbians has some congregations aligning themselves under the Bishop of Uganda. But almost everywhere, Christianity's penetration led to a blending of traditional and Christian beliefs, so that much of Subsaharan Africa is nominally, though not exclusively, Christian (see Fig. G-10). Go to a church in Gabon or Uganda or Zambia, and you may hear drums instead of church bells, sing African music rather than hymns, and see African carvings alongside the usual statuary.

Islam had a rather different arrival and impact. Today, about 32 percent of the realm's population is Muslim. By the time of the colonial invasion, Islam had advanced out of Arabia, across the Sahara, and part-way down the coasts of Africa (particularly along the Indian Ocean). Muslim clerics converted the rulers of African states and commanded them to convert their subjects. They Islamized the savanna states and penetrated into present-day northern Nigeria, Ghana, and Ivory Coast. They encircled and isolated Ethiopia's Coptic Christians and Islamized the Somali people in Africa's Horn. They established beachheads on the coast of Kenya and took over offshore Zanzibar. Arabizing Islam and European Christianity competed for African minds, but Islam proved to be a far more pervasive force. The tension between Islam and Christianity continues in the twenty-first century (see photo), and is one of the defining regional characteristics of the African Transition Zone elaborated Chapter 6B.

URBANIZATION AND SOCIAL CHANGE

As can be discerned in Appendix B, Subsaharan Africa remains the least urbanized world realm, but people are moving to its towns and cities at an accelerating pace. Today, 37 percent of the Subsaharan African population resides in urban settlements. This means that over 325 million people (more than the entire current population of the United States) now live in towns and cities, of which many were founded and developed by the colonial powers. But the infrastructure of the cities has been unable to keep up with the tide of incoming migrants.

The biggest African cities became centers of embryonic national core areas, and many of them incorporated government headquarters. This formal sector [16] of the city used to be the dominant one, with governmental control and regulations affecting civil service, business, industry, and all

of their workers; these districts were endowed with the largest and most modern buildings. Today, however, African cities look different. From a distance, the skyline resembles that of a modern urban center. But in the streets, on the sidewalks right below the shop windows, there are hawkers, basket weavers, jewelry sellers, garment makers, wood carvers—a second economy, most of it beyond governmental control. This informal sector [17] now dominates most African cities. It is peopled by the rural immigrants, who also work as servants, apprentices, construction workers, and in countless other menial jobs. Millions of these migrants cannot find formal employment and are condemned to living in squalid circumstances in the squatter-settlement tracts around (as well as inside) nearly all of Africa's cities.

EMERGING AFRICA

Despite colonial legacies, formidable environmental challenges, and a long history of serious adversity, Africa in the early twenty-first century is taking a turn for the better. Although conditions remain harsh in many places the achievements of the past decade are quite encouraging, even stunning in some cases. We have already noted some of these successes, including a substantial decline in the infant mortality rate and progress toward containing malaria and HIV/AIDS. As a more general indicator of health and well-being, life expectancy overall has increased by about 6 years since 2000. And there is more.

Annual economic annual growth in the realm over the past decade has averaged 5-6 percent and for certain countries it has been higher than that (Fig. 6A-11). As a whole, this realm outperformed all other realms except East Asia, and as of mid-2013 it exhibited the highest growth rate in the world; moreover, among the ten fastest growing national economies since 2005, no fewer than six were located here. Notwithstanding Subsaharan Africa's low level of development in absolute terms, it has been moving upward with remarkable speed. And with higher national incomes as well as an expanding tax base, government spending and investments have increased accordingly, especially in the spheres of public health and education (secondary school enrollment has grown by almost 50 percent during the last ten years).

However, as Figure 6A-11 shows, economic performance across this realm has been highly uneven. The fastest growing countries tend to located on the coast, away from the troubled African Transition Zone across the north, and are generously endowed with natural resources. The poorest performers are first and foremost the victims of war or political mismanagement: South Sudan's economy shrank by about a third in just two years, from 2010 to 2012, and Zimbabwe had an average negative annual growth of nearly −3 percent.

A typical urban landscape in Subsaharan Africa. This aerial view of the city of Arusha (population: ca. 550,000) in northern Tanzania shows a signature feature of the settlement layout of urban Africa: an irregular pattern of low-rise, low-density development. It reflects a general lack of planning, complex land ownership issues, and piecemeal as well as patchwork investment in construction.

© Jan Nijman

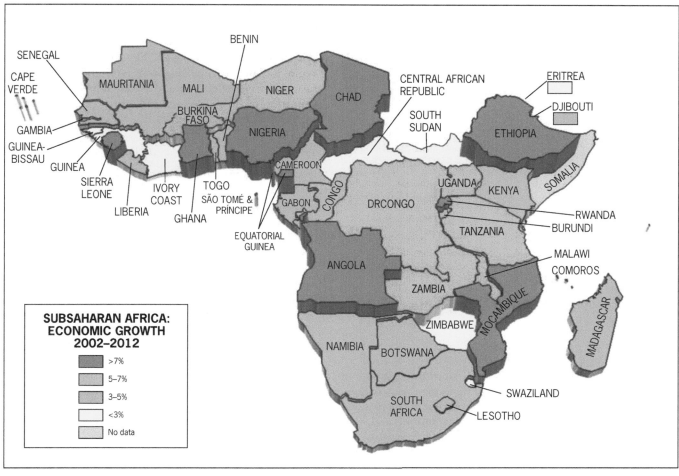

FIGURE 6A-11

© H. J. de Blij, P. O. Muller, J. Nijman, and John Wiley & Sons, Inc.

Middle-class youths at a cultural festival in Kampala, Uganda, during the summer of 2012. Demands for education, cultural goods, computer and Internet use, and access to leading entertainment media are surging, and upscale consumption is on the rise in many of Subsaharan Africa's cities.

© Yannick Tylie/Corbis

But, overall, the economy in most of the realm shows more vibrancy than ever and, with the recent subsidence of wars and violent conflict, democracy is taking hold as well. A number of countries that used to be notorious for perennial strife, including Angola, Sierra Leone, and Chad, have turned a corner and stabilized. Democratic advances, in the form of open elections and a free press, have been especially notable in parts of Southern and West Africa. Political dislocation, repression, and dysfunction do persist in various countries, of which Zimbabwe is the most glaring example—but the Mugabe regime in Harare is fast becoming an anomaly.

Vulnerable Growth

Subsaharan Africa's fate in modern times has been tied to foreign intervention and outside interests. That is still true today as the realm is being drawn into the global economy. Foreign direct investment between 2002 and 2012 more than tripled from U.S. $11 billion to $35 billion. Outside investors

TABLE 6A-1
Fastest Growing Subsaharan Economies (2002–2012) and Leading Exports (2012)

	% Annual GDP Growth	1st and 2nd Biggest Export Products
Equatorial Guinea	10.8	oil, timber
Angola	10.6	oil, diamonds
Ethiopia	8.9	coffee, hides
Nigeria	7.5	oil, cocoa
Chad	7.5	cotton, oil
Moçambique	7.4	aluminum, coal
Sierra Leone	7.3	diamonds, rutile
Ghana	7.2	gold, cocoa
Rwanda	7.2	coffee, tea
Uganda	7.0	coffee, fish
Tanzania	6.9	gold, sisal
DRCongo	6.2	diamonds, copper
Zambia	6.1	copper, minerals

are primarily interested in Africa's natural resources, and much of their capital is used for improving the infrastructure needed to transfer valuable commodities to ports and other exporting centers. Multinational mining and construction companies are especially well represented, and agribusiness corporations, as noted, have been actively buying up the land itself.

Whereas foreign investments are needed and can make vital contributions to a developing economy, the concern is that they provide too little in terms of manufacturing or even processing of raw materials, the kind of economic activity that adds value to a stage of production. Table 6A-1 lists the fastest growing economies of Subsaharan Africa together with their two leading export products in terms of monetary value. In every case, these exports are raw materials, commodities that have fared well in the global marketplace in recent years, particularly because of massive demand from China.

Although Subsaharan Africa has been successfully riding the global commodity boom, there are drawbacks and heightening risks when a realm's economy is so one-sided. First, many resources are finite, and at some point mineral and energy reserves are going to be depleted. Second, heavy reliance on commodity exports means heavy dependence on world market prices that can fluctuate suddenly and substantially. Third, even if international commodity prices are high, the terms of trade tend to be unbalanced if an exporting country must import high-value-added manufactured goods such as cars and computers. And finally, raw-material exporting makes only a modest contribution to the employment economy because it involves minimal domestic processing.

The bottom line here is that governments must focus on using their revenues, while they last, to invest in education as well as diversifying the economy. African governments must also be wary of relying too heavily on a limited number of major foreign customers from outside the realm (China, Japan, Europe). The best way to begin weaning themselves away is to intensify trading relations with neighbors and other Subsaharan African countries to forge greater economic interdependence within this realm.

The Need for Supranationalism

Figure 6A-11 indicates no clear regional patterns of economic growth, which is strongly tied to the uneven distribution of natural resources across Subsaharan Africa. In other respects, particularly consumption and the availability of services such as health and education, geography plays a major role because so many places in this far-flung realm are still quite inaccessible. Transportation costs can constitute 75 percent of the price of food in cities in Malawi, Rwanda, or Uganda; not surprisingly, prices are even higher than that in the remote rural areas of such landlocked countries. Farmers almost everywhere have a hard time getting their produce to market because of bad roads and/or nonexistent rail connections. Trade across borders is heavily shackled by tariffs, unnecessary controls (not to mention ubiquitous demands for bribes), and other protectionist measures. Consider this: intrarealm trade accounts for only 13 percent of total trading activity in Subsaharan Africa compared to almost 70 percent in Europe. Even in South America, where regional integration is also a significant challenge, internal trade is nearly twice as high as in Africa.

To overcome such disadvantages, African states must improve international cooperation, continentwide as well as regionally. The Organization of African Unity (OAU) was established for this purpose in 1963 and was superseded by the African Union (AU) in 2001. In 1975, the Economic Community of West African States (ECOWAS) was established by 15 countries to promote trade, transportation, industry, and social affairs in that region. And in the early 1990s, important steps were taken when 12 countries joined in forming the Southern African Development Community (SADC) and when the Common Market for Eastern and Southern Africa (COMESA) was created. Hence, the institutional structures for integration exist (indeed, there is a need to streamline the various initiatives) and exports across the realm are today at an all-time high. Now it is a matter of summoning the considerable political will to create lasting regional cooperation and realmwide interdependence.

If there is one geographic realm that is subject to stereotypical judgment, it is Subsaharan Africa. All too often, this one is portrayed as a single, monolithic, economic basket case, where dysfunctional government goes hand in hand with economic underperformance, frequent famines, and aimless violence. In the 2010s, that characterization couldn't be further off the mark. Subsaharan Africa not only exhibits enormous geographic, cultural, and economic diversity but also harbors the world's newest emerging market. Economic forecasts tell of another decade lying ahead in which growth and development here is likely to outstrip that of all other realms. In the early 1960s, when much of Africa became politically independent, there was short-lived talk about the 'wind of change' bringing self-determination to these new countries. Instead, adversity was the overwhelming fate of so many of the realm's inhabitants. Now, after an especially traumatic half-century, the 'wind of change' is once again gathering force, prospects are brightening, and Subsaharan Africa is evolving into a realm of hope.

POINTS TO PONDER

- Shipping a new car from China to Tanzania costs less than hauling it from Tanzania to neighboring Uganda.

- Subsaharan Africa is home to 69 percent of all HIV/AIDS cases in the world.

- The realm contains about four-dozen countries; the number of languages spoken within it is estimated to be between 1300 and 2000.

- China's deepening impact on Subsaharan Africa is expanding steadily through activities ranging from trade to investment to education. Brazil, too, is increasingly making its presence felt here.

- At the end of the first two decades of this century, Subsaharan Africa is likely to have recorded the fastest economic growth among all the world geographic realms.

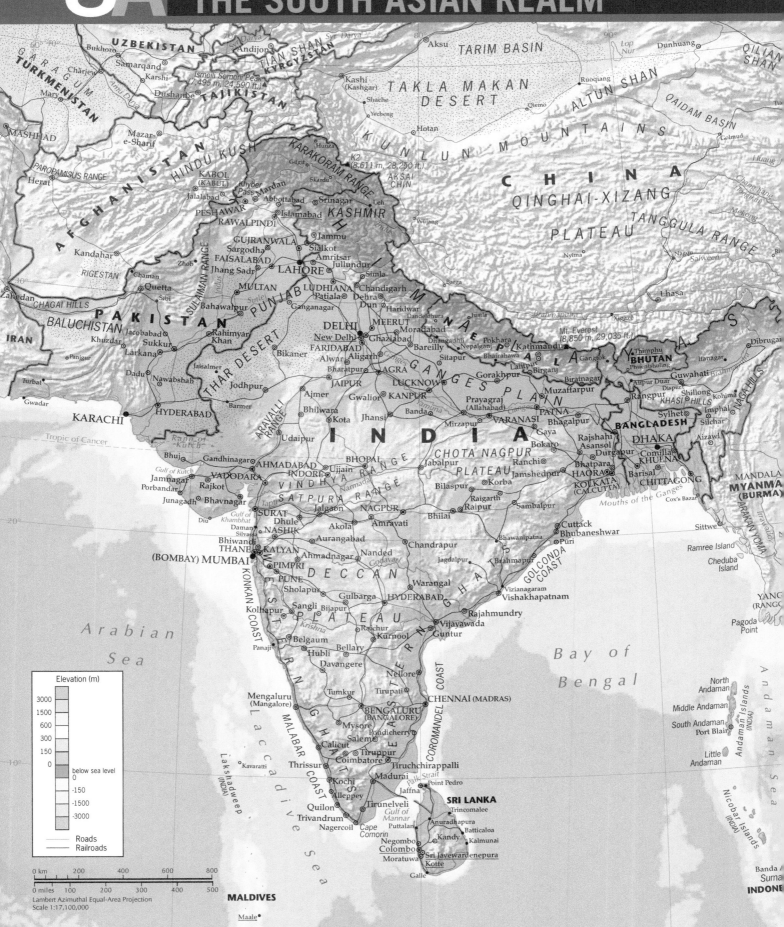

DEFINING the Realm

IN THIS CHAPTER

- South Asia as a birthplace of religions
- Cutting-edge IT, backward agriculture
- Two nuclear powers quarrel over Kashmir
- The Indian Ocean: A crucial geopolitical arena
- South Asia's missing girls

CONCEPTS, IDEAS, AND TERMS

Monsoon 1
Social stratification 2
Indo-European languages 3
Dravidian languages 4
Partition 5
Refugees 6
Forward capital 7
Terms of trade 8
Neoliberalism 9
Population geography 10
Population density 11
Physiologic density 12
Demographic transition 13
Fertility rate 14
Demographic burden 15
Population pyramid 16
Sex ratio 17

FIGURE 8A-1 © H. J. de Blij, P. O. Muller, and John Wiley & Sons, Inc.

South Asia is a realm of almost magical geographic names: Mount Everest, Kashmir, the Khyber Pass, the Ganges River. There was a time when this realm was legendary and prized. Remember that it was "India" and its fabled wealth that the European explorers were after, from Vasco da Gama to Columbus to Magellan. Before them, the fourteenth-century North African geographer Ibn Battuta had traveled overland to South Asia, and his writings about its riches were met with astonishment and even disbelief. From the sixteenth century onward, European trading companies derived enormous profits from commerce in this realm.

However, by the late nineteenth century South Asia seemed to have become remote from the affairs of the world—hungry, weak, exploited, the prototype of the global periphery. Even after independence in 1947, India as well as the other countries of this realm long remained among the world's poorest. For decades, population growth outstripped economic expansion.

Today, for a number of reasons, South Asia commands the world's attention once again. It became the most populous geographic realm on Earth in 2011 (see the Data Table in Appendix B). Two of its states, India and Pakistan, often find themselves in conflict and both are nuclear powers. In the remote mountain hideaways of Pakistan, a terrorist organization's leaders planned attacks that changed the skyline of New York and presaged the battleground of Iraq. In the ports of India, a growing navy reflects the emergence of the Indian Ocean as a new global geopolitical arena in which China, too, is asserting itself. Meanwhile, outsourcing by U.S. companies to India has become a hot topic, and India's spectacular rise in information technology has changed that industry. Our daily lives will increasingly be affected by what happens in this crowded and restive part of the world.

DEFINING THE REALM

THE GEOGRAPHIC PANORAMA

The Eurasian landmass incorporates all or part of 6 of the world's 12 geographic realms, and of these half-dozen none is more clearly defined by nature than the one we call South Asia. Figure 8A-1 shows us why: the huge triangular subcontinent that divides the northern Indian Ocean between the Arabian Sea and the Bay of Bengal is so sharply demarcated by mountain walls and desert wastes that you could take a pen and mark its boundary, from the Naga Hills in the far east through the Great Himalaya and Karakoram in the north to the Hindu Kush and the Iran-bordering wastelands of Baluchistan in the west. Note how short the distances are over which the green of habitable lowlands turns to the dark brown of massive, snowcapped mountain ranges.

South Asia's kaleidoscope of cultures may be the most diverse in the world, proving that neither formidable mountains nor forbidding deserts could prevent foreign influences from further diversifying an already variegated realm. We will encounter many of these influ-

ences in this chapter and the next, but South Asia also possessed one unifying force of sorts: the British Empire, which in its late-nineteenth-century heyday came to hold

> **Entering the beautiful medieval walled city of Jaisalmer in India's Thar Desert, not far from the border with Pakistan.**

© Jan Nijman

182

major geographic qualities of

SOUTH ASIA

1. South Asia is clearly defined physiographically, and much of the realm's boundary is marked by mountains, deserts, and the Indian Ocean.

2. South Asia's great rivers, especially the Ganges, have for tens of thousands of years supported huge population clusters.

3. South Asia, and especially northern India, was the birthplace of major religions that include Hinduism and Buddhism.

4. Due to the realm's natural boundaries, foreign influences in premodern South Asia came mainly via a narrow passage in the northwest (the Khyber Pass).

5. South Asia covers just over 3 percent of the Earth's land area but contains nearly 24 percent of the world's human population.

6. South Asia's annual monsoon continues to dominate life for hundreds of millions of subsistence and commercial farmers. Failure of the monsoon cycle spells economic crisis.

7. Certain remote areas in the realm's northern mountain perimeter are a dangerous source of friction between India and both Pakistan and China.

8. South Asia is still predominantly rural with hundreds of thousands of small villages; but it also contains some of the biggest cities in the world.

sway over all of it in a *raj* (period of rule) that endured through the mid-twentieth. When, in the immediate aftermath of World War II, the British wanted to transfer their authority to a single regional government, local objections swiftly nullified this notion. That regional government would have been Hindu-dominated, but Muslims concentrated in the realm's eastern and western flanks refused, as did a pair of small kingdoms in the mountainous north as well as the Buddhist-dominated southern island then called Ceylon (now Sri Lanka). Negotiations and compromises produced partition and the political boundaries seen in Figure 8A-1. As a result, India, the realm's giant, is flanked by six countries (in clockwise order, Pakistan, Nepal, Bhutan, Bangladesh, Sri Lanka, and the Maldives) as well as a remaining disputed territory in the far north, Kashmir.

Since Islam is Pakistan's official religion (India has none) and that faith is a key criterion in defining the realm we designated as North Africa/Southwest Asia, should Pakistan be included within the latter? The answer lies in several aspects of Pakistan's historical geography. One criterion is ethnic continuity, which links Pakistan to India rather than to Afghanistan or Iran. Another factor involves language: although Urdu is Pakistan's official language, English is the *lingua franca*, as it is in India. Still another factor, of course, is Pakistan's evolution as part of the British Indian Empire. Furthermore, the boundary between Pakistan and India does not signify the eastern frontier of Islam in Asia. As we shall see, more than 200 million of India's 1.3 billion citizens are Muslims (which is just about as many as there are in all of Pakistan), and millions live very close to the Indian side of the border whose creation cost so many lives in 1947. And not only are Pakistan and India linked in the cultural-historical arena: they are locked in a deadly and dangerous embrace in embattled Kashmir.

The tight integration of Pakistan with South Asia will not surprise you after studying the realm's physiography in Figure 8A-1: the natural boundary in this part of the realm lies west of the Indus River, not east of it. Pakistan today remains part of a realm that changes not in the Punjab, but at the Khyber Pass, the highland gateway to Afghanistan.

SOUTH ASIA'S PHYSIOGRAPHY

From snowcapped peaks to tropical forests and from bone-dry deserts to lush farmlands, this part of the world presents a virtually endless array of environments and ecologies, a diversity that is matched by its cultural mosaic. The broad outlines of this realm's physiography are best understood against the backdrop of its fascinating geologic past.

A Tectonic Encounter

As Figure 8A-2 shows, the spectacular relief in the north of this realm resulted initially from the collision of two of the Earth's great tectonic plates (see Fig. G-4). About 10 million years ago, after a lengthy geologic journey following the breakup of the supercontinent Pangaea (see Chapter 6A), the Indian Plate encountered Eurasia. In this huge, slow-motion, accordion-like collision, parts of the crust were pushed upward, thereby creating the mighty Himalaya mountain range. That process is still going on—at the rate of 5 millimeters (0.2 in) per year—and this is one of the most earthquake-prone areas in the world. One major outcome of the tectonic collision was that the northern margins of the South Asian realm were thrust upward to elevations where permanent snow and ice make the landscape appear polar. The march of the seasons melts enough

TECTONIC EVOLUTION OF SOUTH ASIA

EURASIAN PLATE

Himalayas

INDIA
Today

10 million
years ago

SRI LANKA

38 million
years ago

Equator

55 million
years ago

INDIAN
OCEAN

71 million
years ago

"INDIA"
landmass

0   400   800 Kilometers
0   200   400 Miles

SRI LANKA

Modified after USGS drawing.

FIGURE 8A-2   © H. J. de Blij, P. O. Muller, J. Nijman,
and John Wiley & Sons, Inc.

of this snow in spring and summer to sustain the great rivers below, providing water for farmlands that support hundreds of millions of people. The Ganges, Indus, and Brahmaputra all have their origins in the Himalaya. Only south of the Ganges Basin does the massive plateau begin that marks the much older geologic core of the Indian Plate as it drifted northeastward toward Eurasia.

The Monsoon

Physical geography, therefore, is crucial here in South Asia—but not just on and below the surface. What happens in the atmosphere is critical as well. The name "South Asia" is almost synonymous with the term **monsoon [1]** because the annual rains that come with its

onset, usually in June, are indispensable to subsistence as well as commercial agriculture in the realm's key country, India.

Figure 8A-3 shows how the monsoon works. As the South Asian landmass heats up during the spring, a huge low-pressure system forms above it. This low-pressure system begins to draw in vast volumes of air from over the ocean onto the subcontinent. When the inflow of moist oceanic air reaches critical mass in early June, the **wet monsoon** has arrived. It may rain for 60 days or more. The countryside turns green, the paddies fill, and another dry season's dust and dirt are washed away. The region is reborn (see photo pair). The moisture-laden air flowing onshore from the Arabian Sea is forced upward against the Western Ghats, cooling as it rises and condensing large amounts of rainfall. The other branch of the wet monsoon originates in the Bay of Bengal and gets caught up in the convection (rising hot air) over northeastern India and Bangladesh. Seemingly endless rain now inundates a much larger area, including the entire North Indian Plain. The Himalaya mountain wall blocks the onshore airstream from spreading into the Asian interior and the rain from dissipating. Thus the moist airflow is steered westward, drying out as it advances toward Pakistan. After persisting for weeks, this pattern finally breaks down and the wet monsoon gives way to periodic rains and, eventually, another dry season. Then the anxious wait begins for the next year's summer monsoon, for without it India would face disaster. In much of rural India, life can hang by a meteorological thread.

Physiographic Regions

Figure 8A-3 underscores South Asia's overall division into three physiographic zones: northern mountains, southern plateaus, and, in between, a wide crescent of river lowlands.

The arrival of the annual rains of the wet monsoon transforms the Indian countryside. By the end of May, the paddies lie parched and brown, dust chokes the air, and it seems that nothing will revive the land. Then the rains begin, and blankets of dust turn into layers of mud. Soon the first patches of green appear on the soil, and by the time the monsoon ends all is green. The photo on the left, taken just before the onset of the wet monsoon in the west-coast State of Goa, shows the paddies before the rains begin; three months later this same countryside looks as on the right.

© Steve McCurry/Magnum Photos, Inc.   © Steve McCurry/Magnum Photos, Inc.

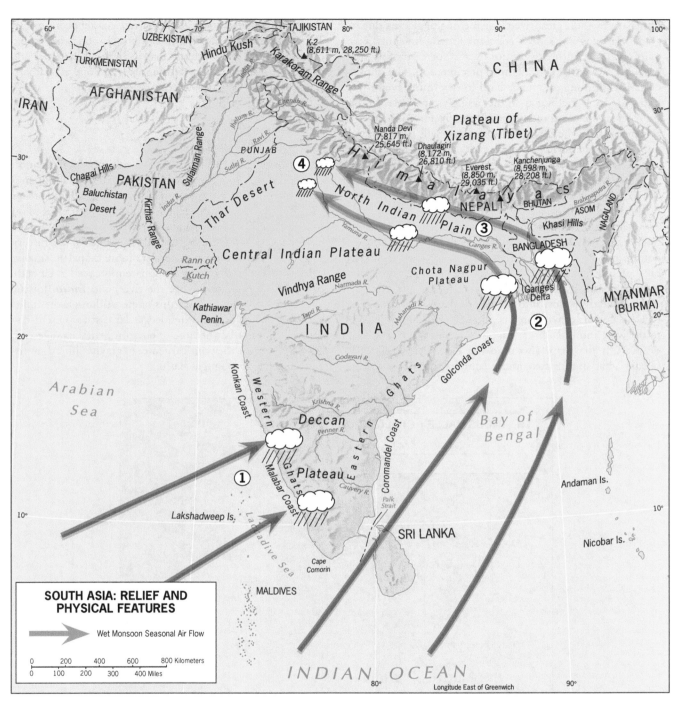

FIGURE 8A-3

© H. J. de Blij, P. O. Muller, and John Wiley & Sons, Inc.

The ***northern mountains*** extend from the Hindu Kush and Karakoram ranges in the northwest through the Himalaya in the center (Everest, the world's tallest peak, lies on the crestline that forms the Nepal-China border) to the ranges of Bhutan and the Indian State of Arunachal Pradesh in the east. Dry and barren in the west on the Afghanistan border, the ranges become green and tree-studded in Kashmir, forested in the lower-lying sections of Nepal, and even more densely vegetated in Arunachal Pradesh. Transitional foothills, with many deeply eroded valleys cut by rushing meltwater, lead to the river basins below.

The belt of ***river lowlands*** extends eastward from Pakistan's lower Indus Valley (the area known as Sindh) through India's wide Gangetic Plain and then on across the great double delta of the Ganges and Brahmaputra in Bangladesh (Fig. 8A-3). In the east, this physiographic region is often called the North Indian Plain. To the west lies the lowland of the Indus River, which rises in Tibet, crosses Kashmir, and then bends southward to receive its major tributaries from the Punjab ("Land of Five Rivers") to the east.

With so much of the realm, and so many of its people, depending on the water transported down from the High

Himalaya by these great rivers, the melting of glaciers due to global warming is a serious concern. The Brahmaputra, for example, relies on meltwater for over 20 percent of its volume, the remainder coming from precipitation. The impact of global warming is actually hard to determine even if we know the ice is melting at an increasingly rapid rate. In the short term, increased melting will actually add to the river's volume, but as the glaciers shrink there will be a tipping point at which meltwater will suddenly and rapidly decrease. Some models indicate this is likely to occur as soon as mid-century, with potentially devastating consequences for populations at lower elevations that have depended on this water for millennia.

Peninsular India is mainly plateau country, dominated by the massive ***Deccan***, a tableland built of lava sheets that poured out when India separated from Africa during the breakup of Pangaea. The Deccan (meaning "South") tilts toward the east, so that its highest areas are in the west and most of the rivers flow into the Bay of Bengal. North of the Deccan lie two other plateaus, the Central Indian Plateau to the west and the Chota Nagpur Plateau to the east (Fig. 8A-3). On the map, also note the Eastern and Western Ghats: "ghat" means step, and it connotes the descent from

Deccan Plateau elevations to the narrow coastal plains below. The onshore winds of the annual wet monsoon bring ample precipitation to the Western Ghats; as a result, here lies one of India's most productive farming areas and one of southern India's largest population concentrations.

BIRTHPLACE OF CIVILIZATIONS

Indus Valley Civilization

A complex and technologically advanced civilization emerged in the Indus Valley by about 2500 BC, simultaneous with other Bronze Age "urban revolutions" in Egypt and Mesopotamia. The Indus Valley civilization was centered on two major cities, Harappa and Mohenjo-Daro, which may have been capitals during different periods of its history (Fig. 8A-4); in addition, there were more than 100 smaller urban settlements. The locals apparently called their state ***Sindhu***, and both ***Indus*** (for the river) and ***India*** (for the later state) may derive from this name. Although the influence of this civilization extended as far east as present-day Delhi, it did not last because of environmental change and, perhaps, because the political center of gravity shifted southeastward into the Ganges Basin.

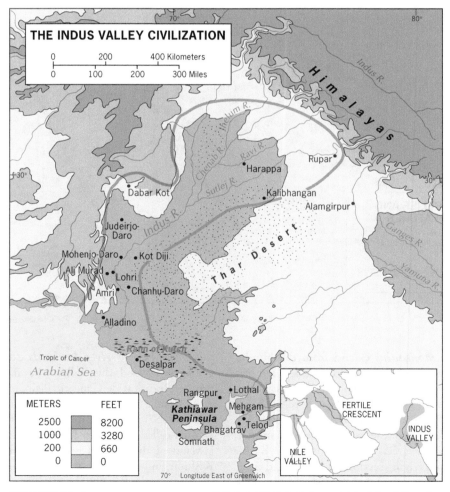

FIGURE 8A-4   © H. J. de Blij, P. O. Muller, and John Wiley & Sons, Inc.

Aryans and the Origins of Hinduism

Around 1500 BC, northern India was invaded by the **_Aryans_** (peoples speaking Indo-European languages based in what is today Iran). As the Iron Age dawned in India, acculturated Aryans began the process of integrating the Ganges Basin's isolated tribes and villages into a new organized system, and urbanization made a comeback. The Aryans brought their language (Sanskrit, related to Old Persian) and a new social order to the vast riverine flatlands of northern India. Their settlement here was also accompanied by the emergence of a religious belief system, **_Vedism_**. Out of the texts of Vedism and local creeds there arose a new religion—**_Hinduism_**—and with it a new way of life.

It is thought that the arrival and accommodation of Aryans in this new society forged a system of social stratification [2] that would solidify the powerful position of the Aryans and be legitimized through religion. Starting about 3500 years ago, a combination of regional integration, the organization of villages into controlled networks, and the emergence of numerous small city-states produced a hierarchy of power among the people, a ranking from the very powerful (Brahmins—highest-order priests) to the weakest. This class-based **_caste system_** of Hinduism is highly controversial in the West (and among groups of Indians too) because of its rigidity and the ways in which it justifies structural inequality. Those in the lowest castes, deemed to be there because they deserved it given their past lives, are worst off, without hope of advancement and at the mercy of those ranking higher on the social ladder. In recent years, the caste system appears to be eroding from the combined effects of globalization, economic growth, and urbanization; this is true for India's bigger cities, but much less so for the majority of people in the country who still reside in rural areas.

Although Hinduism spread across South Asia and even reached the Southeast Asian realm (especially Cambodia and Indonesia), Indo-European languages never took hold in the southern portion of the subcontinent. As Figure 8A-5 shows, Indo-European languages [3] (several of which are rooted in Sanskrit) predominate in the western

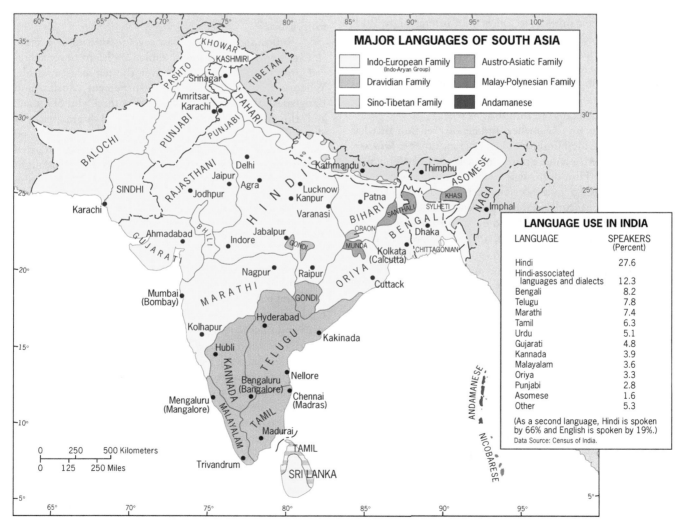

FIGURE 8A-5

© H. J. de Blij, P. O. Muller, J. Nijman, and John Wiley & Sons, Inc.

and northern parts of the realm, whereas the southern languages belong to the Dravidian [4] family—languages that were indigenous to the realm even before the arrival of the Aryans. But these are not fossil languages: they remain vibrant today and have long literary histories. Telugu, Tamil, Kanarese (Kannada), and Malayalam are spoken by some 275 million people. In India's northern and northeastern fringes, Sino-Tibetan languages predominate, and smaller pockets of Austro-Asiatic speakers can be found in eastern India and neighboring Bangladesh.

Buddhism and Other Indigenous Religions

Hinduism is not the only religion that emerged in this realm. Around 500 BC, *Buddhism* arose in the eastern Ganges Basin in what is today the Indian State of Bihar. The famous story of the "enlightenment" of the Prince Siddhartha (the Buddha) took place in the town of Bodh Gaya, and his following soon expanded in all directions. The appeal of Buddhism was (and is) especially strong among lower-caste Hindus, and substantial numbers have converted through the ages. Even some prominent ancient Hindu kings were known to have turned to Buddhism, prompting their subjects to follow suit. Interestingly, Buddhism emerged inside India, but its ultimate influence was felt beyond the realm in Southeast and East Asia. Today, less than 1 percent of the population of India adheres to Buddhism (80 percent are Hindu), but it is the state religion in Bhutan and a large majority (more than 70 percent) of Sri Lankans are Buddhist as well.

Another (much smaller) indigenous religion that has evolved alongside Hinduism since ancient times is *Jainism*, often described as a more purist, principled, and deeply spiritual form of Hinduism. It is especially well known for its uncompromising stand on nonviolence and vegetarianism. Jains today constitute less than 1 percent of the population in India. Finally, we should take note of *Sikhism* as another of the realm's indigenous religions, a blend of sorts of Islamic and Hindu beliefs. This religion, practiced by about 2 percent of the population, is of course much younger; it emerged around AD 1500, a few centuries after Islam became a dominating force in much of the South Asian realm.

FOREIGN INVADERS

The Reach of Islam

In the late tenth century, Islam came rolling like a giant tide across South Asia, spreading across Persia and Afghanistan, through the high mountain passes, into the Indus Valley, across the Punjab, and into the Ganges Basin, converting virtually everybody in the Indus Valley and foreshadowing the emergence, many centuries later, of the Islamic Republic of Pakistan. By the early thirteenth century, the Muslims had established the long-surviving and powerful *Delhi Sultanate*, which expanded across much of the northern tier of the peninsula. The Muslims also came by sea, arriving at the Ganges-Brahmaputra Delta and spreading their faith from the east as well as the west, in the process laying the foundation of today's predominantly Islamic state of Bangladesh.

In the early 1500s, a descendant of Genghis Khan named Babur placed his forces in control of Kabol (Kabul) in Afghanistan, and from that base he penetrated the Punjab and challenged the Delhi Sultanate. In the 1520s, his Islamicized Mongol armies ousted the Delhi rulers and established the *Mughal (Mogul) Empire*.

By most accounts, Mughal rule was at times remarkably enlightened, especially under the leadership of Babur's grandson Akbar, who expanded the empire by force but adopted tolerant policies toward Hindus under his sway; Akbar's grandson, Shah Jahan, made his enduring mark on India's cultural landscape through such magnificent architectural creations as the Taj Mahal in the city of Agra.

Nonetheless, by the early eighteenth century the Mughal Empire was in decline. Maratha, a Hindu state in the west, expanded not only into the peninsular south but also northward toward Delhi, capturing the allegiance of local rulers and weakening Islam's hold. Fractured India now lay open to still another foreign intrusion, this time from Europe.

Reflecting on more than seven centuries of Islamic rule in South Asia, it is remarkable that Islam never achieved proportional dominance over the realm as a whole. Whereas Pakistan is more than 96 percent Muslim and Bangladesh 91 percent, India—where the Delhi Sultanate and the Mughal Empire were centered—remains only about 15 percent Muslim today. Islam may have arrived like a giant tide, but Hinduism stayed afloat and outlasted the invasion. It also withstood the European onslaught that culminated in the incorporation of the entire realm into the British Empire.

The European Intrusion

By the middle of the eighteenth century, the British had taken over much of the trade in South Asia. Their power was imposed through the East India Company (EIC), which represented the empire but whose main purpose was economic control. The British took advantage of the weakened and fragmented power of the Mughals and followed a strategy commonly known as "indirect rule." They left local rulers in place as long as they extracted the desired trading arrangements. In fact, thanks to arrangements with the British, many local maharajas became wealthier than ever before: from northern to southern India, you can find beautiful palaces (now often converted to either museums or hotels) that were built by these rulers, often as recently as the late nineteenth or early twentieth century.

The EIC not only controlled trade with Europe in spices, cotton, and silk goods, but also India's longstanding commerce with Southeast Asia, which until then was in the hands of Indian, Arab, and Chinese merchants. This system worked well (for the British and their Indian trade partners) for almost a century, but by then political developments and heightened tensions were making it inevitable that the British government itself would take over from the EIC and assume responsibility. Thus "East India" became part of the British colonial empire in 1857—a *raj* that would endure for the next 90 years—and Queen Victoria officially became its empress 20 years later.

Colonial Transformation

British colonialism in South Asia coincided with the Industrial Revolution in Europe, and the impact of Britain on the realm must be understood in that context. South Asia became, in large part, a supplier of raw materials needed to keep the factories going in Manchester, Birmingham, and other industrial centers in Britain. For instance, when the supply of cotton from the American South came to a halt during the U.S. Civil War in the early 1860s, the British quickly encouraged (and indeed enforced) cotton production in what is today western India.

When the British took power in South Asia, this was a realm with already considerable industrial development (notably in metal goods and textiles) and an active trade with both Southeast and Southwest Asia. The colonialists saw this as competition, and soon India was exporting raw materials and importing manufactured products—from Europe, of course. Local industries declined, and Indian merchants lost their markets.

Colonialism did produce some assets for India. The country was bequeathed one of the most extensive transport networks of the colonial era, particularly the railroad system—even though the network focused on interior-to-seaport linkages rather than fully interconnecting the various parts of the country. British engineers laid out irrigation canals through which millions of hectares of land were brought into cultivation. Coastal settlements that had been founded by Britain developed into major cities and bustling ports, led by Bombay (now renamed Mumbai), Calcutta (now Kolkata), and Madras (now Chennai). These three cities still rank among India's largest urban centers, and their cityscapes bear the unmistakable imprint of colonialism (see photo in *From the Field Notes*).

British rule also produced a new elite among the South Asian natives. They had access to education and schools that combined English and Indian traditions, and their Westernization was reinforced through university education in Britain. This elite drew from Hindu and Muslim communities, and it was to play a major part in the rising demands for self-rule and independence. These demands started to gather momentum in the early twentieth century and could no longer be denied when World War II came to an end in the mid-1940s.

From the Field Notes . . .

© H.J. de Blij

"More than a half-century after the end of British rule, the centers of India's great cities continued to be dominated by the Victorian-Gothic buildings the colonizers constructed here. This also is evidence of a previous era of globalization, when European imprints transformed urban landscapes. Walking the streets of some parts of Mumbai (the British called it Bombay) you can turn a corner and be forgiven for mistaking the scene for London, double-decker buses and all. One of the British planners' major achievements was the construction of a nationwide railroad system, and railway stations were given great prominence in the urban architecture. I had walked up Naoroji Road, having learned to dodge the wild traffic around the circles in the Fort area, and watched the throngs passing through Victoria (now Chhatrapati Shivaji) Station. Inside, the facility is badly worn, but the trains continue to run, bulging with passengers hanging out of doors and windows."

www.conceptcaching.com

THE GEOPOLITICS OF MODERN SOUTH ASIA

Partition and Independence

Even before the British government decided to yield to demands for independence, it was clear that British India would not survive the coming of self-rule as a single political entity. As early as the 1930s, Muslim activists were promoting the idea of a separate state. As the colony moved toward independence, a major political crisis developed that eventually resulted in the separation of India and Pakistan. But partition [5] was no simple matter. True, Muslims were in the majority in the western and eastern sectors of British India, but smaller Islamic clusters were scattered throughout the realm. Furthermore, the new boundaries between Hindu and Muslim communities had to be drawn right through areas where both sides coexisted—thereby displacing millions (see photo).

The consequences of this migration for the social geography of India were especially far reaching. Comparing the country's 1931 and 1951 distributions of Muslims in Figure 8A-6, you can see the impact on the Indian Punjab and in what is today the State of Rajasthan. (Since Kashmir was mapped as three entities before the partition and as one afterward, the change there represents an administrative, not a major numerical, alteration.) Even in the east a Muslim exodus occurred, as reflected on the map by the State of West Bengal, adjacent to Bangladesh, where the Islamic component in the population declined substantially.

The world has seen many refugee [6] migrations but none involving so many people in so short a time as the one resulting from British India's partition (which occurred on Independence Day, August 15, 1947). Scholars who study the refugee phenomenon differentiate between "forced" and "voluntary" migrations, but as this case underscores, it is not always possible to separate the two. Many Muslims, believing they had no choice, feared for their future in the new India and joined the stampede. Others had the means and the ability to make a decision to stay or leave, but even these better-off migrants undoubtedly sensed a threat.

The great majority of Hindus who lived on the "wrong" side of the border moved as well. The Hindu component of present-day Pakistan may have been as high as 16 percent in 1947 but is barely more than 1.5 percent today; in Bangladesh, which was named East Pakistan at the time of partition, it declined from 30 percent to around 9 percent today. Partition therefore created an entirely new cultural and geopolitical landscape in South Asia.

India–Pakistan

From the moment of their separate creation, India and Pakistan have had a tenuous relationship. Upon independence, present-day Pakistan was united with present-day Bangladesh, and the two countries were respectively called West Pakistan and East Pakistan. As we have noted, the basis for this scheme was Islam: in both Pakistan and Bangladesh, Islam is the state religion. Between the two Islamic wings of Pakistan lay Hindu India. But there was little else to unify the Muslim easterners and westerners, and their union lasted less than 25 years. In 1971, a costly war of secession, in which India supported East Pakistan, led to the collapse of this unusual arrangement. East Pakistan, upon its "second independence" in 1971, took the name Bangladesh; and since there was no longer any need for a "West" Pakistan, that qualifier was dropped and the name Pakistan remained on the map.

India's encouragement of independence for Bangladesh emphasized the continuing tension between Pakistan and India, which had already led to war in 1965, to further conflict during the 1970s over Jammu and Kashmir, and to periodic flare-ups over other issues. During the Cold War, India tilted toward Moscow, while Pakistan found favor in Washington because of its strategic location adjacent to Afghanistan. Armed conflict between the two South Asian countries seemed to be a regional matter—until the early 1990s, when their arms race took on ominous nuclear proportions.

Flight was one response to the 1947 partition of what had been British India, resulting in one of the greatest mass population transfers in human history. Here, two trainloads of eastbound Hindu refugees, fleeing (then) West Pakistan arrive at the station in Amritsar, the first city inside India."

© Bettmann/CORBIS

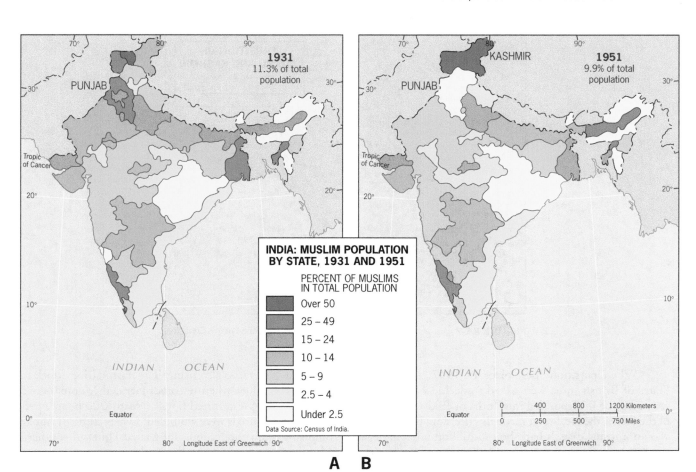

FIGURE 8A-6

© H. J. de Blij, P. O. Muller, and John Wiley & Sons, Inc.

Since then, the specter of nuclear war has hung over the conflicts that continue to embroil Pakistan and India, a concern not just for the South Asian realm but for the world as a whole. No longer merely a decolonized, divided, and disadvantaged country trying to survive, Pakistan has taken a crucial place in the political geography of a geographic realm in turbulent transition.

The relationship between India and Pakistan is especially sensitive because there are still so many Muslims in India. Massive as the 1947 refugee movement was, it left far more Muslims in India than those who had departed. The number of Muslims in India declined sharply, but it remained a huge minority, one that was growing rapidly to boot. By 2013, it surpassed 200 million, just over 15 percent of the total population—the largest cultural minority in the world and almost 10 percent larger than Pakistan's entire population (188 million).

What this means is that a sizeable portion of India's population tends to have more or less "natural" sympathies vis-à-vis Pakistan. Their presence works at times as a brake on hawkish Indian policies toward Islamabad. On the other hand, conflict with Pakistan can have detrimental effects on Hindu-Muslim relations inside India, and over the years has led to communal violence and deadly clashes. This issue is further complicated today by the Indian Muslims' alleged role in terrorist activities in India, orchestrated from Pakistan.

Contested Kashmir

When Pakistan became an independent state following the partition of British India in 1947, its capital was Karachi on the south coast, near the western end of the Indus Delta. As the map shows, however, the present capital is Islamabad. By moving the capital from the "safe" coast to the embattled interior, and by placing it on the doorstep of the contested territory of Kashmir, Pakistan announced its intent to stake a claim to its northern frontiers. And by naming the city Islamabad, Pakistan proclaimed its Muslim foundation here in the face of the Hindu challenge. This politico-geographical usage of a national capital can be assertive, and as such Islamabad exemplifies the principle of the forward capital [7].

Kashmir is a territory of high mountains surrounded by Pakistan, India, China, and, along more than 50 kilometers (30 mi) in the far north, Afghanistan (Fig. 8A-7). Although known simply as Kashmir, the area actually consists of several political divisions, including the Indian State properly referred to as Jammu and Kashmir, a major bone of contention between India and Pakistan.

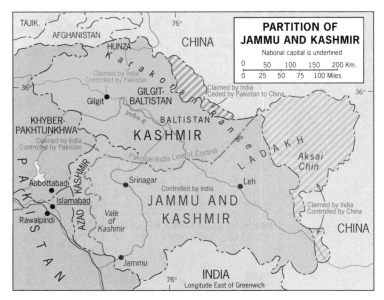

FIGURE 8A-7   © H. J. de Blij, P. O. Muller, and John Wiley & Sons, Inc.

When partition took place in 1947, the existing States of British India were asked to decide whether they wanted to be incorporated into India or Pakistan. In most of the States, the local ruler made this decision, but Kashmir was an unusual case. It had about 5 million inhabitants at the time, nearly three-quarters of them Muslims, but the maharajah of Kashmir himself was a Hindu. When he decided not to join Pakistan and instead aimed to retain autonomous status, this was answered with a Muslim uprising supported by Pakistan. The maharajah, in turn, called for help from India. After more than a year's fighting and through the intervention of the United Nations, a cease-fire line left most of Jammu and Kashmir (including nearly four-fifths of the territory's population) in Indian hands. Eventually, this line—now known as the Line of Control—began to appear on maps as the final boundary settlement, and Indian governments have proposed that it be so recognized.

With about two-thirds of the Kashmiris still Muslim, Pakistan has for decades demanded a referendum in Jammu and Kashmir in which the people can decide for themselves to remain with India or become part of Pakistan. India has refused, arguing that there is a place for Muslims in secular India but not for Hindus in the Islamic Republic of Pakistan. Given the specter of terrorism in India and the dangerous precedent of a concession in light of India's enormous ethnic and regional diversity, the Kashmir conflict has been left to smolder and is unlikely to be resolved for years to come.

The Specter of Terrorism

Comparatively successful as the integration of India's Muslim communities into the fabric of the Indian state has been, the risk of Islamic violence, directed against Indian society in general, is also rising. The most daring attack to date was in 2008, when terrorists targeted Mumbai's two most upscale, Westernized hotels. Nearly 200 people perished and hundreds were wounded. Live pictures of smoke billowing from the famous Taj Mahal Hotel in southern Mumbai were seen around the world.

The group responsible for the most recent attacks was *Lashkar-e-Taiba* (the Party of the Righteous), a Pakistan-based organization that among other things aims to return Kashmir to Islamic rule. These events have significant implications for India, where the overwhelming majority of Muslim citizens have remained uninvolved in extremist causes. It seems that a small number of Indian Muslims are joining local terrorist cells with links to Pakistan and perhaps other Islamic countries. Their terrorist acts lead to investigations and a reactionary climate that offend ordinary and peaceful Indian Muslims, radicalizing a number of them and expanding the market for Islamic militancy. It is still too early to gauge the potential impact of this development on a country that has long and justly prided itself on its multicultural democracy, but the portents for India's political, social, and economic geography are obviously serious.

In the meantime, Pakistan's northwestern frontier is effectively managed by the Taliban, the Afghan Islamic extremists who also have a history of collaboration with al-Qaeda. This border zone with Afghanistan is well beyond the control of the Pakistani government. U.S. efforts to defeat the Taliban in Afghanistan continued in 2013, but were thwarted by the Taliban's ability to move back and forth across this border. Thus the United States exerts increasing pressure on Islamabad to confront the Taliban on the Pakistani side of the border in this remote mountain refuge.

It is a delicate geopolitical chess game. Pakistan is careful not to alienate its Islamic base even if it despises the

Regional ISSUE   Who Should Govern Kashmir?

KASHMIR SHOULD BE PART OF PAKISTAN!

"I don't know why we're even debating this. Kashmir should and would have been made part of Pakistan in 1947 if that colonial commission hadn't stopped mapping the Pakistan–India boundary before they got to the Chinese border. And the reason they stopped was clear to everybody then and there: instead of carrying on according to their own rules, separating Muslims from Hindus, they reverted to that old colonial habit of recognizing "traditional" States. And what was more traditional than some Hindu potentate and his minority clique ruling over a powerless majority of Muslims? It happened all over India, and when they saw it here in the mountains they couldn't bring themselves to do the right thing. So India gets Jammu and Kashmir and its several million Muslims, and Pakistan loses again. The whole boundary scheme was rigged in favor of the Hindus anyway, so what do you expect?

Here's the key question the Indians won't answer. Why not have a referendum to test the will of all the people in Kashmir? India claims to be such a democratic example to the world. Doesn't that mean that the will of the majority prevails? But India has never allowed the will of the majority even to be expressed in Kashmir. We all know why. About two-thirds of the voters would favor union with Pakistan. Muslims want to live under an Islamic government. So people like me, a Muslim carpenter here in Srinagar, can vote for a Muslim collaborator in the Kashmir government, but we can't vote against the whole idea of Indian occupation.

Life isn't easy here in Srinagar. It used to be a peaceful place with boats full of tourists floating on beautiful lakes. But now it's a violent place with shootings and bombings. Of course we Muslims get the blame, but what do you expect when the wishes of a religious majority are ignored? So don't be surprised at the support our cause gets from Pakistan across the border. The Indians call them terrorists and they accuse them of causing the 60,000 deaths this dispute has already cost, but here's a question: why does it take an Indian army of 600,000 to keep control of a territory in which they claim the people prefer Indian rule?

Now this so-called War on Terror has made things even worse for us. Pakistan has been forced into the American camp, and of course you can't be against 'terrorism' in Afghanistan while supporting it in Kashmir. So our compatriots on the Pakistani side of the Line of Control have to stay quiet and bide their time. But don't underestimate the power of Islam. The people of Pakistan will free themselves of collaborators and infidels, and then they will be back to defend our cause in Kashmir."

KASHMIR BELONGS TO INDIA!

"Let's get something straight. This stuff about that British boundary commission giving up and yielding to a maharajah is nonsense. Kashmir (all of it, the Pakistani as well as the Indian side) had been governed by a maharajah for a century prior to partition. What the maharajah in 1947 wanted was to be ruled by neither India nor Pakistan. He wanted independence, and he might have gotten it if Pakistanis hadn't invaded and forced him to join India in return for military help. As a matter of fact, our Prime Minister Nehru prevailed on the United Nations to call on Pakistan to withdraw its forces, which of course it never did. As to a referendum, let me remind you that a Kashmir-wide referendum was (and still is) contingent on Pakistan's withdrawal from the area of Kashmir it grabbed. And as for Muslim 'collaborators', in the 1950s the preeminent leader on the Indian side of Kashmir was Sheikh Muhammad Abdullah (get it?), a Muslim who disliked Pakistan's Muslim extremism even more than he disliked the maharajah's rule. What he wanted, and many on the Indian side still do, is autonomy for Kashmir, not incorporation.

In any case, Muslim states do not do well by their minorities, and we in India generally do. As far as I am concerned, Pakistan is disqualified from ruling Kashmir by the failure of its democracy and the extremism of its Islamic ideology. Let me remind you that Indian Kashmir is not just a population of Hindus and Muslims. There are other minorities—for example, the Ladakh Buddhists—who are very satisfied with India's administration but who are terrified at the prospect of incorporation into Islamic Pakistan. You already know what Sunnis do to Shi'ites in Pakistan. You are aware of what happened to ancient Buddhist monuments in Taliban Afghanistan (and let's not forget where the Taliban came from). Can you imagine the takeover of multicultural Kashmir by Islamabad?

To the Muslim citizens of Indian Kashmir, I, as a civil servant in the Srinagar government, say this: look around you, look at the country of which you are a subject. Muslims in India are more free, have more opportunities to participate in all spheres of life, are better educated, have more political power and influence than Muslims do in Islamic states. Traditional law in India accommodates Muslim needs. Women in Muslim-Indian society are far better off than they are in many Islamic states. Is it worth three wars, 60,000 lives, and a possible nuclear conflict to reject participation in one of the world's greatest democratic experiments?

Kashmir belongs to India. All inhabitants of Kashmir benefit from Indian governance. What is good for all of India is good for Kashmir."

Vote your opinion at www.wiley.com/go/deblijpolling

AP/Wide World Photos

Smoke billows from the landmark Taj Mahal Hotel in Mumbai on November 29, 2008. The Taj was one of several sites in southern Mumbai that were simultaneously targeted for attack by Islamic militants. The siege lasted four days and almost 200 people died in the violence. Indian commandos killed all of the terorists but one, who was captured, tried, sentenced to death, and executed in 2012. It was not the first time that such terrorism had struck India and, unfortunately, not the last: in early 2013, bombings killed a dozen people in the southern city of Hyderabad.

China's control over Tibet (called Xizang by the Chinese) and its efforts to influence the lives of Tibetans both within and outside Tibet create additional issues. To the dismay of Beijig, Tibet's exiled Dalai Lama calls India his second home. In recent years China has been pressuring the government of Nepal, wedged between India and Tibet, to discourage Tibetan immigration and to constrain the activities of Tibetans already in the country. Farther east, China claims the bulk of India's State of Arunachal Pradesh ("land of the dawn-lit mountains"), based on the assertion that the boundary, established in 1914, was never ratified by Beijing—even though it was approved by the then-independent Tibetans themselves. China has also claimed rights to a small area in northern India located between Sikkim and Bhutan on the basis that the people there are Tibetans and therefore belong under Chinese jurisdiction.

China's power is felt in other ways. In recent years the Chinese have announced plans to construct dams on the Tibetan headwaters of the upper Brahmaputra River, potentially jeopardizing water supply in both northeastern India and Bangladesh. Kashmir is by no means the only place along South Asia's northern frontier where trouble can erupt at any time.

northern extremists, and it is fearful of an economically stronger India and its growing ties to the United States. India is deeply concerned about Pakistan's role in terrorism on Indian soil and, even worse, the possibility of fundamentalists taking control of Pakistan's nuclear arsenal; at the same time, it must also guard against increased tensions between Hindus and Muslims inside India. India is also impatient with American reluctance to choose its side in the Kashmir conflict. The United States, in turn, is sympathetic to the world's largest democracy but needs Pakistan to be an ally in the global counterterrorism campaign. Each of these parties is walking a tightrope, where the slightest mistake could have deadly consequences.

Chinese Border Claims

An overview of this realm's geopolitical framework would not be complete without noting the powerful and sometimes invasive presence of China. As Figure 8A-7 shows, China claims the northeastern extension of Jammu and Kashmir State. This issue has been quiet in recent years, but officially neither China nor India shows any sign of conceding

Indian Ocean Geopolitics

China needs access to markets for its products and supplies of raw materials to sustain its rapidly growing industrial production, and a major part of this access runs through the Indian Ocean. Along the way, it is extending Chinese political and military power through the expansion of its navy in the Indian Ocean and building bases in Pakistan, Myanmar, and Bangladesh. India, increasingly concerned about Chinese intentions, has responded by building its own new alliances with such Southeast Asian states as Indonesia and Vietnam.

From a broader pan-Asian perspective (South and East), geopolitical developments are increasingly a matter of U.S.-China-India relations in which China is asserting itself in the Indian Ocean Basin as well as along the northern Indian border; in which India's economic rise has given it a new assertiveness in the political arena; and in which the United States is ideologically inclined to sympathize with India while the imperatives of political reality motivate it to steer toward maintaining the traditional political balance of power between the two Asian giants. The future could be a U.S.-Chinese-Indian condominium or, more

DELHI NEW AND OLD

FLY DIRECTLY OVER the Delhi–New Delhi conurbation into its new international airport (opened in 2010), and you may not see the place at all. A combination of smog and dust creates an atmospheric soup that can limit visibility to a few hundred meters for weeks on end. Relief comes when the rains arrive, but Delhi's climate is mostly dry. The tail-end of the wet monsoon reaches here during late June or July, but altogether the city only gets about 60 centimeters (25 in) of rain a year. When the British colonial government decided to leave Calcutta more than a century ago and build a new capital city adjacent to Delhi, conditions were different. South of the old city lay a hill about 15 meters (50 ft) above the surrounding countryside, on the right bank of the southward-flowing Yamuna River, a tributary of the Ganges. Compared to Calcutta's hot, swampy environment, Delhi's was agreeable. In 1912 it was not yet a megacity. Skies were mostly clear. Raisina Hill became the site of a New Delhi.

This was not the first time rulers chose Delhi as the seat of empire. Ruins of numerous palaces mark the passing of powerful kingdoms. But none brought to the Delhi area the transformation the British did. In 1947, the Indian government decided to keep its headquarters here. In 1970, the metropolitan-area population exceeded 4 million. By 2014, it was a staggering 24.8 million, India's largest urban region.

Delhi is popular as a seat of government for the same reason as its ongoing expansion: the city has a fortuitous relative location. The regional topography creates a narrow corridor through which all land routes from northwestern India to the North Indian Plain must pass, and Delhi lies in this gateway. Thus the twin cities not only contain the government functions; they also anchor the core area of this massively populated country.

Old Delhi was once a small, traditional, homogeneous town. Today Old and New Delhi form a multicultural, mul-

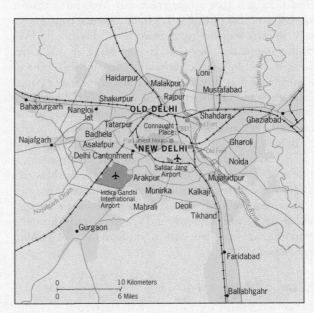

© H. J. de Blij, P. O. Muller, and John Wiley & Sons, Inc.

tifunctional urban giant. From above, the Delhi conurbation looks like an inkblot, a nearly concentric region that has steadily expanded in all directions. The fastest growth has been to the south, where formerly separate towns and satellite cities such as Faridabad are now part of this sprawling conurbation. Gurgaon is especially well-known, a leading activity hub south of the airport that has witnessed explosive growth over the past 15 years or so, an agglomeration of IT companies, international call centers, and new middle-class residential developments. Another sign of Delhi's modernization is the construction of a new, heavy-rail transit system, aimed at providing some relief to the metropolitan area's massive congestion and pollution problems.

likely, a continued informal alliance of the United States and India seeking to put the brakes on China's assertiveness. U.S. support for Indian membership in the United Nations Security Council is but one manifestation of this evolving U.S.-India relationship.

There is some indication of a rapprochement between the two Asian giants. In a notable turnaround, a Chinese spokesperson in early 2013 indicated that China would not oppose Indian membership in the Security Council. Perhaps most importantly, growing economic interdependence will help to keep things in check. China wants to penetrate India's vast and growing consumer markets. China-India trade is growing rapidly, surpassing U.S. $75 billion in 2012 ($58 billion from China to India and less than one-third of that in the other direction). China runs a significant surplus, and this reflects, up to now, the fact that the **terms of trade [8]**

are to China's advantage: India supplies mainly raw materials while China sells finished goods with a higher added value. In 2010, the two pledged to increase their trade to $100 billion by 2015, with India (so far unsuccessfully) seeking to reduce its trade deficit.

EMERGING MARKETS AND FRAGMENTED MODERNIZATION

In recent years, optimistic reports in the media have been proclaiming a new era for South Asia, marked by rising growth rates for the realm's national economies, rewards from globalization and modernization, and increasing integration into the global economy. India, obviously the key to the realm, has even been described as "India Shining" during this wave of enthusiasm.

And indeed, a combination of circumstances, ranging from America's involvement with Pakistan in the campaign against terrorism to the real estate and stock market booms in India, suggest that a new era has arrived. But consider this: well over half of India's 1.3 billion people continue to live in poverty-stricken rural areas, their villages and lives virtually untouched by what is happening in the cities (where, tens of millions of urban dwellers inhabit some of the world's poorest slums). Fully a third of Pakistan's population lives in abject poverty; female literacy is still below 50 percent. Half of the people of Bangladesh, and nearly half of those in the realm as a whole, live on the equivalent of one U.S. dollar per day or less. It is estimated that half the children in South Asia are malnourished and underweight, a majority of them girls—this at a time when the world is able to provide adequate calories for all its inhabitants, if not sufficiently balanced daily meals. It still remains to be seen whether the benefits of newfound economic growth can be spread around widely enough to improve the lot of South Asia's masses.

Economic Liberalization

Most countries in this realm have liberalized their economies since the late 1980s as part of a worldwide turn toward neoliberalism [9]. This involves privatization of state-run companies, lowering of international trade tariffs, reduction of government subsidies, cutting of corporate taxes, and overall deregulation to spur business activity. It was an important change from previous times in which markets were tightly controlled by unyielding central governments that since independence had espoused ideologies opposed to unrestrained capitalism. A change of direction was unavoidable. The ineffective policies of the past, continuing grinding poverty, and near fiscal bankruptcy demanded support from the International Monetary Fund; the IMF, in turn, insisted on structural reforms.

The results of these reforms have been especially noticeable in India, Bangladesh, and Pakistan, where economic growth rates climbed to levels never seen before (Fig. 8A-8). Most of this growth is in manufacturing, services, finance, and, in India, information technology (IT). A more open economy has attracted increased foreign investment, and during the past two decades a new (urban) middle class has emerged. This steadily expanding new class may account for only 25 percent or so of the population, but in South Asia that translates into more than 400 million people—a huge new consumer market for an array of products ranging from cars to smartphones. Nevertheless, that still leaves well over a billion South Asians who have *not* attained middle-class status, for whom almost nothing has changed, who remain overwhelmingly dependent on agriculture, and who are not likely to log on to the new information economy anytime soon.

One striking feature of the South Asian realm, then, is that even if the majority of the people live traditional

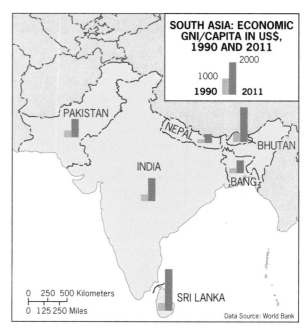

FIGURE 8A-8 © H. J. de Blij, P. O. Muller, J. Nijman, and John Wiley & Sons, Inc.

lives in rural villages, there are also a fair number of megacities in which social and economic change is the order of the day. The urban regions of Mumbai, Delhi–New Delhi, Kolkata, Dhaka, and Karachi all contain populations larger than 15 million that have grown rapidly over the past two decades. Their density is often overwhelming, environmental conditions are poor, and the contrast between rich and poor is usually staggering. But almost always it is better to be poor in the city than in the countryside, simply because cities offer opportunities that do not exist in the villages—which helps to explain the burgeoning flow of rural-to-urban migrants that drives the growth of towns and cities all across South Asia.

The Significance of Agriculture

More than half of the entire workforce of South Asia is employed in agriculture, ranging from about 43 percent in Pakistan to about 75 percent in Nepal. But overall productivity is low, and the contribution of agriculture to the national economy is only around 20 percent. Incomes in rural areas are much lower than in major cities, and the same is true for the standard of living. Almost 70 percent of South Asia's population is rural, and even those who do not work in agriculture tend to rely on it indirectly.

Millions of lives every year depend on a good harvest. As Figure 8A-3 shows, the wet monsoon brings life-giving rains to the southwestern (Malabar) coast, and a second branch from the Bay of Bengal sweeps across north-central India toward Pakistan, losing strength (and moisture) as it proceeds. This means that amply watered eastern India and Bangladesh as well as the southwestern

From the Field Notes . . .

© Jan Nijman

"During my travels in northeastern India in early 2011, I visited some agricultural areas in the Brahmaputra Valley that benefit from plentiful irrigation. Tea and rice are two major crops. Because big companies run the large tea plantations, many of the rice farmers have to make do with small plots of land. Here a farmer in Asom State shows off part of his rice harvest. I encountered him and several others at a small, machine-operated mill shop. Note that the rice is brown—milling it removes the bran layer and makes the rice white. 'We have the best rice in all of India,' he proudly said, as he slowly poured it from his hand back into the bag. Having enjoyed some excellent meals in the area, I could not disagree."

www.conceptcaching.com

coastal strip grow rice as their staple crop; but drier northwestern India and Pakistan raise wheat.

Farmers' fortunes tend to vary geographically, as can be illustrated in the situation on either side of India's Western Ghats upland. The monsoon rains are generally plentiful along the coast-paralleling, western slopes of this linear highland, from the southern tip of the subcontinent as far north as the vicinity of Mumbai. Here you can see the hillside vegetation assume all shades of fresh green come the month of June, a sure sign that the harvest will be bountiful. But on the eastern (rain shadow) side and deeper into the interior of the Deccan Plateau, it is a different story. The rains come less often and do not last as long. Farming becomes a gamble with nature, and life becomes precarious. Many of the farmers here are members of lower castes, landless and indebted, and have the hardest time making ends meet. Almost every year, Maharashtra's inland districts report several thousand (!) farmer suicides as desperately poor peasants end their lives because they can no longer provide for their families.

It is clear that the majority of people in this realm depend on agriculture and that governments must aim their economic policies at improving agricultural productivity to raise the standard of living in rural areas. But they have a long way to go. The demands on governments are many, and they often seem distracted by economic sectors that can make a faster and greater contribution to the tax base, such as manufacturing, financial services, and IT—economic activities that almost always are centered on the big cities far from the impoverished countryside.

SOUTH ASIA'S POPULATION GEOGRAPHY

Given its enormous human content, the South Asian realm's areal size is relatively quite small. It totals less than 40 percent of the size of similarly populous East Asia. Comparing the world's two giants shows that China's territory is almost three times as large as India's. The total population of Subsaharan Africa is less than half of South Asia's, in an area almost five times as large. Adjectives such as "teeming," "overcrowded," and "crammed" are often used to describe the realm's habitable living space, and with good reason. South Asia's intricate cultural mosaic is tightly packed, with only the deserts in the west and the mountain

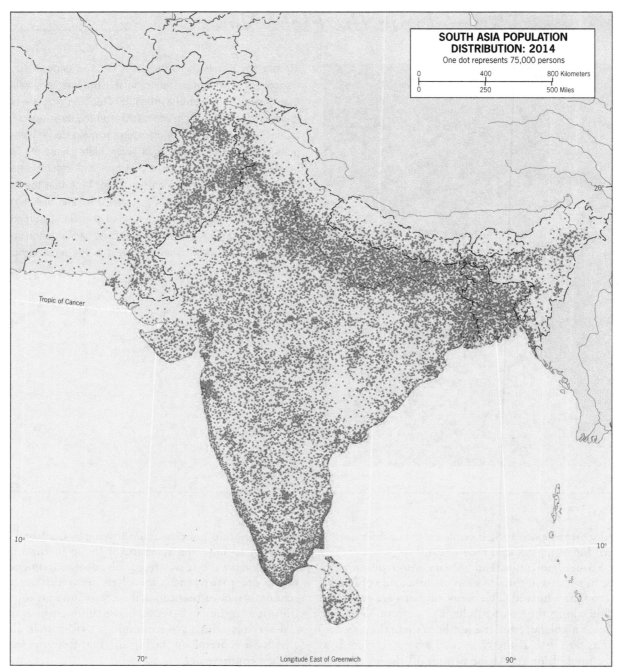

SOUTH ASIA POPULATION
DISTRIBUTION: 2014
One dot represents 75,000 persons

FIGURE 8A-9

© H. J. de Blij, P. O. Muller, and John Wiley & Sons, Inc.

fringe in the north displaying extensive empty spaces. The outlines of the densely populated river basins are clearly visible in the dot patterns of the population distribution map (Fig. 8A-9).

The field of population geography [10] focuses on the characteristics, distribution, growth, and other aspects of spatial demography in a country, region, or realm as this relates to soils, climates, land ownership, social conditions, economic development, and other factors. In the South Asian context, it is useful to concentrate on four demo-graphic dimensions: the role of density; the demographic transition; demographic burdens; and the gender bias in birth rates. As we shall see, population issues are often more complicated than they first appear.

Population Density and the Question of Overpopulation

Population density [11] measures the number of people per unit area (such as a square kilometer or square mile) in a country, province, or an entire realm. We distinguish

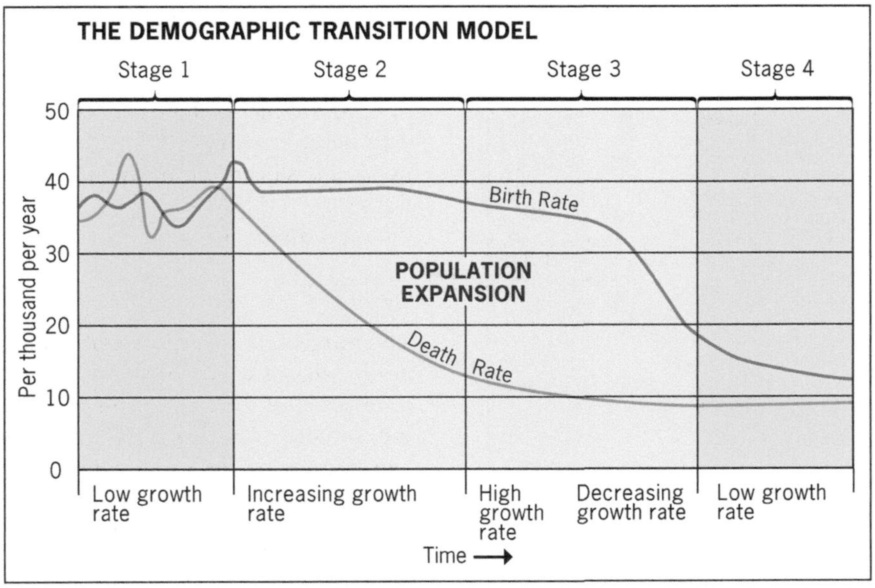

THE DEMOGRAPHIC TRANSITION MODEL

FIGURE 8A-10   © H. J. de Blij, P. O. Muller, and John Wiley & Sons, Inc.

between two types of measures. **Arithmetic density** is simply the number of people per area, usually a country. **Physiologic density [12]** is a more meaningful measure because it takes into account only land that is arable and can be used for food production. Please take a careful look at the data displayed for South Asia in Appendix B, and you will see that, for example in Pakistan, the two measures are quite different because of that country's large deserts and inhospitable mountain ranges.

Until recently, South Asia's persistent poverty was often related to its enormous and rapidly growing population and its high population densities. The idea was that there were simply "too many mouths to feed"—the realm was "overpopulated." The notion of **overpopulation** can be compelling and seems to make sense at an intuitive level since every country or region can be thought of as having a limited "carrying capacity."

But things are more complex than that. If you look again at Appendix B, you will find that some countries with high densities, such as the Netherlands or Japan, are doing very well, and it is not necessarily because they have an impressive natural resource base (neither does). The point is that high density in itself is not always a problem and that, in certain circumstances, population can be considered as a **human resource**. If productivity is high, there does not appear to be a problem, but if productivity is low, then large populations can be a drain on the economy. Countries with high education levels, institutional effectiveness, and technological know-how are able to use their natural resources more efficiently.

Thus in South Asia, with large numbers of people still illiterate and undereducated, population tends to function as a *burden* rather than a resource. The problem is not so much that there are too many, but that too many

are not sufficiently productive. The good news is that, as a result of higher economic growth rates stemming from economic reforms, there is more money to invest in education. The bad news so far is that not enough of this money is actually being spent that way.

The Demographic Transition

The relevance of population issues to development goes far beyond density, which is really just a snapshot of the population pattern at a moment in time. It gets more interesting—and more complicated—when we relate population change to economic trends. For instance, for a considerable time South Asia's population grew faster than the realm's economy. Clearly that was a problem because more and more people had to survive on less. Today, fortunately, it is the other way around: in most of the realm, the economy is growing faster than the population.

The term demographic transition [13] refers to a structural change in birth and death rates resulting, first, in rapid population increase and, subsequently, in declining growth rates and a stable population (Fig. 8A-10). The United States and other highly developed countries had already passed through this transition by the mid-twentieth century, and most countries in the South Asian realm are in the third stage today. Note that Stage 2 and part of Stage 3, with high birth rates and low death rates (due to medical advances), entail a population expansion. In South Asia, this expansion occurred from the 1950s through the 1970s. The key issue, of course, is for birth rates to come down so that overall growth rates will drop and the population will stabilize. This is happening today, but the process is not yet complete.

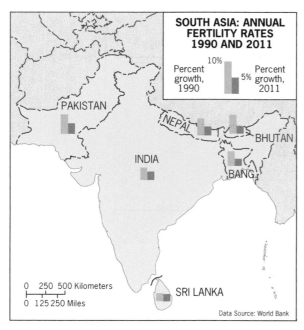

FIGURE 8A-11

© H. J. de Blij, P. O. Muller, J. Nijman, and John Wiley & Sons, Inc.

Figure 8A-11 shows how fertility rates [14] (the number of births per woman) have dropped across the realm over the past quarter-century. Only Sri Lanka seems to have completed the transition, although Bhutan is now very close. Elsewhere, fertility rates are still too high (India by itself has been adding about 15 million people per year during the past decade), but at least they are trending in the right direction.

Demographic Burdens

The immediate significance of demography to economics lies in what is called the demographic burden [15]. This term refers to the proportion of the population that is either too old or too young to be productive and that must be cared for by the productive population. Typically, the most productive population in developing countries is represented in the age cohorts between 20 and 50 years. A country with low death rates and high birth rates will have a relatively large share of old and young people, and thus a large demographic burden. Obviously, the way to reduce this burden is to lower birth rates.

Let us now examine Figure 8A-12 and compare today's population pyramids [16] (diagrams showing the

POPULATION PYRAMIDS: INDIA AND CHINA, 2014–2039

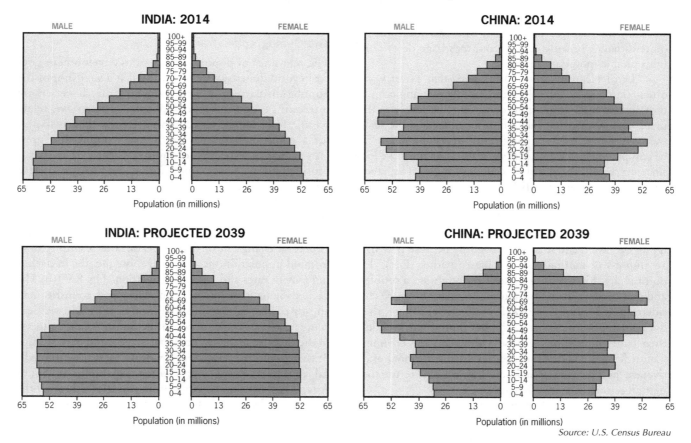

Source: U.S. Census Bureau

FIGURE 8A-12

© H. J. de Blij, P. O. Muller, J. Nijman, and John Wiley & Sons, Inc.

age–sex structure) for India and China. The latter has been more successful in curtailing births since 1980, so China now faces a lower demographic burden than India. But, interestingly, what is advantageous today can become a disadvantage tomorrow. Look at Figure 8A-12 again and see what the population profiles are projected to be 25 years from now. Assuming that India will be able to further reduce its birth rate in the coming years, its demographic burden will be less than China's one generation from now. In China, today's productive cohort will have moved on to old age, thereby adding to its national demographic burden. It is another reason for India boosters to be optimistic about the future. Yet some other major hurdles remain, and certain forms of birth control are as morally reprehensible as they are economically counterproductive.

© Jan Nijman

A group of girls in a park in Delhi showing off their henna tattoos. "Mehndi" is a centuries-old festive tradition involving decorative painting on the hands and wrists. The designs usually wear off in a few weeks' time.

The Missing Girls

Issues of family planning and birth control shed some fascinating light on the "fragmented modernization" of South Asia. As we saw, the realm finds itself in an advanced stage of the demographic transition wherein birth rates have begun to decrease. But take a good look at India's population pyramid for 2014 and note that among young children boys far outnumber girls. In fact, males outnumber females well into middle age.

Traditionally, boys are valued more than girls because they are thought to be more productive income-earners, because they are entitled to land and inheritance, and because they do not require a dowry at the time of marriage. When a couple gets married (often arranged, and at a young age), the bride comes into the care of the groom's family, where she also contributes her work in and around the house. For this, the bride's family must provide a dowry that can impose a major expense on her parents. For these reasons, the birth of a boy is a greater cause for celebration than that of a girl. "Raising a daughter," as one saying goes, "is like watering your neighbor's garden."

One reason for the high fertility rates in the past was that families would continue to have children until there were enough sons to take care of the parents in their old age (the girls, after all, would be taking care of their future husband's parents). Hence, this gender bias is in itself a major factor in South Asia's population growth—but that is not the only problem. When a poor couple repeatedly produces girls and not boys, in some instances the family decides to end the life of the newborn daughter. It is this *female infanticide* or *gendercide* that causes the unnatural gender bias in South Asia's population profiles (the same applies to parts of China as well).

But why—as the economic situation has improved, as birth rates have receded, and as modernization has begun to set in—do we still observe this skewed sex ratio [17]? The answer is that with fewer children, the importance of having at least one boy has for many families become even more pressing. And here is where "modernization" throws another curve ball: newly available technologies of ultrasound scanning plus rising incomes (i.e., the growing affordability of a scan) have induced many families to determine the gender of the unborn child and decide on abortion if the child is female. Thus in recent years the sex ratio has become more, not less, skewed, and the most extreme ratios are now found in some of the most developed parts of the realm, such as the Indian States of Punjab and Haryana.

In the long run, of course, this leads to a shortage of females, which becomes particularly apparent at marriage age. In some areas, families now face a problem in finding brides for their sons, and this "bachelor angst," in turn, is leading to a change in attitudes. Look at India's population pyramid for 2039 and note that over the next quarter-century the sex ratio is expected to become less skewed.

Discrimination against women and girls in South Asia is expressed in a variety of ways in daily life. One matter that is now receiving more attention is the lack of sanitation for females. In many workplaces, schools, slum neighborhoods, and public spaces, women still have no (or insufficient) access to toilets. For safety and

From the Field Notes . . .

"Strolling the grounds of one of India's leading high-tech companies, Wipro, in the southern city of Bengaluru (formerly Bangalore), I was struck by the thought that their use of the word 'campus' was right on target: the great majority of the 33,000 employees on this site (120,000 in total) are in their mid-20s and almost all have a college degree; a large number of them are involved in research and product development; and the layout of the premises could easily be mistaken for a

(well-funded) university. This Silicon Valley-like campus is the heart of the company's booming outsourcing and consulting business. The company is active in almost all major Indian cities and has a sizeable global presence. I was shown around by Rohit, a 26-year-old with a bachelor's degree in engineering from an Indian college and an MBA from Singapore National University. He reveled in the opportunity: 'I joined the company just four months ago in their marketing division and feel extremely fortunate. Everybody wants this job! It's a great professional opportunity and the salary is very good.' And Bengaluru is a pleasant place to live: at 900 meters (3000 ft) above sea level, even the summer weather is tolerable. Bengaluru, however, is growing so rapidly that its infrastructure cannot keep up, so that congestion, traffic jams, and commuting times are all growing as well."

© Jan Nijman   www.conceptcaching.com

personal reasons women need more privacy, but often that is not available. In India, an estimated 330 million females lack proper access to toilets, with major implications for health and social functioning. Imagine a small rural school with one toilet (if indeed there is one): it will be used by boys at the exclusion of girls. Girls will have no access at all the entire day. This simple fact leads to girls missing school and even dropping out. Recent efforts by development organizations to install toilets for girls have so far only led to significant decreases in female-student dropout rates.

Still, it is difficult to make generalizations about gender relations across this populous realm, in part because of religious and regional diversity as well as rural-urban differences. To be sure, these are in many respects male-dominated societies, especially at a young age. But it is useful to remember that Pakistan, India, Sri Lanka, and Bangladesh have all had female prime ministers who held their countries' most powerful political office. That has yet to happen in the United States.

FUTURE PROSPECTS

South Asia is a realm in transition—politically, economically, and demographically. It is a realm that seems clearly bounded by nature, yet it is vitally linked to Southwest Asia and, increasingly, the entire world. It is also a realm that at times is difficult to read. India–Pakistan tensions continue to be a cause for concern, and the specter of terrorism haunts those who wish only to live in peace. This is not just in the hands of the governments of the two biggest states in the realm. Religious movements (Muslim and Hindu) and the way they engage in politics are crucially important, and the United States and China have major roles to play as well.

Economically, there is no question that India's rise will increasingly command the world's attention. Indian transnational corporations will continue to penetrate the global economy, and the growing Indian middle class with its appetite for consumption will increasingly draw interest from producers around the world. That English is the subcontinent's *lingua franca,* and that IT is a leading economic sector, give it an enormous advantage into the future. And the fact that India, the realm's giant, can claim to be the world's largest democracy gives it tremendous credibility.

When, during the next several decades, South Asia passes through the demographic transition; if it keeps the peace; if it continues its leading role in the global IT sector; if its economic growth is used to educate and empower the masses; and if the reorganization of agriculture allows more productive and prosperous lives—and these are all real possibilities—then this populous and wondrous South Asian realm may yet turn out to be the biggest story of the twenty-first century.

POINTS TO PONDER

- The South Asian realm contains three of the world's mightiest rivers and the world's largest human concentration.
- After two-thirds of a century, the conflict over Kashmir is still unresolved.
- The most skewed sex ratios in the population occur in the most prosperous parts of this realm.
- The Indian Ocean may be the world's most crucial geopolitical arena of the twenty-first century.
- Hundreds of millions of females in South Asia suffer from a lack of access to basic human needs, including sanitary facilities.

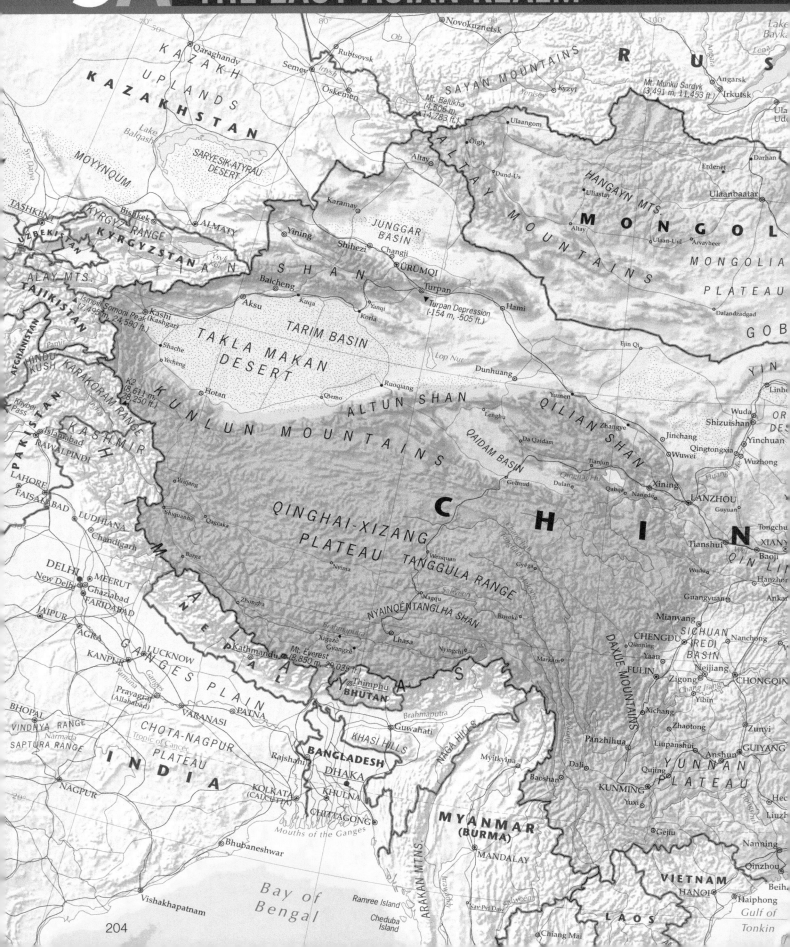

FIGURE 9A-1

© H. J. de Blij, P. O. Muller, and
John Wiley & Sons, Inc.

East Asia is a geographic realm like no other. At its heart lies the world's most populous country, the product of what may be the world's oldest continuous civilization. On its Pacific mainland shores an economic transformation has taken shape with no parallel in world history. Its offshore islands witnessed the first use of atomic weapons on civilian populations and the postwar emergence of one of the world's most powerful economies. Few lives in this world were left unaffected, directly or indirectly, by the momentous events that occurred in East Asia over the past two generations. Just look around you. Chinese-made televisions (and so much more), Japanese-designed automobiles, South Korean smartphones, Taiwanese computers—from toys to textiles and from hardware to software—East Asian products fill streets and stores, homes and hotels.

China is the world's biggest exporter and home to three of the five busiest container ports in the world: Shanghai, Shenzhen, and Hong Kong (shown here). The other two—Singapore and South Korea's Busan—are also located in the Asian Pacific Rim.

© Jan Nijman

DEFINING THE REALM

It has all happened with astonishing speed. Some of us can remember the time when you were no more likely to find anything useful made in China than you were to buy anything from Russia. But after end of the 1960s, things changed rapidly. Japan led the way, turning its World War II defeat into postwar economic triumph. By the mid-1970s, Japan's economic growth—compared to China's seemingly total stagnation—appeared to justify Japan's recognition as a discrete geographic realm, an economic engine for the world

major geographic qualities of EAST ASIA

1. East Asia is encircled by snowcapped mountains, vast deserts, cold climates, and Pacific waters.

2. East Asia was one of the world's earliest culture hearths, and China is one of the world's oldest continuous civilizations.

3. East Asia is the second most populous geographic realm after South Asia; its population remains heavily concentrated in its eastern regions.

4. China, the world's largest state demographically, is the current rendition of an empire that has expanded and contracted, fragmented and unified many times during its long existence.

5. China's sparsely peopled western regions are strategically important to the state, but they lie exposed to minority pressures and Islamic influences.

6. Along China's east coast, an economic transformation launched more than thirty-five years ago is now rapidly expanding westward.

7. Increasing regional disparities and fast-changing cultural landscapes are straining East Asian societies.

8. Japan, one of the economic giants of the East Asian realm, has a history of colonial expansion and wartime conduct that still affects international relations here.

9. East Asia is home to the world's newest superpower as China's economic and political influence is increasingly projected around the globe.

10. The political geography of East Asia contains a number of flashpoints capable of generating conflict, including North Korea, Taiwan, and several island groups in the seas adjoining the realm.

---

and a strong competitor for the top-ranked U.S. economy. But then Hong Kong, South Korea, and autonomous Taiwan began to show the world what other peoples in East Asia were capable of. When the ruler of communist China, the realm's giant, opened the door to an American president in 1972, a pivotal moment in global history (and geography) had arrived. Before the end of the century, China had taken its place as modern East Asia's core. That event in 1972 signified a new direction in Chinese political thinking, and it would facilitate major revisions in economic policy. Today, East Asia is the most dynamic realm in the global economy: led by China, it is changing the world—and in the process is itself undergoing a profound transformation.

THE GEOGRAPHIC PANORAMA

As Figure 9A-1 shows, the East Asian geographic realm forms a roughly triangular wedge between the vast expanses of eastern Russia to the north and the populous countries of South and Southeast Asia to the south, its edges often marked by high mountain ranges or remote deserts. The darker brown on the map designates the highest mountains and plateaus, which create a vast arc north of the Himalayas before bending southward and becoming lower (tan shading) toward Myanmar, Laos, and Vietnam in Southeast Asia. Here in the southwest, where Tibet is located, mountains and plateaus alike are covered by permanent ice and snow, the soaring ranges crumpled up like the folds of an accordion. Three major rivers, their valleys parallel for hundreds of kilometers,

disclose the orientation of this high-relief topography. Northward, note how rapidly the mountains give way to broad, flat deserts whose names appear prominently: the Takla Makan in the far west, the Gobi where China meets Mongolia, the Ordos in the embrace of what looks like a huge meander of a river we will learn more about shortly, the Huang He (Yellow River).

One basin, lodged between high mountains to its west and lower ones elsewhere, and of special interest, is China's Sichuan (Red) Basin. It looks rather small on the map, but is home to more than 120 million people and, we will discover, is important for other reasons as well. In this country of mountains and deserts, living space is at a premium. And speaking of living space, the green areas on the map, which have the lowest relief and (often) the most fertile soils, are home to the vast majority of this realm's population. Here the great rivers that come from the melting ice and snow in the interior highlands have been depositing their sediment load for eons, and when humans domesticated plants and started to grow crops, this was the place to be. That was thousands of years ago—perhaps as long as 10,000 years—and ever since, this has been the largest human cluster on Earth.

But the East Asian realm is not confined to the mainland of mountains and river basins. You can imagine how its offshore islands were populated: the Korean Peninsula seems to form part of a bridge pointing toward the southernmost island of what is today Japan, and from there it seems likely that the early migrants moved farther

Places and Names

AS IN OTHER parts of the world, European colonists in China wrote down the names of places and people as they heard them—and often got them wrong. The Wade-Giles system put such place names as Peking, Canton, and Tien-tsin on the map, but that's not how the Chinese knew them. In 1958, the communist regime replaced the foreign version with the *pinyin* system, based on the pronunciation of Chinese characters in Northern Mandarin, which was to become the standard form of the Chinese language throughout China. The world now became familiar with these same three cities written as Beijing, Guangzhou, and Tianjin. Among prominent Chinese geographic names, only one has not gained universal recognition: Tibet, called Xizang by China but referred to by its old name on many maps for reasons that will become obvious in Chapter 9B.

Pinyin usage may be standard in China today, but China remains a country of many languages and dialects. Not only do minorities speak many different languages, but Mandarin-speakers use numerous dialects—so that when you sit down with some Chinese friends who have just met, it may take just one sentence for one to say to the other "ah, you're from Shanghai!" Migration is changing this, of course. China's population is on the move, and a growing number of residents of Shanghai today were not born in that city. But China's language map is anything but simple. And not just place names, but personal names, too, were revised under pinyin rules. The communist leader who used to be called Mao Tse-tung in the Western media became Mao Zedong. Also remember that the Chinese write their last name first: President Xi Jinping is Jin-ping to his friends and Mr. Xi to others. To the Chinese, therefore, it is Obama Barack, not the other way around.

---

north until they reached Hokkaido. In warmer times, they may even have ventured beyond, onto the Kurile Islands. And in the south, Taiwan lies even closer to mainland China than Japan does to Korea, whereas tropical Hainan Island, the realm's southernmost extremity, is almost—but not quite—connected to the small peninsula that reaches toward it.

In terms of total land area, though, East Asia is mostly mainland—but the islands and their peoples have played leading roles in forging this realm's regional geography. The waters between mainland and islands (the Taiwan Strait, the South China Sea, the East China Sea, the Yellow Sea, the Korea Strait, and others) also figure prominently in the geographic saga of this realm. Today, the Japanese and the Chinese are arguing over the ownership of small islands in these waters, specks of land with large oil reserves and fishing grounds claimed by both sides. So this realm's map is considerably more complicated than that wedge-shaped triangle in Figure 9A-1 initially suggests—even the spellings of many of its contents (see box titled "Places and Names").

POLITICAL GEOGRAPHY

It is all too easy to refer to China when you mean East Asia, because China is the latter's dominant country, contains more than 85 percent of the realm's population, and has taken an increasingly prominent role on the world stage. But there are five other political entities on East Asia's map: Japan, South Korea, North Korea, Mongolia, and Taiwan. Note that we refer here to *political entities* rather than *states*. In this realm, the distinction is important. Taiwan refers to itself as the Republic of China (ROC), but it is not recognized as a sovereign state by most members of the international community; the communist administra-

tion in Beijing, capital of the People's Republic of China (PRC), regards Taiwan as part of China and as a temporarily wayward province. And North Korea is widely viewed as a rogue state, a brutal and archaic dictatorship that has failed its people terribly. Having compiled one of the world's most dreadful human rights records, North Korea is not even a fully functional member of the United Nations.

Nevertheless, China is the realm's dominant entity: demographically, economically, and politically. It is important to keep in mind, as you read Chapters 9A and 9B, that portions of what we map today as regional components of China were not part of the country in the past, and that other areas now lying outside China are regarded by many Chinese as Chinese property (for example, a large sector of the Indian State of Arunachal Pradesh and portions of the Russian Far East). As we will see, China's imperial past saw the state expand and contract and expand again, leaving unfinished business on land as well as at sea. On such issues, Chinese emotions can run quite deeply.

Six hundred years ago China already was the largest nation on the planet, its history encompassing thousands of years, its unmatched fleets exploring lands and peoples in South Asia and East Africa, its technologies unequaled. But even the Chinese could not curb the growing presence of Europe's colonial powers, and eventually the British, French, Russians, and Germans accomplished the unthinkable—taking control over most of the Chinese state. When the Japanese emulated the Europeans and forged their own colonial empire, much of it at China's expense, humiliation was complete—and never forgotten. To this day, the sense that China's borders (including those with Russia and India) were imposed by outsiders is never far from the surface.

Gambling With Nature

THE CATASTROPHIC NATURAL disaster that hit Japan in March 2011 overwhelmed the northeastern coast of its main island (Honshu) as well as the country as a whole—but it did not come as a surprise. The Earth's crustal dynamics in this part of the realm guarantees earthquakes at a relentless frequency (see Fig. G-5).

As Figure 9A-2 shows, it all stems from the configuration of the underlying tectonic plates that converge on Japan. Consider the distribution of all those smaller quakes before and after the big one. Any one of them could have been the epicenter, and it is obvious that the entire east coast of Japan lies in the danger zone, including all of the gigantic conurbation centered on Tokyo. So even the misfortunes that befell Japan on March 11, 2011 could have been far worse.

All Japanese, and especially the nearly 30 million living in and around Tokyo, know about the "70-year" rule: over the past three and a half centuries, the Tokyo area has been struck by major earthquakes roughly every 70 years—in 1633, 1703, 1782, 1853, and 1923. The Great Kanto

Earthquake of 1923 set off a firestorm that swept over the city and took the lives of an estimated 143,000 people. Tokyo Bay virtually emptied of water; then a killer tsunami roared back in, sweeping everything before it.

Today, metropolitan Tokyo is decidedly more vulnerable than it was a century ago. True, building regulations are stricter and civilian preparedness is better. But entire expanses of industries have been built on landfill that will liquefy; the city is honeycombed by underground gas lines that will rupture and stoke countless fires; congestion in the area's maze of narrow streets will hamper rescue operations; and many older high-rise buildings do not have the structural integrity that has lately emboldened builders to erect skyscrapers in excess of 50 stories. Add to this the burgeoning population of the greater Kanto Plain—which surpasses 40 million on what may well be the most dangerous 4 percent of Japan's territory—and we realize that the next major earthquake along northern Japan's Pacific coast could produce an ever bigger disaster than the historic Tohoku quake of 2011.

ENVIRONMENT AND POPULATION

To understand the complex physical geography of East Asia shown in Figure 9A-1, it is useful to refer back to Figures G-4 and G-5 in the introductory chapter. The high, snowcapped mountain ranges of the realm's southwestern interior result from the gigantic collision of the Indian and Eurasian tectonic plates (see Fig. 8A-2), pushing the Earth's crust upward and creating not only the mountain ranges of which the Himalaya is the most famous, but also popping up the enormous, domelike Qinghai-Xizang (Tibetan) Plateau. In Figure G-5, note the high incidence of earthquakes associated with this collision, converging on a narrow zone of instability that crosses southwestern China and stretches into Southeast Asia. The calamitous 2008 earthquake (magnitude 7.9) in Sichuan Province that killed almost 90,000 originated in this danger zone but was only one in an endless series that will continue to take its toll (the latest occurring here in April 2013—a 7.0 temblor that killed at least 200 and injured more than 10,000).

From Figure G-5 it is also obvious that the Pacific Ring of Fire, with its lethal combination of volcanism and earthquakes, endangers Japan far more than it does China. This threat became a horrific reality on March 11, 2011 when a monstrous 9.0-magnitude earthquake struck off Japan's northeastern coast near the city of Sendai. Figure 9A-2 shows the configuration of the underlying tectonic plates that converge on Japan. The Pacific Plate moves westward at an average of 7–10 centimeters (3–4 in) per year, and the only way it can do so is by pressing forward (or subducting) *beneath* the North American Plate (Japan sits atop the western tip of the latter). It was the most powerful Japanese quake ever recorded, and one of the five

biggest in the world since 1900. Even worse, this massive temblor and its torrent of violent aftershocks triggered a series of devastating tsunamis [1] (seismic sea waves) that swept across the narrow, densely populated coastal plains

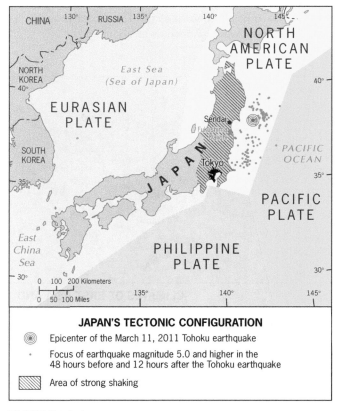

FIGURE 9A-2   © H. J. de Blij, P. O. Muller, J. Nijman, and John Wiley & Sons, Inc.

JAPAN'S TECTONIC CONFIGURATION

◎ Epicenter of the March 11, 2011 Tohoku earthquake

· Focus of earthquake magnitude 5.0 and higher in the 48 hours before and 12 hours after the Tohoku earthquake

▨ Area of strong shaking

© Kyodo/XinHua/Xinhua Press/Corbis

Houses and other buildings being washed away by massive tsunami waves minutes after the gigantic Tohoku earthquake of March 11, 2011. Virtually the entire area around the city of Sendai was destroyed, including this satellite town of Natori. It was a truly apocalyptic event: first the magnitude-9.0 quake, then the tsunamis, and finally the radioactive pollution emitted by the damaged reactors of the Fukushima Daiichi nuclear complex 95 kilometers (60 mi) south of Sendai (see Fig. 9A-2).

that hug the shoreline of Honshu (Japan's largest island) north of the Tokyo area (see photo). And as if the destruction and death left behind was not enough, the leakage of radioactivity from a heavily damaged nuclear-power complex near Fukushima south of Sendai (Fig. 9A-2) may have caused serious future health problems in the local population. Now officially known as the Tohoku earthquake, its final death toll was reckoned to be about 21,000.

The vulnerability of Japan to such disasters results from a dangerous combination of circumstances: it is located in a particularly active tectonic-plate collision zone, and many of the country's habitable (and most densely populated) areas are confined, low-lying plains on the islands' east coast open to flooding by Pacific tsunamis. Not surprisingly, the location of most Japanese nuclear power plants along these susceptible shorelines has now become a hotly debated issue.

Looking at the map of East Asian climates (Fig. 9A-3, left map), we should not be surprised that the western and northern sectors of this realm are dominated by conditions that do not favor substantial population clusters. Permanent snow and ice cover much of the area mapped as **H** (highland climes) including Tibet (Xizang) and Qinghai. Northward, the **B** climates (desert and steppe) prevail because this vast expanse lies about as far from maritime influences (and moist air masses) as you can get in Asia. Mongolia is one of the driest countries in the world, but even here—and also in frosty Tibet—there are places where people manage to eke out a living. But the map leaves no doubt as to why the great majority of East Asians inhabit the eastern part of this realm.

When we compare the climates prevailing in the East Asian realm to those familiar to us in North America (Fig. 9A-3, right map), it is immediately obvious that the **C** or humid-temperate climates are more extensive in the United States than in East Asia. Note especially the comparative location of the milder **Cfa** climate, which in the United States extends beyond 40° North latitude up to New England, but which in China yields to colder **D** climates at a latitude equivalent to Virginia's. Thus the capital, Beijing,

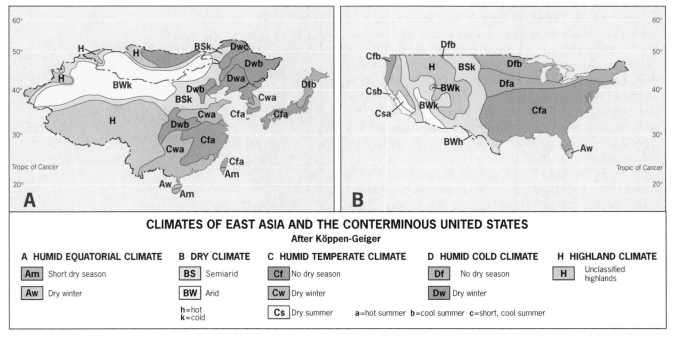

CLIMATES OF EAST ASIA AND THE CONTERMINOUS UNITED STATES
After Köppen-Geiger

A HUMID EQUATORIAL CLIMATE	B DRY CLIMATE	C HUMID TEMPERATE CLIMATE	D HUMID COLD CLIMATE	H HIGHLAND CLIMATE
Am Short dry season	**BS** Semiarid	**Cf** No dry season	**Df** No dry season	**H** Unclassified highlands
Aw Dry winter	**BW** Arid	**Cw** Dry winter	**Dw** Dry winter	
	h=hot k=cold	**Cs** Dry summer		

a=hot summer b=cool summer c=short, cool summer

FIGURE 9A-3   © H. J. de Blij, P. O. Muller, and John Wiley & Sons, Inc.

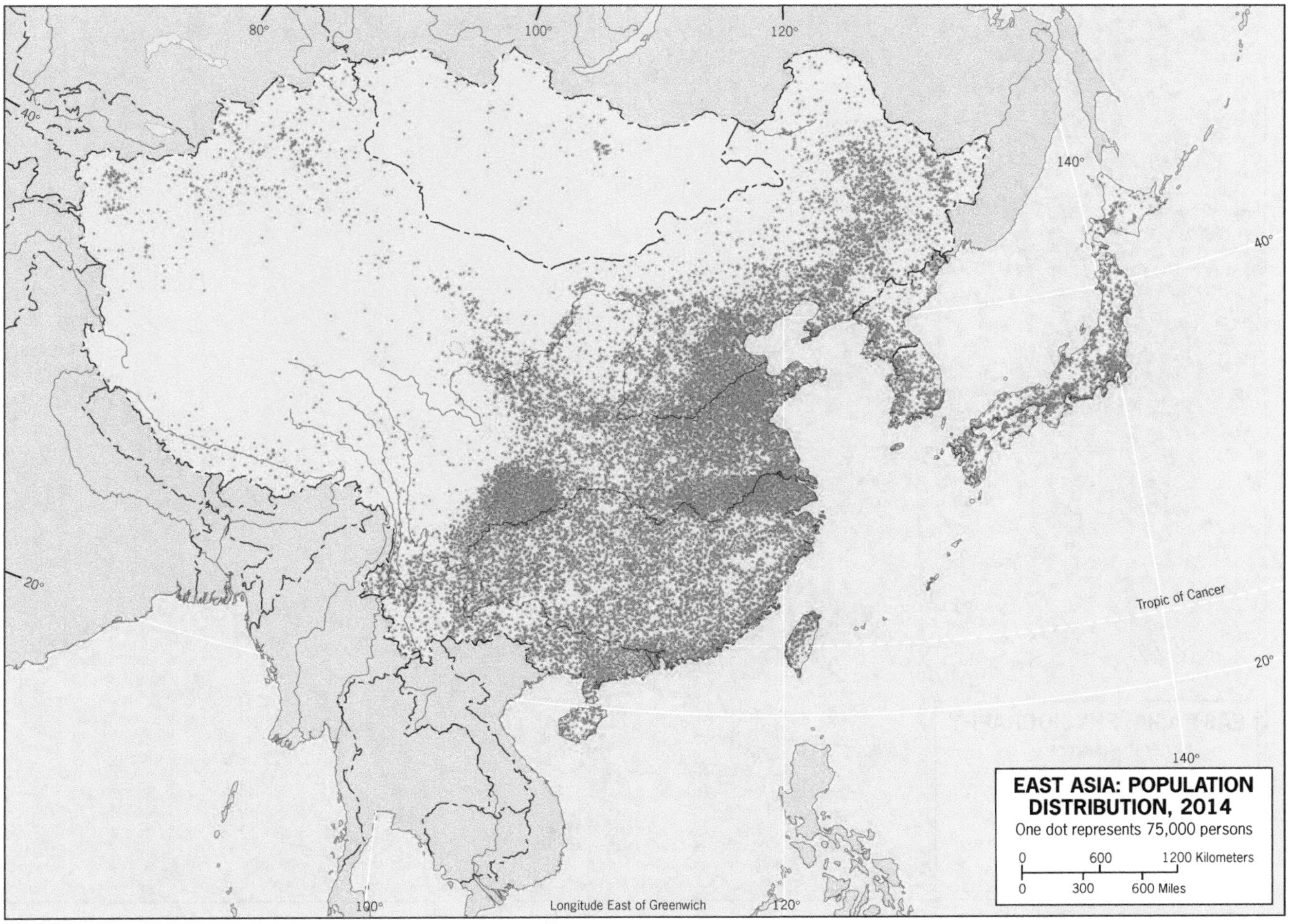

FIGURE 9A-4   © H. J. de Blij, P. O. Muller, and John Wiley & Sons, Inc.

has the warm summers but long, bitterly cold winters characteristic of *D* climates. Take a closer look at Figure 9A-3 and it is clear that both the Korean Peninsula and the Japanese islands lie astride this transition from *C* to *D* climates. South Korea is significantly milder and moister than North Korea, and Japan's largest island (Honshu) is temperate in the south but cold in the north. Not surprisingly, the least densely populated major island of Japan is northernmost Hokkaido, where the climate is rather like that of northern Wisconsin.

Comparing just the United States and China, note that whereas *C* or *D* climates prevail over more than half of the U.S., these climates predominate over less than one-third of China—even though the United States has only 317 million people compared to China's nearly 1.4 billion. That is what makes the population distribution map (Fig. 9A-4) so noteworthy: the overwhelming majority of East Asia's people are located in the easternmost one-third of the realm's territory, creating the biggest, most densely settled population cluster in the world, which mainly depends on the limited green-colored area in Figure 9A-1.

Several times in earlier chapters of this book we have noted the capacity of humans to live under virtually all

environmental circumstances; technological developments enable the survival of year-round communities in Antarctica, on oil platforms at sea, in the driest of deserts, and on the highest of plateaus. But the world population distribution map (Fig. G-8) still reminds us how we got our modern start—through crop-raising and herding. The fertile river basins and coastal plains of East Asia supported ever-larger farming populations, whose descendants still live on that same land: for all its current industrialization and urbanization, just under half the population of China remains rural to this day. Environment, in the form of elevation, relief, water supply, soil fertility, and climate played the crucial role in the evolution of the population distribution displayed in Figure 9A-4—and will continue to do so for centuries to come.

The Great Rivers

China is in some respects the product of four great river systems and their basins, valleys, deltas, and estuaries. These rivers and their tributaries are visible, but do not stand out as clearly in Figure 9A-1 as they do on the physiographic map (Fig. 9A-5). So important are they as

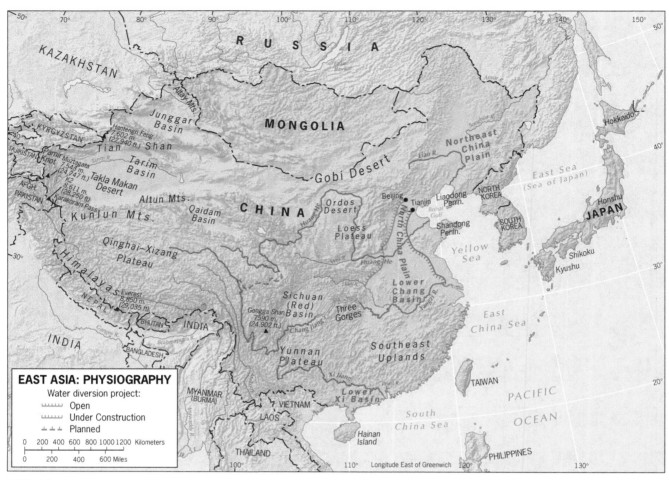

FIGURE 9A-5

© H. J. de Blij, P. O. Muller, J. Nijman, and John Wiley & Sons, Inc.

designators of the realm's regional geography that we should acquaint ourselves with them here. Of the four, the two in the middle are in many ways the most important: the **Huang He** (Yellow River) that makes a huge loop around the Ordos Desert and then flows across the North China Plain into the Bohai Gulf, and the **Yangzi** River, probably the most famous river in China's historical geography, called the **Chang Jiang** (Long River) upstream.

As the map shows, the Yellow River and its tributaries form the sources of water vital to the historic core area of China, the North China Plain, where the capital, Beijing, is located. The Yangzi River is the major artery of the Lower Chang Basin; by its mouth lies China's largest city, Shanghai, and in its middle course the water flow is controlled by the world's biggest dam (see photo). Both the Huang and the Yangzi rivers originate in the snowy mountains of the Qinghai-Xizang Plateau, a reminder that these remote environments are critical to hundreds of millions of people who live thousands of kilometers away.

The other two rivers have much shorter courses, but the **Pearl** River outlet of the one in the south, the **Xi Jiang** (West River), forms an estuary that has become China's (and East Asia's) greatest hub of globalization—an ongoing saga discussed in Chapter 9B. This is where you find

Hong Kong and, right next to it, the fastest-growing major city in the history of humankind—Shenzhen.

Finally, the northernmost of China's four major rivers, the **Liao** River, originates near the margin of the Gobi Desert and then forms an elbow as it crosses the Northeast China Plain to reach the Bohai Gulf flowing southward. Here the climate is colder, low relief scarcer, agriculture lagging, and population smaller than in the more southerly river basins, but mineral resources create opportunities for mining and industry. Each of East Asia's river-based clusters has its own combination of potentials and problems.

But even these major river systems, together with China's lesser ones, are increasingly pressed to satisfy the country's ever-growing demands for water. In order to meet these urgent needs, China has embarked on the massive South-North Water Transfer Project to bring new supplies to its thirsty northeastern core area, especially metropolitan Beijing and Tianjin (Fig. 9A-5). When completed, the entire project will annually divert more than 40 billion cubic meters of water from the Chang River to the north. The Eastern Route (following China's Grand Canal) opened in 2013, and the Central Route is expected to begin operating in 2014; the Western Route in the rugged highlands of the upper Chang and Huang basins is still in the planning stage. This

© Wen Zhenxiao/Xinhua Press/Corbis

Three Gorges Dam is emblematic of China's contemporary "era of the megaproject." The dam wall rises 180 meters (600 ft) above the inundated valley floor of the Chang/Yangzi River. It is 2 kilometers (1.2 mi) wide and creates a reservoir—largest of its kind in the world—that extends more than 600 kilometers (400 mi) upstream.

gargantuan project, however, comes with a price that is not only monetary: the reservoirs and canals along the Central Route will submerge more than 300 square kilometers of land, forcing well over 300,000 people from their homes in Henan and Hubei provinces.

Along the Coast

East Asia's Pacific margin is a jumble of peninsulas and islands. The Korean Peninsula looks like a near-bridge from Asia to Japan, and indeed it has served as such in the past. The Liaodong and Shandong peninsulas protrude into the Yellow Sea, which continues to silt up from the sediments of the Huang and Liao rivers. Off the mainland lie the islands that have played such a crucial role in the modern human geography of Asia and, indeed, the world: Japan, Taiwan, and Hainan. Japan's environmental range is expressed by cold northern Hokkaido and warm southern Kyushu, but Japan's core area lies on its main island, Honshu. As Figure 9A-1 shows, myriad smaller islands flank the mainland and dot the East and South China seas. As we will discover, some of these smaller islands significantly affect the political geography of this realm.

NATURAL RESOURCES

Given that the East Asian realm contains nearly one-fourth of the world's population, it is not difficult to imagine the magnitude of the demand for natural resources here. The world first received notice of this about a hundred years ago when Japan's imperial expansion was in part driven by the need for raw materials to feed its rapidly expanding industrialization. Today, East Asia's demand for natural resources is expressed not in imperialism but in the global

marketplace: it is driving a commodity boom all over the world, from Russia to Australia to Brazil to Subsaharan Africa.

While China was moribund under its early communist administration, and before post–World War II Japan embarked on its headlong rush to become a world economic power, East Asia's requirements remained modest by global standards. But then Japan's economic success, followed by China's swift adoption of market economics, created unimagined and unprecedented needs.

Japan, about the size of Montana but with a population of more than 100 million, showed what lay ahead. With limited domestic resources to support large-scale manufacturing, the Japanese set up global networks through which flowed commodities ranging from oil and natural gas to iron ore and chemicals. Urbanizing and modernizing populations demand ever more consumer goods, and Japanese products poured onto domestic as well as foreign markets. Japanese-owned fleets of freighters plied the oceans, and for a while Japan even became remote Australia's top-ranked customer for commodities.

When China took off in the 1980s, economic geographers cast a wary eye on the geologic map. Until then, China's biggest resource had been its fertile, river-deposited alluvium (silt): despite the communist regime's best efforts, state-run industries planned to satisfy domestic needs were no match for globalizing Japan. Most Chinese were farmers. Staving off famine was a never-ending preoccupation. But when China opened its doors to the world, and its cities burgeoned even as its industries proliferated, its needs—for oil, natural gas, metals, food, electricity, water—multiplied. Before long, China had replaced Japan as Australia's number-one customer. And Chinese manufacturers and suppliers searched for commodities from Indonesia to Iraq and from Tanzania to Brazil. If China holds an advantage, it is in the so-called *rare earth* elements not commonly known, such as thulium (used in lasers), praseodymium (aircraft parts), lanthanum (electric automobiles), and promethium (X-ray equipment). By some measures, East Asia contains almost 95 percent of the known deposits of these minerals, which are also increasingly utilized in missile technology and "green" energy applications.

But China clearly needs the world because East Asia's storehouse of other known resources is not encouraging (Fig. 9A-6). Coal reserves are widespread and can satisfy the expanding coal-fired energy system (but only at the cost of thousands of miners' lives every year). Although oil reserves, are also widespread, they tend to be rather modest and diminishing. Deposits in northeastern and far western China are the largest; moreover, exploration is proceeding offshore. Yet nothing in China compares with the massive iron ore deposits and plentiful ferroalloys available to Russia when it

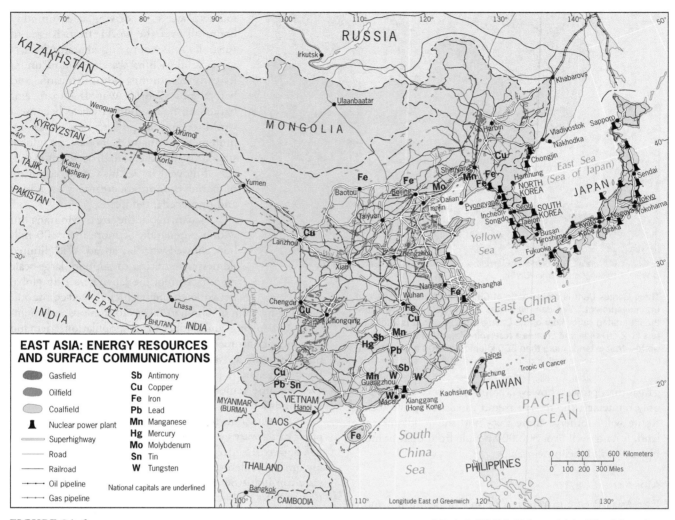

EAST ASIA: ENERGY RESOURCES
AND SURFACE COMMUNICATIONS

⬬ Gasfield	**Sb** Antimony
⬬ Oilfield	**Cu** Copper
⬭ Coalfield	**Fe** Iron
⚓ Nuclear power plant	**Pb** Lead
═══ Superhighway	**Mn** Manganese
── Road	**Hg** Mercury
── Railroad	**Mo** Molybdenum
┼─┼ Oil pipeline	**Sn** Tin
┼─┼ Gas pipeline	**W** Tungsten

National capitals are underlined

FIGURE 9A-6

© H. J. de Blij, P. O. Muller, and John Wiley & Sons, Inc.

industrialized to meet the Nazi challenge; and nothing in China can match the abundant gas and oil reserves of contemporary Russia, let alone the massive deposits of Southwest Asia's Persian Gulf region. Hence China competes with Japan for energy pipelines from Russia and with other sources for its industrial raw materials. So in just a few short years, China has become both the world's biggest consumer as well as its leading exporter.

East Asia's ascent to the globalizing world's principal stage has put it in the forefront of regional development, but at a high environmental cost in terms of air and water pollution (see photo). The East Asian geographic realm is now in the midst of an industrial, social,

In China's headlong rush to become a global economic power, environmental concerns have always taken a back seat. Thus it is hardly surprising that a recent study reported atmospheric pollution in 2010 was a factor in well over one million premature deaths countrywide. This scene along Beijing's Guangha Road during rush hour in February 2013 particularly underscores the daily challenge facing urban residents. In fact, days before this picture was taken, air pollution measurements here broke the global record for smog by a wide margin—registering *30 times* higher than the World Health Organization's uppermost "safe" level! The unusually-shaped structure to the right, one of Beijing's newest landmarks, is CCTV Tower, headquarters of state-run China Central Television, the PRC's broadcasting behemoth that controls a vast network of 22 channels that reach more than a billion viewers.

© Liu Liqun/Corbis

AMONG THE REALM'S GREAT CITIES . . .

XIAN, ANCIENT AND MODERN

THE CITY KNOWN today as Xian in Shaanxi Province is the site of one of the world's oldest urban centers. It may have been a settlement during the Shang-Yin Dynasty more than 3000 years ago; it was a town during the Zhou Dynasty, and the Qin emperor was buried here along with 6000 life-sized terracotta soldiers and horses, reflecting the city's importance. During the Han Dynasty (ca. 200 BC to AD 200) the city, then called Chang'an, was one of the greatest centers of the ancient world, the Rome of ancient China. Chang'an formed the eastern terminus of the Silk Route, a storehouse of enormous wealth. Its architecture was unrivaled, from its ornamental defensive wall with elaborately sculpted gates to the magnificent public buildings and gardens at its center.

Situated on the fertile loess plain of the upper Wei River, Chang'an was the focus of ancient China during crucial formative periods. After two centuries of Han rule, political strife led to a period of decline, but the Sui emperors rebuilt and expanded Chang'an when they made it their capital. During the Tang Dynasty, Chang'an again became a magnificent city with three districts: the ornate Palace City; the impressive Imperial City, which housed the national administration; and the busy Outer City containing the homes and markets of artisans and merchants.

After its Tang heyday the city again declined, although it remained a bustling trade center. During the Ming Dynasty it was endowed with some of its architectural landmarks, including the Great Mosque marking the arrival of Islam; the older Big Wild Goose Pagoda dates from the influx of Buddhism. After the Ming period, Chang'an's name was changed to Xian (meaning "Western Peace"), then to Siking, and in 1943 back to Xian again.

Having been a gateway for Buddhism and Islam, Xian in the 1920s became a center of Soviet communist ideology.

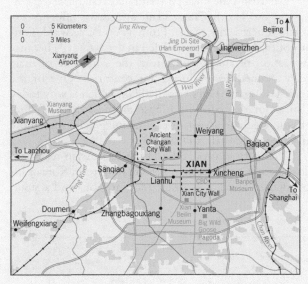

© H. J. de Blij, P. O. Muller, J. Nijman, and John Wiley & Sons, Inc.

The Nationalists, during the struggle against the Japanese, moved industries from the vulnerable east coast to Xian, and when the communists took power they enlarged Xian's industrial base still further. The present city (population: 5.4 million) lies southwest of the famed tombs, its cultural landscape now dominated by a large industrial complex that includes a steel mill, textile factories, chemical plants, and machine-making facilities. Little remains (other than some prominent historic landmarks) of the splendor of times past, but Xian's location on the main railroad line to the vast western frontier of China sustains its long-term role as one of the country's key gateways.

and political revolution the outcome of which is far from clear.

HISTORICAL GEOGRAPHY

We in the Western world often take it for granted that the pivotal events that led to the domestication of animals and the selective farming of plants, the herding of livestock and the harvesting of crops, the storage of produce and the growth of villages into towns, all began in what we now call the Middle East. The story of rivers ebbing and flowing, the "lessons" of natural irrigation, the planned harvesting of grains, the rise of cities, and the organization of the earliest states is the story of "Western" civilization—the saga of Mesopotamia and the Tigris-Euphrates Basin, and ancient Egypt and the Nile. From the Fertile Crescent, we were always

taught, these revolutionary changes diffused outward to other parts of Eurasia and then to the rest of the world.

The Chinese have long taken a different view, and we now know from extensive archeological research that East Asia was one of the few places in the world where the process of state formation [2] occurred independently thousands of years ago, and that the modern Chinese state could trace its roots to that ancient time, long before there was a Greece or a Rome.

Ancient China

We now know that the East Asian realm was forged from numerous cultures that flourished around 6000 BC during the early Neolithic [3] (New Stone Age) in several areas, including the Lower Chang Basin to the south and even beyond. Crops like millet, rice, and wheat were domesticated here, independently of developments in the Middle East, and urbanization and state formation followed suit.

Eventually, the most powerful states established themselves on the North China Plain and their influence extended far across the realm. From 1766 BC onward, Chinese political history is chronicled in dynasties [4] because a succession of rulers came from the same line of male descent, sometimes enduring for centuries. One of the longest-lasting dynasties was the Han, which is why today we speak of the ethnic Chinese as the *People of Han.* Dynastic rule ended just over a century ago, after more than three-and-a-half millennia.

The cultural geography of the East Asian realm acquired a common base that, despite long-term Korean independence as well as Japanese modifications and adaptations to the Chinese norms they had borrowed, acquired an overall Chinese denomination. Buddhism matured in China and diffused to Japan; *Confucianism* infused Korean kingdoms. In Japan, where local tradition places the country's beginnings in 660 BC, the ruling elites borrowed heavily from Chinese culture, including town plans, building styles, legal models, and even writing systems.

Peoples of the East Asian Realm

If we were studying the East Asian realm six centuries ago, during China's Ming Dynasty, we would have had no doubt as to the location of core and periphery. China was the core. Encircling the Chinese state in the periphery were not only the Koreans and the Japanese but also the Mongols and Tatars to the north and northwest; the Kazakhs, Kyrgyz, Tajiks,

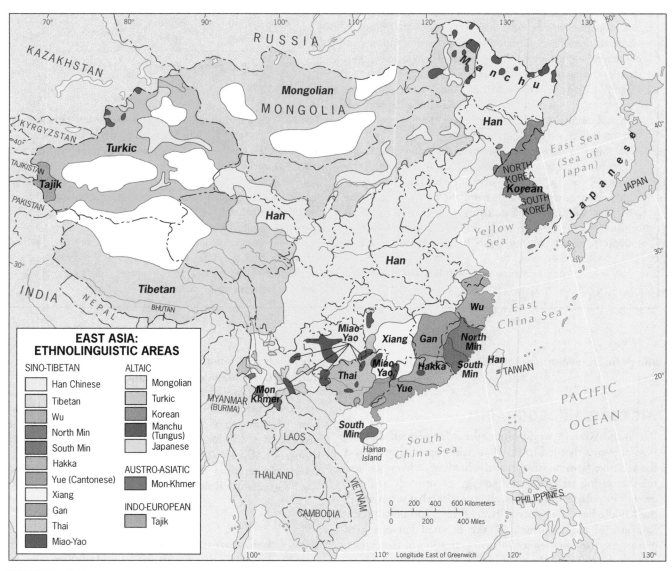

FIGURE 9A-7

© H. J. de Blij, P. O. Muller, and John Wiley & Sons, Inc.

and Uyghurs to the west; the Tibetans, Nepalese, and others to the southwest; and peoples too numerous to identify individually to the south, including both majorities (Burmans, Thais, Vietnamese) and minorities in states that were still forming in South and Southeast Asia.

Like all empires, the China of the Ming emperors expanded and contracted over time, but during the next—and final—dynasty, that of the Qing (whose rule began in AD 1644), many of the states and peoples just mentioned fell under Chinese rule. But it was the emperors' last hurrah: European and Japanese imperialists challenged Qing rule, took control over most of the state's core area, ousted the Chinese from much of the periphery, and left the country in chaos, bringing about the end of nearly 3700 years of dynastic rule in 1911.

But by that time, the ethnic geography of East Asia had become highly complicated. Even after losing control over peoples from Korea to Vietnam and from Mongolia to Burma (now called Myanmar), the Chinese state of the twentieth century still governed numerous minorities. East Asia today, therefore, remains an especially complex mosaic of ethnicities and languages.

Figure 9A-7 highlights the cultural diversity of a realm in which China dominates numerically, but where infusions from elsewhere are evident. We already know of the Mongols, the Muslim Uyghurs, and the Buddhist Tibetans; but the most varied and most numerous minority groups inhabit the southeastern corner of this realm, from

the island of Hainan to the mouth of the Yangzi River. For example, the Yue language, middle green on the map (it used to be called Cantonese), is the common language in the pivotal Pearl River Estuary. Many of the other minority tongues shown here have links to Southeast Asian languages.

And do not be misled by what the map seems to show about Han Chinese. Officialdom, the elites, and the well-educated speak Standard Chinese (also called "Mandarin"), with those in the south somewhat less true to the Beijing-area version than those in the north. But ordinary people in villages a few kilometers apart may not be able to understand each other at all. What they are able to do is read the characters in which Standard Chinese (locally called *Putonghua*) is written. And so, wherever you are in China, when you watch an anchorperson read the news on television, you will see a moving ticker below showing in characters what is being said on-screen. Viewers in Sichuan may not understand the newscaster in Beijing, but still will be able to get the news by reading the crawl.

The ethnolinguistic mosaic of the East Asian realm is paralleled by regional variations in belief systems that are discussed in Chapter 9B, because beliefs—their origins, diffusion, and current regional expression—all reflect the diverse ways that cultural and political geographies are interconnected in this populous realm.

CHINA'S HISTORICAL ROLE WITHIN EAST ASIA

Chinese Empires and Dynasties

China's great antiquity, as noted above, is chronicled in dynasties, the earliest of which are still shrouded in mystery. But, as with any long-existing state, some of China's dynastic rulers proved more productive than others. Some dynasties bequeathed long-term geographic legacies to the state. Others molded the Chinese nation. The Han Dynasty did both, which again is why even today we speak of the Chinese as the ***People of Han***.

But the Zhou Dynasty, centuries before the Han, witnessed the arrival of Buddhism in China, saw Confucius walk the pathways of the north, started the building of the Great Wall (see photo), and, in another context, spread the use of chopsticks for eating. Confucianism [5] was to become China's guiding philosophy for two millennia (see box titled "Confucius").

More than a thousand years after the Han Dynasty, something happened that the Russians would understand. The Mongols drove the local rulers from power and took over the state. But instead of imprinting

The Great Wall of China, portions of it built and rebuilt from the seventh century BC to the sixteenth century AD, primarily aimed at fending off Mongol invaders (see Fig. 9A-8). Some parts are completely gone but other sections have been renovated in recent times, such as this one about 65 kilometers (40 mi) north of Beijing.

© Jan Nijman

Confucius

CONFUCIUS (*Kongfuzi* in pinyin) was China's most influential philosopher and teacher. His ideas dominated Chinese life and thought for over 20 centuries. Confucius was born in 551 BC and died in 479 BC. Appalled at the suffering of ordinary people during the Zhou Dynasty, he urged the poor to assert themselves and demand explanations for their harsh treatment by the feudal lords. He tutored the indigent as well as the privileged, giving the poor an education that had hitherto been denied them and ending the aristocracy's exclusive access to the knowledge that constituted power.

Confucius's revolutionary ideas extended to the rulers as well as the ruled. He abhorred supernatural mysticism and cast doubt on the divine ancestries of China's aristocratic rulers. Human virtues, not godly connections, should determine a person's place in society, he taught. Accordingly, he proposed that the dynastic rulers turn over the reins of state to ministers chosen for their competence and merit.

His earthly philosophies notwithstanding, Confucius took on the mantle of a spiritual leader after his death. His thoughts, distilled from the mass of philosophical writing (including Daoism) that poured forth during his lifetime, became the guiding principles of the formative Han Dynasty. The state, he said, should not exist just for the power and pleasure of the elite; it should be a cooperative system for the well-being and happiness of the people.

With time, a mass of writings evolved, much of which Confucius never wrote. At the heart of this body of literature lay the *Confucian Classics*, 13 texts that became the basis for education in China for 2000 years. From government to morality and from law to religion, the *Classics* were Chinese civilization's guide. The entire national system of education (including the state examinations through which everyone, poor or privileged, could enter the civil service and achieve political power) was based on the *Classics*. Confucius championed the family as the foundation of Chinese culture, and the *Classics* prescribe a respect for the aged that was a hallmark of Chinese society.

But his philosophies also were conservative and rigid, and when the colonial powers penetrated China, his ideas came face to face with practical Western education. For the first time, some Chinese leaders began to call for reform and modernization, especially of teaching. Confucian principles, they said, could guide an isolated China, but not China in the new age of competition.

The communists who took power in 1949 attacked Confucian thought on all fronts. The *Classics* were abandoned, indoctrination pervaded education, and, for a time, even the family was viewed as an institution of the past. Here the communists miscalculated. It proved impossible to eradicate two millennia of cultural conditioning in a few decades. As soon as China entered its post-Mao period in 1976, public interest in Confucius surged, and the shelves of bookstores again sagged under the weight of his writings. The spirit of Confucius will pervade physical and mental landscapes in China for generations to come.

Mongol rules on their Chinese subjects, the Mongols underwent Sinicization [6] or, as it is sometimes said, Hanification [7]—that is, they adopted many of the ways of the People of Han. Hostility between the Mongols and the Chinese never diminished, however. Marco Polo saw it first-hand during his early medieval travels to "Cathay" (the name used for Northern China) and reported on it when he returned to Europe.

Mongol (Yuan Dynasty) rule ended in 1368, and it is amazing that, in the five and a half centuries dynastic China was subsequently to endure, only two dynasties were to rule: the Ming (1368–1644) and the Qing (1644–1911). The Ming, ruling their empire from the Forbidden City in Beijing (where ordinary mortals were forbidden entry), started out triumphantly: they annexed northern Korea, Mongolia, even Myanmar (Burma). They dispatched huge fleets into Pacific and Indian Ocean waters to explore the wider world. But it all came crashing down under conditions we talk a great deal about today: climate change. A major environmental shift called the *Little Ice Age* that had struck Europe in the previous century now afflicted Ming China. Wheatfields lay barren. With 100 million mouths to feed, the em-

perors worried about revolution. They burned the fleets, built barges, and extended the Grand Canal from the Lower Chang Basin to transport rice to the hungry north. But the Ming Dynasty never recovered its initial verve.

By the mid-1600s, the Manchus, a northern people with historic Mongol-Tatar links, saw their opportunity and seized control in Beijing. The People of Han are still shaking their heads about it—a people numbering about a million managed to grab the reins of power over a nation of several hundred million. The invaders adopted Chinese ways, kept the Ming systems of administration and education, called themselves Qing, and set about expanding the empire. As noted earlier, it was the emperors' last hurrah—although a long-drawn-out one. The Qing Empire became the largest Chinese empire ever (Fig. 9A-8), but it was stretched thin, failed to modernize, and could not withstand the nineteenth-century onslaught of foreign powers on its shores. Our map shows the maximum dimensions the Qing Empire acquired as well as the colonial domains the Europeans, Russians, and Japanese appropriated. Thus 36 centuries of dynastic rule over China soon ended in war, revolution, chaos, and the final collapse in 1911.

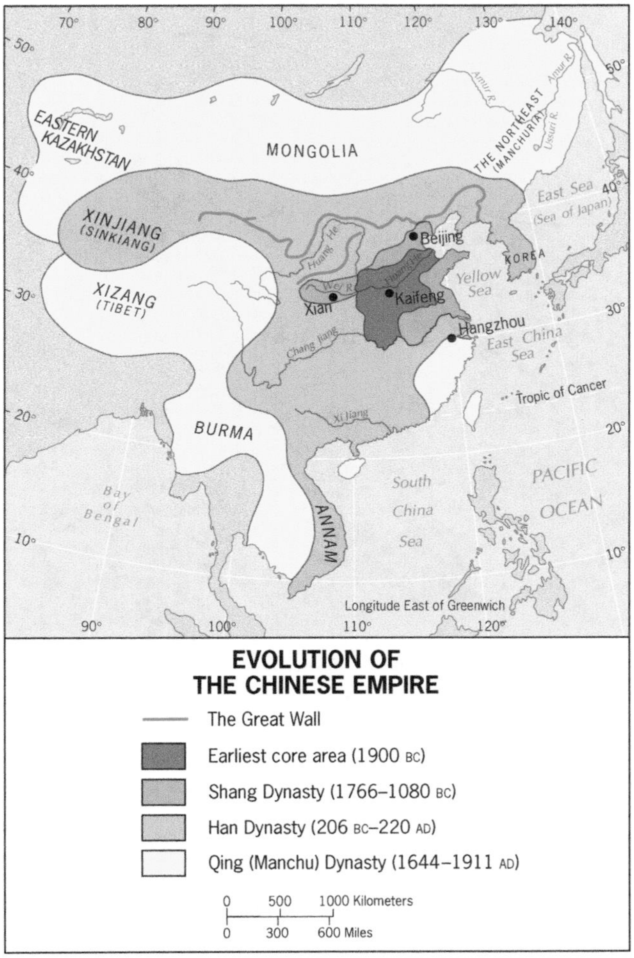

FIGURE 9A-8

© H. J. de Blij, P. O. Muller, and
John Wiley & Sons, Inc.

EVOLUTION OF THE CHINESE EMPIRE

— The Great Wall

Earliest core area (1900 BC)

Shang Dynasty (1766–1080 BC)

Han Dynasty (206 BC–220 AD)

Qing (Manchu) Dynasty (1644–1911 AD)

cheap manufactures into China, whose handicraft industries succumbed in the face of unbeatable competition. In addition, British merchants imported large quantities of opium from India into China, and soon this addictive intoxicant was destroying the very fabric of Chinese cultural life. When the Qing government tried to resist this influx, the First Opium War (1839–1842) proved disastrous. The victorious British forced China's rulers to acquiesce to opium importation, and the breakdown of Chinese sovereignty was underway. When the Chinese tried that approach again, the Second Opium War 15 years later resulted in the Chinese being forced to allow the cultivation of the opium poppy in China itself. Very soon thereafter, Chinese society was disintegrating beneath a narcotic tide that proved uncontrollable.

Meanwhile, the modern ethnic complex of Figure 9A-7 was in the making. The Beijing court was forced to grant concessions and leases to foreign merchants; China ceded Hong Kong to Britain even as British ships sailed up the Yangzi to consolidate a huge sphere of influence in China's crucial midsection. Portugal took Macau, Germany established itself on the Shandong Peninsula, the French encroached on China from their Asian colonies farther south, and the Russians entered the Northeast, then still known as *Manchuria.* The Japanese subsequently invaded Korea, annexed the Ryukyu Islands (they still possess them, including Okinawa, today), and colonized Formosa (now called Taiwan) in 1895.

All over China, under the doctrine of *extraterritoriality,* the British and other colonial powers carved out **concessions** in which Europeans, as well as Russians and Japanese, were immune from local Chinese law (see box titled "Extraterritoriality"). Some of these urban enclaves, business as well as residential, were even off-limits to Chinese citizens. In many other buildings, parks, and additional facilities, Chinese found themselves unable to enter without permission from the entrenched foreigners. This contributed to the loss of face that helped provoke the so-called Boxer Rebellion of 1900, when bands of revolutionaries roamed cities and countryside, attacking and killing not only foreigners but also their Chinese collaborators. It was

China in Disarray

Figure 9A-9 provides only a mere hint of China's disarray. Chinese emperors (and their subjects) had come to regard the state as invincible, but the colonial powers demonstrated otherwise. Economically, the colonialists imported

---

Extraterritoriality

DURING THE NINETEENTH century, as China weakened and European colonial invaders entered China's coastal cities and sailed up its rivers, the Europeans forced China to accept a European doctrine of international law—**extraterritoriality [8]**. Under this doctrine, foreign states and their representatives are immune from the jurisdiction of the country in which they are based. Today this applies to embassies and diplomatic personnel. But in Qing (Manchu) China, it went far beyond that.

The European, Russian, and Japanese invaders established as many as 90 *treaty ports*—extraterritorial enclaves in

China's cities under unequal treaties enforced by gunboat diplomacy. In their "concessions," diplomats and traders were exempt from Chinese law. Not only port areas but also the best residential suburbs of large cities were declared to be "extraterritorial" and made inaccessible to Chinese citizens. In the city of Guangzhou (Canton of colonial times), Sha Mian Island in the Pearl River was a favorite extraterritorial enclave. A sign at the only bridge to the island stated, in English and Cantonese, "No Dogs or Chinese."

FIGURE 9A-9

© H. J. de Blij, P. O. Muller, and John Wiley & Sons, Inc.

a portentous uprising, put down with great loss of life by a multinational force consisting of British, Russian, French, Italian, German, Japanese, and American soldiers. China had no friends to call upon.

Revolutionary China

Even as China's public order continued to disintegrate, a better-organized revolutionary movement arose: the so-called Nationalist movement under a prominent leader named Sun Yat-sen. Blaming the sclerotic dynastic regime for China's troubles, these Nationalists in 1911 mounted a fierce attack on the emperor's garrisons all over China. Within a few months the 267-year-old Qing Dynasty was overthrown, and with it the system that had survived for thousands of years at China's helm.

The Nationalists, however, faced insurmountable problems in their own efforts to impose a new order on chaotic China. They did negotiate an end to the extraterritorial treaties, and, because of their well-orchestrated military campaign, they did acquire greater legitimacy than the previous regime had when confronting colonial interests. But the Nationalist government set up its base in the southern city of Canton (now Guangzhou), leaving another would-be government to attempt to rule from Peking (Beijing), the old imperial headquarters. Meanwhile, in 1921, a group of intellectuals in Shanghai founded the Chinese Communist Party; one of its prominent co-founders was a young man named Mao Zedong.

During the chaotic 1920s, the Nationalists and the Communist Party at first cooperated, with the remaining foreign presence their joint target. After Sun Yat-sen's death in 1925, Chiang Kai-shek became the Nationalists' leader, and by 1927 the foreigners were on the run, escaping by boat and train or falling victim to rampaging Nationalist forces. But soon the Nationalists began purging communists even as they pursued foreigners, and in 1928, when Chiang established his Nationalist capital in the city of Nanjing on the banks of the lower Yangzi, it appeared that the Nationalists would emerge victorious from their campaigns. They had driven the communists ever deeper into the interior, and by 1933 the Nationalist armies were on the verge of encircling the last communist stronghold in the area around Ruijin in Jiangxi Province. This led to a momentous event in Chinese history: the **Long March**. Nearly 100,000 people—soldiers, peasants, leaders—marched westward from Ruijin in 1934, a communist column that included Mao Zedong and Zhou Enlai. Nationalist forces rained down attack after attack on the marchers, and of the original 100,000, about three-quarters were eliminated. But new sympathizers joined along the way (see the route marked in Fig. 9A-9), and the 20,000 survivors found a refuge in the remote mountainous interior of Shaanxi Province, 3200 kilometers (2000 miles) away. There, they prepared for a renewed campaign that would eventually bring them to power.

JAPAN'S HISTORICAL ROLE IN EAST ASIA

From Isolationism to Imperialism

Since the seventeenth century, Japan had cultivated and enforced a strict policy of isolationism [9]. Foreign influences were shunned, the Japanese people were not allowed to travel outside of Japan, and foreigners were not tolerated on Japanese soil. Contact with the outside world was extremely limited, therefore, and even trade was heavily restricted. For some time during the seventeenth and eighteenth centuries, the Dutch East India Company obtained the exclusive right to trade with Japan, but Company personnel were prohibited from setting foot on Japanese soil. So the Japanese built a small artificial island in Nagasaki Bay named Deshima where Dutch ships could dock and sailors stretch their legs. Japanese workers would cross the bridge to the island to haul the cargo ashore, but the foreigners were strictly confined to Deshima.

But as Western imperial powers (especially the British and the French) imposed their designs on Asia, isolationism became an increasingly unrealistic option for Japan because it did not want to end up itself one day as a colonial prize of the Europeans. The Industrial Revolution had yet to reach Japan, and its ability to wage war was premodern compared to the more advanced military technology (e.g., steamships) of the Western powers. Prodded by a local show of force by the U.S. Navy in the 1850s, the so-called **Meiji Restoration** (the return of "enlightened rule" focused on the Emperor Meiji) in 1868 introduced a wholesale change of Japanese foreign policy: away from isolationism and aimed at rapid modernization. Japan had decided to emulate the West.

After these modernizers took control of Japan, they turned to Britain for guidance in reforming their nation and its economy. During the decades that followed, the British advised the Japanese on the layout of cities and the construction of a railroad network, the location of industrial plants, and the organization of education. The British influence is still visible in the Japanese cultural landscape: the Japanese, like the British, drive on the left side of the road. (Consider how this affects the effort to open the Japanese market to U.S.-made automobiles!)

The Japanese reformers of the late nineteenth century undoubtedly saw many geographic similarities between Britain and Japan. At that time, most of what mattered in Japan was concentrated on the country's largest island, Honshu (literally, *mainland*). The ancient capital, Kyoto, lay in the interior, but the modernizers wanted a coastal, outward-looking headquarters. So they chose the town of Edo, situated on a large bay where Honshu's eastern coastline bends sharply (Fig. 9A-1). They renamed the place **Tokyo** (meaning *eastern capital*), and little more than a century later it was the largest urban agglomeration on Earth. Honshu's coasts were also close to mainland Asia, where raw materials and potential markets for Japanese products could be found. Importantly, the notion of a greater Japanese empire, too, was inspired in part by British example.

But the Japanese reformers who oversaw this process of modernization [10] managed to build on, not replace, Japanese cultural traditions. We in the Western world tend to equate modernization with Westernization [11]: urbanization, the spread of transport and communications facilities, the establishment of a market (money) economy, the breakdown of local traditional communities, the proliferation of formal schooling, and the acceptance and adoption of foreign innovations. In Japan, and later in other East and Southeast Asian countries, modernization was viewed as progress mainly confined to the introduction of new technologies and better methods of production. Modernization served to increase efficiency, from producing goods to running railroads to fighting war. But modernization need not affect culture, especially cultural norms and values. In their view, a society can be modernized without being Westernized.

In this context, Japan's modernization was a novelty. Having long resisted foreign intrusion, the Japanese did not achieve the transformation of their society by importing a Trojan horse; it was guided by Japanese planners, building on the existing Japanese infrastructure, to fulfill Japanese objectives. Certainly, the Japanese imported foreign technologies and adopted innovations from the British and others, but the Japan that was built, a unique combination of modern and traditional elements, was essentially a Japanese achievement.

Japan in China

By the end of the 1880s, Japan had already built the strongest military force in East Asia and was prepared to use it. The so-called First Sino-Japanese War of 1894–1895 resulted in a Japanese victory: a long-term Japanese presence on the mainland in the Northeast, Japanese control of Korea, and the effective Japanese annexation of Taiwan (renamed Formosa). If it was not yet clear that power in East Asia

had shifted to Japan, this would become obvious when the Japanese defeated Russia in their brief war of 1904–1905, both powers having had imperialist designs on northeastern China (the Russians were especially interested in Port Arthur, the Yellow Sea port now known as Dalian). Along the way, Japan became ever more aggressive in its foreign policy: in 1910, it annexed Korea; in 1931, it took firm control of Manchuria (Northeast China); in 1940, it invaded French Indochina, the U.S.-controlled Philippines, the Dutch East Indies (now Indonesia), and the British colonies of Burma and modern-day Malaysia; and finally, on December 7, 1941, it ignited World War II in the Pacific by attacking the United States at Pearl Harbor in Hawai'i (Fig. 9A-10).

The Japanese-Chinese conflict during this era had exposed the weakness of China, and that in turn fueled a drive for change (and rehabilitation) among the Chinese. Although many foreigners fled China during the 1920s and 1930s, others took advantage of the opportunities presented by the contest between the Nationalists and

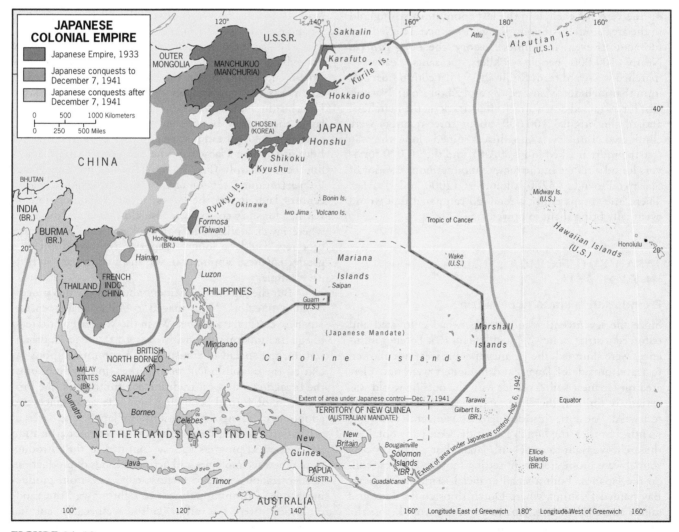

FIGURE 9A-10

© H. J. de Blij, P. O. Muller, and John Wiley & Sons, Inc.

communists. The Japanese took control over the Northeast, and when the Nationalists proved unable to dislodge them, they established a puppet state there, appointed a Manchu ruler to represent them, and named their possession *Manchukuo*.

The inevitable full-scale war between the Chinese and the Japanese broke out in 1937, with the Nationalists bearing the brunt of it (providing the communists with even more time and room to regroup). Figures 9A-9 and 9A-10 show how much of China the Japanese conquered. The Nationalists moved their capital inland to Chongqing, and the communists controlled the territory centered on Yanan to the north. China had been effectively broken into three pieces.

POST—WORLD WAR II EAST ASIA

Communist China

After the U.S.-led Western allies defeated Japan in 1945, the civil war in China quickly resumed. The United States, hoping for a stable and friendly government in China, attempted to mediate the conflict but at the same time recognized the Nationalists as the legitimate government. The United States also aided the Nationalists militarily, destroying any chance of genuine and impartial mediation. By 1948, it was quite clear that Mao Zedong's well-organized militias would defeat Chiang Kai-shek's forces. The remnants of Chiang's faction gathered Chinese treasures and valuables and then fled to the nearby island of Taiwan. There they swiftly acquired control of the government and proclaimed their own Republic of China. Meanwhile, on October 1, 1949, standing in front of the assembled masses at the Gate of Heavenly Peace in Beijing's Tiananmen Square, Mao Zedong proclaimed the birth of the People's Republic of China.

Under communism, Chinese society was completely overhauled and the dynasties soon seemed part of an ancient past. Benevolent or otherwise, the dynastic rulers of old China headed a country in which—for all its splendor, strength, and cultural richness—the fate of landless people and of serfs often was indescribably miserable; in which floods, famines, and diseases could decimate the populations of entire regions without any help from the state; in which local lords could (and often did) repress the people with impunity; in which children were sold and brides were purchased. The European intrusion made things even worse, bringing slums, starvation, and deprivation to the millions who had moved to the cities.

The communist regime, dictatorial and brutal though it was, attacked China's weaknesses on several fronts, mobilizing virtually every able-bodied citizen in the process. Land was confiscated from the wealthy; farms were collectivized; dams and levees were built with the hands of thousands; the threat of hunger for millions receded; health conditions improved; child labor was reduced; literacy was encouraged.

At the same time, the regime committed colossal errors and engaged in systematic repression of its own people at an unheard of scale. The so-called ***Great Leap Forward*** (the propaganda term for what this was supposed to be) became what was perhaps the worst human-engineered catastrophe in the history of the world. A combination of delusional attempts at revolutionary glory, economic incompetence, and extreme ruthlessness is estimated to have caused between 30 and 45 million deaths—mostly as a direct result of starvation, but with many others falling victim to murder, torture, and exhaustion due to forced labor. The idea was to enforce labor-intensive industrialization through the compulsory enlistment of large rural populations. But the results were inferior industrial products and a horrific disruption of agriculture.

Mao ruled China from 1949 to 1976, long enough to leave lasting imprints on the state. Another aspect of his communist ideology had to do with population. Like the Soviets (and influenced by a horde of Soviet advisors and planners), Mao refused to impose or even recommend any population policy, arguing that such a policy would represent a capitalist plot to constrain China's human resources. As a result, China's population mushroomed explosively during his rule.

Yet another disastrous episode of Mao's rule was the so-called ***Great Proletarian Cultural Revolution***, launched during his final decade in power (1966–1976). Fearful that Maoist communism was becoming contaminated by Soviet "deviationism" and concerned about his own stature as its revolutionary architect, Mao unleashed a vicious campaign against what he viewed as emerging elitism in society. He mobilized young people living in cities and towns into cadres known as Red Guards and commanded them to attack "bourgeois" elements throughout China, criticize Communist Party officials, and root out "opponents" of the system. The results were truly staggering: thousands of China's leading intellectuals died; moderate leaders were purged; and teachers, elderly citizens, and older revolutionaries were tortured to make them confess to crimes they did not commit. As the economy suffered, food and industrial production declined steadily. Violence and famine killed as many as 30 million people as the Cultural Revolution spun out of control. One of those who survived was a Communist Party leader who had himself been purged and thereafter been reinstated—Deng Xiaoping. Deng was destined to emerge as the country's leader in the post-Mao period of economic transformation.

Japan's Defeat and Recovery

During World War II, Japan had expanded its domain farther than the architects of the 1868 modernization could ever have imagined. But by 1945, when American nuclear bombs devastated two Japanese cities and produced surrender shortly thereafter, the expansionist era was over and the country lay in ruins. But once again, aided this time by an enlightened U.S. postwar administration, Japan surmounted

From the Field Notes . . .

© H.J. de Blij

© H.J. de Blij

"Visiting the Peace Memorial Park in Hiroshima is a difficult experience. Over this site on August 6, 1945 began the era of nuclear weapons use, and the horror arising from that moment in history, displayed searingly in the museum, is an object lesson in this time of nuclear proliferation. In the museum is a model of the city immediately after the explosion (the red ball marks where the detonation occurred), showing the total annihilation of the entire area with an immediate loss of more than 80,000 people and the death from radiation of many more subsequently. In the park outside, the Atomic Bomb Memorial Dome, the only building to partially survive the blast, has become the symbol of Hiroshima's devastation and of the dread of nuclear war."

www.conceptcaching.com

The Wages of War

JAPAN AND THE former Soviet Union never signed a peace treaty to end their World War II conflict. Why? There are four reasons, and all of them are on the map just to the northeast of Japan's northernmost large island, Hokkaido (see Fig. 9A-1). Their names are Habomai, Shikotan, Kunashiri, and Etorofu. The Japanese call these rocky specks at the southern end of the Kurile Island chain their "Northern Territories." The Soviets occupied them just before the end of the war and never gave them back to Japan. Now they are part of Russia, and the Russians have not given them back either.

The islands themselves are no great prize. During World War II, the Japanese brought 40,000 forced laborers, most of them Koreans, to mine the minerals there. When Russia's Red Army overran them in 1945, the Japanese were ordered out, and most of the Koreans fled. Today the population of about 19,000 is overwhelmingly Russian, most of them members of the military based on the islands and their families. At their closest point the islands are only 5 kilometers (3 mi) from Japanese soil, a constant and visible reminder of Japan's defeat and loss of land. Moreover, territorial waters

bring Russia even closer, so that the islands' geostrategic importance far exceeds their economic potential.

All attempts to resolve this issue have failed. In 1956, Moscow offered to return the two smallest, Shikotan and Habomai, but the Japanese declined, demanding all four islands back. In 1989, then-Soviet President Mikhail Gorbachev visited Tokyo in the hope of securing an agreement. The Japanese, it was widely reported, offered an aid-and-development package worth U.S. $26 billion to develop Russia's eastern zone—its Pacific Rim and the vast resources of the eastern Siberian interior. This would have begun the transformation of Russia's Far East, stimulated the ports of Nakhodka and Vladivostok, and made Russia a participant in the spectacular growth boom of the western Pacific Rim.

But it was not to be. Subsequently, Russian presidents Yeltsin, Putin, and Medvedev also were unable to come to terms with Japan on this issue, facing opposition from the islands' inhabitants and from their own governments in Moscow. And so the Second World War, nearly 70 years after its conclusion, continues to cast a shadow over this northernmost segment of the Asian Pacific Rim.

disaster. The Japanese were forced to accept a new constitution, and territorial adjustments were imposed (see the box titled "The Wages of War"). The new constitution stipulated that the country could not spend more than 1 percent of its GDP on the military and it had to accept the permanent stationing of American troops on its soil. This was meant to constrain Japan in terms of any possible future expansionist urges—and it probably did. It also induced Japan to shift its focus from military might to economic prowess. And once again everything turned out to be extraordinarily successful.

EAST ASIA'S ECONOMIC STATURE

Japan's Postwar Transformation

Japan's accelerated economic recovery and rise to the status of world economic superpower was one of the greatest success stories of the second half of the twentieth century. Japan had lost a war and an empire, but now was scoring many economic victories in a new global arena. Japan became an industrial giant, a technological pacesetter, a fully urbanized society, a political power, and one of the most affluent nations on Earth.

Japan once again proved adept at emulating the West: by 1980, the U.S. automobile industry had effectively been competed out of the market by the likes of Toyota and Honda. The very same thing happened in the domain of consumer electronics and other high-technology products. Japan did it better and cheaper than anyone else. Cities everywhere have reliable Japanese cars on their streets; people across the globe listen to Japanese portable audio players; laboratories the world over use Japanese optical equipment. From microwave ovens to smartphones, from oceangoing ships to high-definition TVs, Japanese-designed products flood global markets—even if many of these Japanese companies now have their products made in China.

For the past two decades, however, it should be noted that Japan's economy has been virtually stalled. Even though it is still the third-biggest economy in the world, it has lost much of its dynamism and momentum. Japan's current challenges are elaborated in Chapter 9B.

The Asian Tigers

The Japanese economic miracle was replicated, in turn, by the four Asian Tigers [12]: Hong Kong, South Korea, Taiwan, and Singapore. In the 1960s and 1970s, they embarked on similar strategies that resulted in rapid industrialization propelled by the attraction of foreign investment and the creation of export processing zones for the manufacturing of high-value-added goods [13], including computers, mobile phones, kitchen appliances, and a plethora of electronic devices. The Tigers quickly became trading nations, and they particularly oriented themselves to the most affluent Western markets. Today, it is no coincidence that most of the world's largest ports are located on the shores of East Asia (see photo on the opening page of this chapter), with their exports shipped mainly to North America and Europe.

Note that the Asian Tigers (as well as Japan) share yet another characteristic: while they all implemented significant market liberalization measures (e.g., reducing tariffs or limits on foreign investment), they also maintained strong central governments that exerted a major, sometimes authoritarian influence on their economies. It might even be argued that this is a reflection of "Asian values" reminiscent of Confucius—especially loyalty to the family, the corporation, and the nation combined with the suppression of individual desires.

China's Economic Miracle

After Mao Zedong's death in 1976, China began a historic metamorphosis that was to have the widest global impact. The essence of China's transformation was comparable to what the Asian Tigers had achieved earlier: the creation of a favorable environment for foreign investment to support the growth of a manufacturing sector mostly geared toward exports. Chinese wages, at least initially, were kept low, and training programs were aimed at constantly upgrading the skills of the local workforce. At the same time, political conditions remained stable because in China, more than anywhere else, the government maintains tight controls. This was (and is) a communist state—but one that proved to be extremely adept at understanding how global capitalism operates and how to put it

Hong Kong Island (left photo), long the focus of a British Crown Colony (until 1997) but always closely linked to adjacent mainland China, is one of the most densely built-up areas in the world, with its high-rise towers crammed together cheek by jowl. This former city-state has a major, globally-oriented central business district and offers a high-end residential lifestyle for those who can afford it. English is still the chief language and many multinational corporations have major offices here. And just a short ferry ride across the water to the north lies Hong Kong's port and Kowloon (right photo), a decidedly less internationalized sector of the metropolis—still vibrant but with a lower cost of living and catering primarily to ethnic Chinese residents.

© Jan Nijman

© Jan Nijman

From the Field Notes . . .

"I could not quite believe my eyes when I came upon this Starbucks in the middle of Beijing's Forbidden City: this icon of American consumerism, wrapped in ancient Chinese architecture, in the heart of this revered complex, in a country that calls itself communist? It was back in 2004 that the Chinese authorities had agreed to allow the Starbucks café on the premises in return for a hefty financial contribution to ongoing restoration efforts. But not everybody agreed this was a good idea. Several Chinese groups protested against this "'erosion" of Chinese culture, and by 2007 the government felt compelled to reverse its decision. The deal was rescinded and Starbucks was evicted from the Forbidden City. It was a splendid illustration of the pragmatism that marks the culture of the Chinese and permeates their economic policies. Call it capitalism or authoritarianism, but the Chinese prefer to do whatever works given the circumstances, and they have little time for ideological principles."

© Jan Nijman   www.conceptcaching.com

to use. These days, pragmatism has unmistakably become the hallmark of Chinese policies.

It was as if Japan and its Tiger emulators had merely been warm-ups for East Asia's main economic act: the colossal rise of China. In less than a quarter of a century, China emerged as the most dynamic and fastest-growing component of the world economy. To be sure, Japan and the Tigers had experienced double-digit growth rates as well, but it is a different story altogether when the leading character is a country of more than a billion people. In 2010, China surpassed Japan to become the second-largest economy in the world, and its ascent steadily proceeds in this decade.

GEOPOLITICS IN EAST ASIA

Sino-Japanese Relations

It should not come as a surprise that Chinese-Japanese relations are problematic. A hundred years ago, China was in disarray and Japan was taking East Asia by storm—as well as by force. The contrast was stark: one was a wounded civilization, the other was beating the Western powers at their own game (at least for a time). Japan proudly proclaimed to stand for pan-Asian ideals, and that is how it legitimized its invasion and occupation of China. But the Japanese committed unspeakable atrocities during their campaign in China. Millions of Chinese citizens were shot, burned, drowned, subjected to gruesome chemical and biological experiments, and otherwise wantonly victim-

ized. When you ask the Japanese, they say World War II began in 1941 when the United States declared war right after Pearl Harbor. When you ask the Chinese, they say World War II began in 1931 when the Japanese invaded Manchuria.

Decades later, when China's economic reforms of the 1980s and 1990s led to a renewed Japanese presence in China, the Chinese public and its leaders called for Japan to acknowledge and apologize for these wartime crimes against humanity. The unqualified apology the Chinese desire, in word and deed, has not been forthcoming. Some Japanese history textbooks still avoid acknowledging what happened to the satisfaction of the Chinese, and surveys indicate strong public sentiment on this still-sensitive issue.

But now that China has surpassed Japan in terms of economic prowess; now that China is the biggest exporter in the world; and now that Japan's economy has been stagnating for nearly a generation—this time it is China that is full of confidence and on its front foot. Although the two countries have close economic ties, their diplomatic relations are strained by clashing interests, historical memory, and cultural friction.

One of the most recent flashpoints to arise involves the Sino-Japanese-Taiwanese dispute over the Senkaku Islands in the East China Sea (Fig. 9A-11). These tiny uninhabited islands were seized by Japan in 1895 but are claimed by the Chinese, who call them the Diaoyu Islands. And they are also claimed by Taiwan, which refers to them as the Diaoyutai Islands. It is not so much the intrinsic

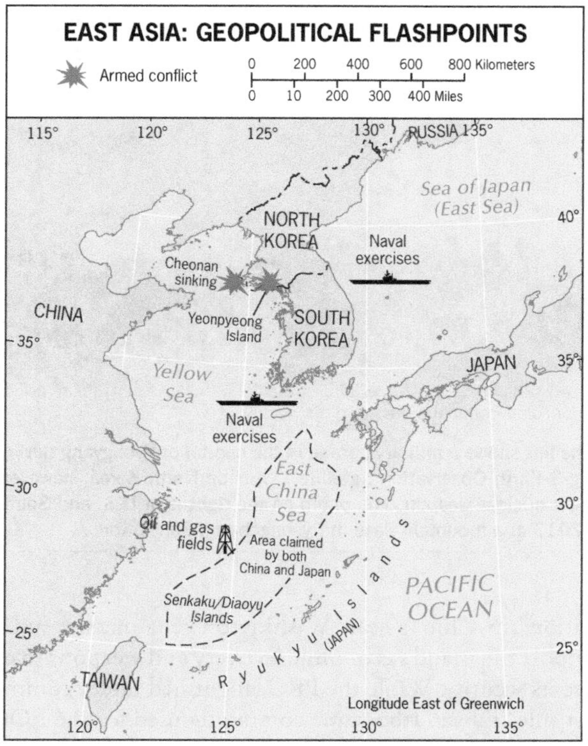

FIGURE 9A-11 © H. J. de Blij, P. O. Muller, J. Nijman, and John Wiley & Sons, Inc.

peninsula, then back northward across the 38th parallel, and finally drew in Chinese armed forces who pushed the front southward again. By 1953, a military stalemate halted the hostilities, and the Korean War ended at the Cease-Fire Line not far from where the 38th parallel had marked the original 1945 boundary. Ever since, a heavily armed demilitarized zone (DMZ) has more or less hermetically sealed North from South—with the two Koreas, having grown apart, still in danger of renewed conflict.

But this is not just a bilateral issue. The Korean conflict has long had realmwide and even global implications. One reason is that North Korea's nuclear capability has been in the hands of perhaps the most repressive and archaic regime on Earth—unreliable, unpredictable, and without scruples. North Korea's nuclear missiles may be intended primarily for South Korea, but (theoretically at least) can also reach China, Russia, Japan and perhaps even North America. Moreover, the North Koreans have carried out three underground nuclear weapons tests since 2006, the last one in February 2013, thereby increasing the possibility of a nerve-wracking East Asian arms race.

The North Korea issue also deepens divisiveness in the realm. South Korea and Japan are diametrically opposed to the regime based in Pyongyang, whereas China takes a far more neutral position, at times even seeming to lend the North Korean regime support. The Chinese appear to use North Korea in their dealings with Japan and the United States, since it is widely thought that China is crucial to containing the North Korean threat.

Ever since the end of the Second World War in 1945, Japan has adhered to a constitution that essentially forbids its rearmament and commits it to a relationship with the United States involving the stationing of tens of thousands of American armed forces on Japanese soil. But Japan's 2009 election campaign brought to the fore an unusually forceful reappraisal of these issues, and public opinion has been shifting toward a stronger military posture and the ouster of U.S. troops. One result of the international community's failure to constrain North Korea's nuclear aspirations may be Japan's military revival. The country has gradually increased its military posture and billions have been invested in a sophisticated missile defense system to protect against potential North Korean (or Chinese) attacks.

The North Koreans, in turn, are aware of latent Chinese support, and this seems to encourage them to test the waters. In 2010, a North Korean submarine torpedoed the *Cheonan*, a South Korean naval vessel patrolling off the west coast of South Korean near the boundary with the North, killing 46 (Fig. 9A-11). South Korea, the United States, Japan, and much of the world strongly condemned this act of violence—yet China pointedly did not.

The death of the North's leader, Kim Jong-il, in December 2011 and the accession of his son, Kim Jong-un, coincided with another critical food shortage among the North Korean people, more desperately in need of outside aid than ever. For a moment, in early 2012, it looked like an agreement had been achieved for U.S. food aid in

value of the islands that is at stake here: it is far more a matter of national pride and entitlement. Moreover, some oil and gas deposits have recently been discovered in this area, and ownership of the islands grants rights to their territorial waters and what lies beneath them. In any event, by 2013 China's heightened belligerence over these 'rocks' had brought Chinese-Japanese relations to their lowest level in decades. It may well be that China has the most compelling claims to these islands, because eighteenth- and nineteenth-century maps (from both China and Japan) seem to corroborate that they were in Chinese hands before the Japanese takeover.

The Korea Factor

Throughout history, the Koreans have repeatedly been divided, partitioned, colonized, and occupied. And even when outsiders were not involved, their indigenous kingdoms struggled for supremacy. During the Qing Dynasty, Chinese emperors intervened at will. As China fell apart after 1900, the Japanese conquered the Korean Peninsula and annexed all of it as their colony in 1910.

When Japan was defeated in 1945, the Allied powers divided Korea for "administrative" purposes. The territory north of the 38th parallel was placed under the control of Soviet forces; south of this latitude, the United States was in control. In 1950, communist forces from North Korea invaded the South in a forced-unification drive, unleashing a devastating conflict that first swept southward across the

© Du Baiyu/Xinhua Press/Corbis

© Park Jin-hee/Xinhua Press/Corbis

North Korea continues to be a major regional security concern. The photo on the left shows a military parade in the capital of Pyongyang during December 2012, celebrating the successful launch of the "Kwangmyongsong-3 Earth Observation Satellite." Outside North Korea, however, it was widely interpreted as a test of a long-range missile capable of delivering a nuclear weapon. The photo on the right is of U.S. and South Korean marines involved in a joint cold-weather training exercise in February 2013 at a mountain base in Pyeongchang, South Korea.

return for a promise to end nuclear (missile) testing—but the deal collapsed a few weeks later following North Korea's (failed) launch of a rocket capable of delivering a ballistic missile. The North Koreans finally managed a successful launch several months later and U.S.-North Korean talks were suspended.

In the spring of 2013, North Korea's blustering reached new heights with repeated threats of "thermonuclear war" against the South and even against the United States. Such threats have been part of a standard playbook in recent years, and tend to coincide with the annual joint military exercises of South Korean and U.S. troops. But this time they were louder than ever, and the unpredictability of the young, untested Kim Jong-un raised alarms throughout the region and well beyond.

Taiwan: The Other China

Mention the island of Taiwan in China, and you are likely to be greeted with a frown and a headshake. Taiwan, your host may tell you, is a problem foreigners do not understand. Virtually all of the 23 million people of Taiwan are Chinese. Taiwan was part of China during the Qing Dynasty. Taiwan was stolen from China by Japanese imperialists in 1895, when it was known as Formosa. Then, when communists and Nationalists were fighting each other for control of mainland China right after World War II, and the communists were about to win, the Nationalists in 1949 fled by plane and boat to Taiwan, where they overpowered the locals. Even as Mao Zedong was proclaiming the birth of the People's Republic of China (PRC) in Beijing, the loser, Chiang Kai-shek, named his regime in Taiwan the Republic of China (ROC)—and told the world that he headed China's "legitimate" government.

The PRC, of course, ridiculed this assertion, but the ROC had powerful friends, especially the United States. Chiang Kai-shek's regime was soon installed at the United

Nations in China's seat. Washington sent massive aid to support the island's economic recovery and weapons to ensure its security. While the PRC languished under communist rule, Taiwan (the name commonly used for the ROC) advanced economically, and over time its political system matured into a functioning (if turbulent) democracy. What the Taiwanese sought was economic prosperity, and they got it.

But to the PRC, Taiwan is regarded as a "wayward province" that must be reunited with the motherland. When U.S. President Nixon arrived in Beijing in 1972 for a historic visit that was to change the world, Taiwan was a bargaining chip. Soon, the ROC's UN delegation was dismissed and representatives of the Beijing government were seated in its place. Many countries around the world that had recognized Taiwan as the legitimate heir to China's leadership now suddenly changed sides. Meanwhile, Beijing's leaders set about trying to isolate the ROC, and to a large extent they succeeded.

Geography, however, was to intervene. With billions of U.S. dollars in reserves, fruitful connections to Overseas Chinese in Southeast Asia, and its emergence as an Asian Tiger economic powerhouse, Taiwan had some significant cards to play—and the Beijing regime discovered it could not afford to deny Taiwanese companies permission to exploit opportunities in the PRC's development zones. And so, via the "back door" of Hong Kong, Taiwanese entrepreneurs built thousands of factories in mainland China, many of them located directly across the Taiwan Strait. Taiwanese businesspeople now pumped hundreds of millions of dollars into China's development boom, and the economies of Taiwan and the PRC found themselves on a path toward ever tighter integration. In 2012, an estimated 27 percent of Taiwan's exports went to China along with substantial Taiwanese foreign direct investment, and at least 800,000 Taiwanese were living and working (temporarily) on the mainland.

Today, even in difficult economic times, per capita annual income in Taiwan exceeds U.S. $20,000—more than triple that of China and on a par with South Korea. Even though a sizeable majority of Taiwanese oppose reunification with the PRC, few would want to see their economic well-being imperiled by political adventures.

China Goes Global

Napoleon once famously described China as a sleeping giant that would shake the world when it finally awoke. China today is indeed awake and changing the world—but it is changing itself and the surrounding East Asian realm even more. A closer look at this transformation within the framework of East Asia's regions is the objective of Chapter 9B.

POINTS TO PONDER

- The fortunes of China and Japan have always seemed to be inversely related: when one was rising, the other was in decline.

- East Asia constitutes the biggest manufacturing complex in the world, but the realm's natural resources are limited.

- In the past decade, China's defense spending has increased by about 12 percent per year, much of it intended to deter the United States from intervening in a possible crisis over Taiwan.

- The impoverished North Korean people continue to suffer horrendous famines and mass imprisonment while their government dedicates massive resources to building nuclear weapons.

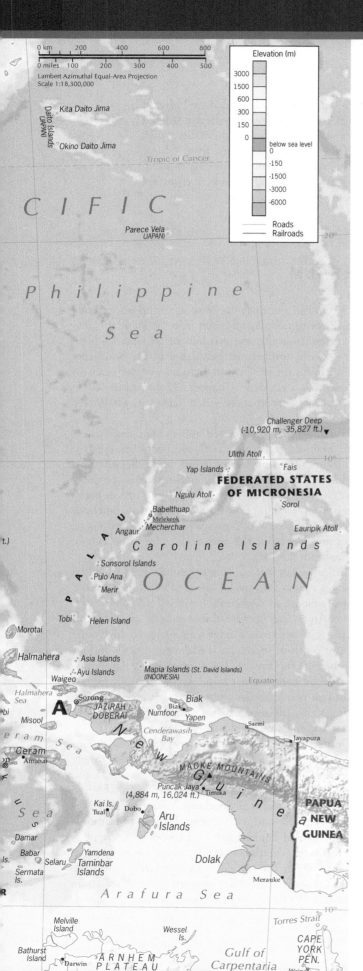

FIGURE 10A-1   © H. J. de Blij, P. O. Muller, and John Wiley & Sons, Inc.

IN THIS CHAPTER

- ◆ Earthquakes, tsunamis, and volcanoes
- ◆ The mixed blessings of palm oil
- ◆ The Overseas Chinese
- ◆ Singapore's centrality
- ◆ ASEAN's impotence
- ◆ Geopolitics in the South China Sea
- ◆ Why the shape of a country matters

CONCEPTS, IDEAS, AND TERMS

Buffer zone	1
Shatter belt	2
Tsunami	3
Biodiversity	4
Overseas Chinese	5
Emerging market	6
Node	7
ASEAN	8
AFTA	9
Antecedent boundary	10
Subsequent boundary	11
Superimposed boundary	12
Relict boundary	13
Compact state	14
Protruded state	15
Elongated state	16
Fragmented state	17
Perforated state	18

S outheast Asia is a realm of peninsulas and islands, a corner of Asia bounded by India on the northwest and China on the northeast (Fig. 10A-1). Its western coasts are washed by the Indian Ocean, and to the east stretches the vast Pacific. From all these directions, Southeast Asia has been penetrated by outside forces. From India came traders; from China, settlers; from across the Indian Ocean, Arabs to engage in commerce and Europeans to build empires; and from across the Pacific, Americans. Southeast Asia has been the scene of countless contests for power and primacy—the competitors have come from near and far.

DEFINING THE REALM

Southeast Asia's geography in some ways resembles that of eastern Europe, even if the physiography is very different. It is a mosaic of smaller countries on the periphery of two of the world's largest states. It has been a buffer zone [1] between powerful adversaries. It is a shatter belt [2] in which stresses and pressures from without and within have fractured the political geography. Like eastern Europe, Southeast Asia exhibits great cultural diversity. This is a realm of hundreds of cultures and ethnicities, numerous languages and dialects, global as well as local religions, and diverse national economies ranging from high- to low-income.

A GEOGRAPHIC OVERVIEW

Figure 10A-1 displays the relative location and dimensions of the Southeast Asian geographic realm, an assemblage of 11 countries situated on the Asian mainland as well as on thousands of islands, large and small, extending from Sumatera* in the west to New Guinea in the east, and from Luzon in the north to Timor in the south. We will become familiar with only the largest and most populous of these islands, but sailing the seas of this part of the world you would pass dozens of smaller ones every day. And if you could stop, you would find even the tiniest populated islands to have their own character resulting from the cultural sources of their residents, the environmental challenges they face and the opportunities they exploit, their modes of dress, and the structure of their dwellings, even the vivid colors with which they often decorate their boats.

The giant of this realm, in terms of both territory and population, is the far-flung *archipelago* (island chain) of Indonesia, labeled appropriately on the map by the largest letters. In the east, the state of Indonesia extends beyond the Southeast Asian realm into the Pacific Realm because it controls the western half of an island—New Guinea—whose indigenous peoples are not Southeast Asian. We focus on this unusual situation later (and on New Guinea as a whole in Chapter 12), but note it here because unusual borders and divided islands are a hallmark of this realm.

In mainland Asia, as noted above, Southeast Asia is bordered by India and China, both sources of immigrants, cultural infusions, economic initiatives, and other relationships evident in the realm's cultural landscapes. Also originating there are rivers that play a central role in the lives of many millions of people south of the realm border. As we will find, the core areas of several of Southeast Asia's most populous countries are located in the basins of major rivers whose sources lie inside China.

Before we get started, it is helpful to get acquainted with the key states of this realm, some of which will already be familiar. North of Indonesia lies the Philippines, well known to Americans because this was once an American colony and is still a source of many immigrants to the United States. Also north of Indonesia is Malaysia, easy to find on the map because its core area lies on the long Malay Peninsula that almost connects mainland Asia with Indonesia. At the tip of that peninsula lies another famous geographic locality: Singapore, the spectacular economic success story of Southeast Asia and a world-city by every measure.

On the Asian mainland, the name Vietnam still resonates in America, which fought a bitter and costly war there in the 1960s and 1970s. As the map shows, Vietnam looks like a sliver of land extending from its border with China to the delta of the greatest of all Southeast Asian rivers, the Mekong. Looking westward, neighboring Laos and Cambodia may not be all that familiar, but next comes centrally positioned Thailand, the dream (and reality) of millions of tourists and one of the world's most fascinating countries. And then, on Southeast Asia's western margin, we come to Myanmar (formerly Burma): here human potential,

---

*As in Africa and South Asia, names and spellings have changed with independence. In this chapter we will use contemporary spellings, except when we refer to the colonial era. Thus Indonesia's four major islands are Jawa, Sumatera, Kalimantan (the Indonesian portion of Borneo), and Sulawesi. Prior to independence they were respectively known as Java, Sumatra, Dutch Borneo, and Celebes.

major geographic qualities of
SOUTHEAST ASIA

1. Southeast Asia extends from the peninsular mainland to the archipelagos offshore. Because Indonesia controls part of New Guinea, its functional region reaches into the neighboring Pacific geographic realm.

2. Southeast Asia, like eastern Europe, has been a shatter belt between powerful adversaries and has a fractured cultural and political geography shaped by foreign intervention.

3. Southeast Asia's physiography is dominated by high relief, crustal instability marked by volcanic activity and earthquakes, and tropical climates.

4. A majority of Southeast Asia's 625 million people live on the islands of just two countries: Indonesia, with the world's fourth-largest population, and the Philippines. The rate of population increase in the Insular region of Southeast Asia exceeds that of the Mainland region.

5. Although the great majority of Southeast Asians have the same ancestry, cultural divisions and local traditions abound, which the realm's divisive physiography sustains.

6. Southeast Asia's political geography exhibits a variety of boundary types and several categories of state territorial morphology.

7. The Mekong River, Southeast Asia's Danube, has its source in China and borders or crosses five Southeast Asian countries, sustaining tens of millions of farmers, fishing people, and boat owners.

8. Singapore is the leading world-city in Southeast Asia and lies at the realm's center of trade and business relations.

9. Southeast Asia contains a number of rapidly emerging markets and fast-growing economies that in some respects follow in the tracks of the neighboring realm of East Asia.

10. China's influence in this realm has increased markedly in recent years and in some instances triggered a local backlash.

© G. Bowater/Corbis Images

A section of a vast palm oil plantation in Sarawak State in the southern part of Malaysian Borneo. These plantations have proliferated in Malaysia and Indonesia, bringing in export revenues but at a mounting environmental cost.

natural endowment, and opportunity were thwarted by a half-century of extremely harsh military rule (that plunged the country into devastating poverty)—which in 2012 quite suddenly relaxed its vise-like grip and reopened Myanmar to the world.

SOUTHEAST ASIA'S PHYSICAL GEOGRAPHY

Physiographically, Southeast Asia is in some ways reminiscent of Middle America, a fractured realm of islands and peninsulas flanking a populous mainland studded with high mountains and deep valleys. It is useful to look back at Figures G-4 and G-5 to see why: both Southeast Asia and Middle America are dangerous places, where the Earth's crust is unstable as tectonic plates are in collision, earthquakes are a constant threat, volcanic eruptions take their toll, tropical cyclones lash sea and land, and floods, landslides, and other natural hazards make life riskier than in most other parts of the world.

In terms of human geography, Southeast Asia is part of the Pacific Rim. But in physiographic terms, it forms part of the Pacific Ring of Fire and all the hazards this designation brings with it. As recently as 2004, an undersea earthquake off westernmost Indonesia caused a tsunami [3] (seismic sea wave) in the Indian Ocean that killed more than 300,000 people along coastlines from Sumatera to Somalia. This was only the latest in an endless string of natural disasters originating in Southeast Asia whose effects were felt far beyond the realm's borders. In 1883, the Krakatau volcano lying between Sumatera and Jawa exploded, resulting in a death toll estimated at more than 36,000. In 1815, the Tambora volcano in the chain of islands east of Jawa known as the Lesser Sunda Islands blew up, darkening skies throughout the world and affecting climates around the planet (the year that followed is still known as the "year without a summer" when crops failed, economies faltered, and people went hungry as far away as Egypt, New England, and France). Research on what may have been the most calamitous of all such eruptions suggests that, about 73,000 years ago, the Toba volcano on Sumatera exploded with such force that its ash and soot not only darkened skies and affected weather, but changed global climate for perhaps as long as 20 years and threatened the very survival of the human population, then still small in number and widely dispersed. In fact, a number of scientists postulate that this eruption caused such widespread casualties that human genetic diversity was significantly diminished.

It therefore goes without saying that high relief dominates Southeast Asia, from the Arakan Mountains in western Myanmar to the glaciers (yes, glaciers!) of New Guinea. Take a close look at Figure 10A-1 and you can see how many elevations approach or exceed 3000 meters (10,000 ft), and, using the elevation guide in the upper right-hand corner, how mountainous and hilly much of the realm's topography is. Lengthy ranges form the backbones not only of islands such as Sulawesi and Sumatera, but also of the Malay Peninsula, most of Vietnam, and the border zone between Thailand and Myanmar. In Figure G-5 it is possible to trace these volcano-studded mountain ranges by their earthquake epicenters and volcanic records.

Exceptional Borneo

But among the islands there is one significant exception. The bulky island named Borneo in Figure 10A-1 has high elevations (Mount Kinabalu in the north reaches 4101 meters [13,455 ft]), yet has no volcanoes and negligible Earth tremors. This island has been called a stable "mini-continent" amid a mass of volcanic activity, a slab of ancient crust that long ago was pushed high above sea level by tectonic forces and was subsequently eroded into its present landscapes. Borneo's soils are not nearly as fertile as those of the volcanic islands, so that an equatorial rainforest developed here that long survived the human population explosion, giving

sanctuary to countless plant and animal species including Southeast Asia's great ape, the orangutan. That era is now ending as human encroachment on Borneo's tropical habitat is accelerating, logging is destroying the remaining forest, and roads and farms are penetrating its interior. Borneo, along with other parts of Indonesia and Malaysia, has also experienced the rapid expansion of palm oil plantations at the expense of tropical woodlands (see box titled "Palm Oil Plantations and Deforestation").

Borneo's tropical forests are a remnant of a much larger stand of equatorial rainforest that once covered most of this realm. Besides Borneo, eastern Sumatera still contains limited expanses of rainforest, including a few orangutan sanctuaries. So does less populous and more remote New Guinea, which was never reached by these great apes. As we noted in the introductory chapter, equatorial rainforests can still be found today in three low-latitude areas of the world: the Amazon Basin of South America, west-equatorial Africa, and here in Southeast Asia. The combination of climatic conditions that sustains these forests—consistently warm temperatures and year-round rainfall—produces the biologically richest and ecologically most complex vegetation regions on Earth. Huge numbers and varieties of trees and other plants grow in very close proximity, vying for space and sunlight both horizontally and vertically. Yet despite all this luxuriant growth, the soils beneath rainforests are nutrient poor. Most of the surface nutrients are derived from the decaying vegetation on the forest floor, which nurture the growth of the next generation of plants. Long-term indigenous inhabitants have developed ways to use the plants, animals, and soils to eke out a living—but when migrant farmers from elsewhere remove the trees to utilize the soil, mistakenly assuming it will be able to support their crops, failure swiftly results. This reality notwithstanding, intensifying population pressure throughout the tropics continues to shrink what remains of the world's rainforests.

Relative Location and Biodiversity

Look again at Figure 10A-1, but in a more general way. The Malay Peninsula, adjacent Sumatera, Jawa, and the Lesser Sunda Islands east of Jawa seem to form a series of stepping stones toward New Guinea, and in the extreme lower-right corner of the map you can see Australia's Cape York Peninsula appearing to reach toward New Guinea. What would happen, you might ask, if sea level were to drop and those narrow bodies of water between the peninsulas and the islands dried up?

That is precisely what occurred—not just once, but repeatedly in the geologic history of Southeast Asia. Long ago, the orangutans whose descendants remain in Indonesia today were able to migrate from the mainland into warmer equatorial latitudes because global sea level dropped during periods of glaciation, and islands separated by water today were temporarily connected by land bridges. More recently, early human arrivals here also got assistance from

Palm Oil Plantations and Deforestation

IN THE MID-NINETEENTH century, it was discovered that the reddish fruit of a species of palm tree in West Africa contained rich oils that could be used for everything from making soap to lubricating steam engines. The European colonial powers, who liked to experiment with different crops throughout their empires to obtain the highest and most profitable yields, eventually learned that these palm trees grew especially well in Southeast Asia. Beginning in the 1930s, oil-palm plantations were established across this realm, particularly in what is now Malaysia and Indonesia. Today, palm oil is used in an enormous range of products; in fact, it is so widely utilized in processed foods that up to half of all products sold in supermarkets contain it.

This form of agriculture is also quite lucrative, because the yields of oil palms per hectare (2.5 acres) are much higher than those of such competing oil crops as soybeans and sunflowers. Moreover, the price of this commodity on global markets has risen steadily over the past few years, triggering successive rounds of production increases. Malaysia and Indonesia have benefited the most, and in 2012 together supplied no less than 85 percent of all the world's palm oil.

The achievement of this success, however, has come at a high price. According to UN agencies, the expansion of oil-palm plantations now constitutes the single biggest threat to tropical forest preservation in the two countries. Most at risk for survival are such key wildlife species as orangutans, pygmy elephants, Sumatran rhinos, and tigers. In 2010, the swiftly expanding closed-canopy palm oil plantations were conservatively estimated to already cover an area the size of Austria,

with about half located in Sumatera and the rest divided about evenly between Borneo and peninsular Malaysia (Fig. 10A-2 below; see also the photo at the beginning of this chapter).

The palm oil industry is now being pressured by various groups to adhere to more sustainable practices, mainly by avoiding start-ups of new plantations in areas of high conservation value, and by introducing a "certified" label for oil produced in a sustainable manner. But progress on this front is slow, and as long as global demand remains high, the temptation to expand production in suitable areas will be hard to resist.

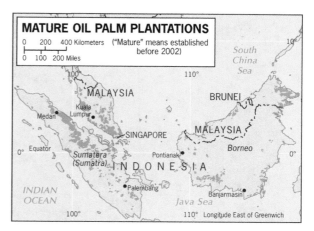

FIGURE 10A-2   © H. J. de Blij, P. O. Muller, J. Nijman, and John Wiley & Sons, Inc.

nature: Australia's Aborigines probably managed to cross what remained of the deeper trenches between islands by building rafts, but their epic journey was facilitated by land bridges as well.

Time and again, therefore, Southeast Asia was a receptacle for migrating species. Combine this with the realm's tropical environments, and it is no surprise that it is known for its biodiversity [4]. Scientists estimate that fully 10 percent of the Earth's plant and animal species are found in this comparatively small realm. Biogeographers can trace the progress of many of these species from the mainland across the archipelago toward Australia, but some were halted by deeper trenches that remained filled with water even when sea levels dropped. An especially deep trench lies in the Lombok Strait between the islands of Bali (next to Jawa) and Lombok (Fig. 10A-1), a key biogeographical boundary (discussed in Chapter 11) first recognized by the naturalist Alfred Russel Wallace, a contemporary of Charles Darwin.

As we shall presently observe, Southeast Asia's biodiversity had a fateful impact on its historical geography. Among the realm's specialized plants, it was the spices that

attracted outsiders from India, China, and Europe, with consequences still visible on the map today.

Four Major Rivers

Water is the essence of life, and among world realms Southeast Asia is comparatively well endowed with moisture (Fig. G-7). Ample, occasionally even excessive, rainfall fills the rice-growing paddies of Indonesia and the Philippines. On the realm's mainland, where annual rainfall averages are somewhat lower and the precipitation is more seasonal, major rivers and their tributaries fill irrigation channels and form fertile deltas. The map of population distribution clearly highlights this spatial relationship between rivers and people, expressed in distinct coastal clustering (Fig. 10A-3).

As Figure 10A-1 reminds us, rivers that are crucial to life in certain realms sometimes have their sources in neighboring realms, a geographic issue that can lead to serious regional discord. What right does an "upstream" state in one realm have to dam, or otherwise interfere with, a river whose flow is vital to a state (or states) downstream?

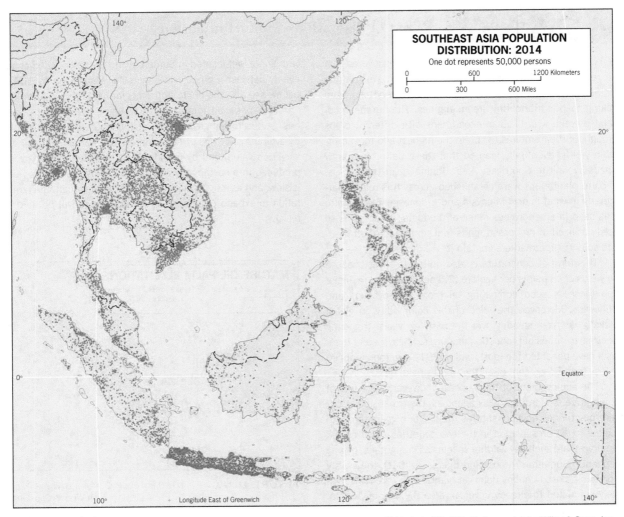

FIGURE 10A-3

© H. J. de Blij, P. O. Muller, and John Wiley & Sons, Inc.

In Southeast Asia's case, three of its four major rivers originate in China: (1) the **Mekong**, which crosses the mainland from north to south; (2) the **Red** River that reaches the sea via its course across northern Vietnam; and (3) the **Irrawaddy**, which forms the lifeline of Myanmar. The fourth is an intra-realm river, the **Chao Phraya**, that functions as the key artery of Thailand.

The Mighty Mekong

From its headwaters high in the snowy uplands of China's Qinghai-Xizang (Tibetan) Plateau, the Mekong River rushes and flows some 4200 kilometers (2600 mi) to its delta in southernmost Vietnam. This "Danube of Southeast Asia" traverses or borders five of the realm's countries, supporting rice farmers and fishing people, forming a transportation route where roads are few, and providing electricity from dams upstream. Tens of millions of people depend on the waters of the Mekong, from subsistence farmers in Cambodia to apartment dwellers in China. The Mekong Delta in southern Vietnam is one of the realm's most densely populated areas and produces enormous harvests of rice.

But problems loom. China is building a series of dams across the Lancang (as the Mekong is called there) to supply surrounding Yunnan Province with electricity. Although such hydroelectric dams should not interfere with water flow, countries downstream worry that a severe dry spell in the interior would impel the Chinese to slow the river's flow to keep their reservoirs full. Cambodia is especially concerned over the future of the Tonlé Sap, a large natural lake whose water is supplied by the Mekong (see Fig. 10B-2). In Vietnam, farmers worry about salt water invading the Delta's paddies should the Mekong's level drop. And the Chinese may not be the only dam builders in the future: Thailand has expressed an interest in building a dam on the Thai-Laos border where it is defined by the Mekong.

In such situations, the upstream states have an advantage over those downstream. Several international organizations have been formed to coordinate development in the Mekong Basin, most notably the Mekong River Commission (MRC) founded more than 50 years ago. China has offered to sell electricity generated by its dams to Thailand, Laos, and Myanmar. Coordinated efforts to reduce

From the Field Notes . . .

"After a three-hour drive by bus southward from Hanoi, we reached the Van Long Nature Reserve in northeastern Vietnam's Red River Delta. It lies in a limestone terrain known as karst, part of the same geology that continues to the north through Halong Bay and into southern China beyond. Karst landscapes are formed through the slow but steady dissolu-

tion of limestone by (naturally) acidic water; the harder rock formations are more resistant to erosion and remain as towers, resulting in unique and sometimes whimsical landforms (left photo). The Van Long Nature Reserve is a biologically rich ecotourism site that was established in 2001 and involves local communities. Women from nearby villages guide visitors around in their basket boats, and they welcome the extra income in an area barely touched by Vietnam's emerging economy (right photo)."

www.conceptcaching.com

© Jan Nijman

© Jan Nijman

deforestation in the Mekong's drainage basin have had some effect. After consultations with the MRC, Australia built a bridge linking Laos and Thailand. There is even a plan to make the Mekong navigable from Yunnan to the coast, creating an alternative outlet for interior China. Sail the Mekong today, however, and you are struck by the slowness of development along this key artery. Wooden boats, thatch-roofed villages, and teeming paddies mark a river still crossed by antiquated ferries and flanked by few towns. Of modern infrastructure, there is very little to observe (see final photo of this chapter). And yet the Mekong and its basin form the lifeline of mainland Southeast Asia's predominantly rural societies.

Rivers and States

Whereas the Mekong impacts the lives of peoples in several Southeast Asian states, the effects of the other three major Southeast Asian rivers are for the most part internal. As Figure 10A-1 shows, the Red River forms the focus for the heavily populated Tonkin Plain in northern Vietnam, where the capital, Hanoi, lies on its banks. In Thailand, the relatively short but crucial Chao Phraya, on which Bangkok is situated, is just one of a series of channels in that river's delta, formed by numerous streams rising in the country's interior. And Myanmar's Irrawaddy River (some of whose headwaters arise in China) crosses that country from north to south, its wide valley one of the world's leading rice-producing areas and its largest city, Yangon, at the corner of its delta.

POPULATION GEOGRAPHY

Examine the map of Southeast Asia's population distribution (Fig. 10A-3), and you are immediately struck by the huge concentration of people on a relatively small island in Indonesia—a cluster larger than any other in the realm,

the four mainland river deltas included. This is Jawa, and its population of close to 150 million not only accounts for well over half of Indonesia's national total but also exceeds that of every other country in the realm.

This population concentration is particularly noteworthy because Indonesia is not yet a highly urbanized country. Today more than half of the Indonesians still live in rural areas, and although Jawa, as shown in Chapter 10B, is the country's most urbanized island, over 60 million of its inhabitants still live off the land. What makes all this possible is a combination of fertile volcanic soil, ample water, and extremely warm temperatures that enable Jawa's farmers to raise three crops of rice in a single paddy during a single year, helping feed a national population still growing faster than the global average. But we should also be aware that the thickest red clusters on Jawa denote fast-growing urban areas, cornerstones in the building of a new economy with increasingly global linkages.

Within Indonesia, the contrasts between Jawa and the four other major islands—Sumatera, Borneo (Kalimantan), Sulawesi, and most especially Indonesian New Guinea—reflect the core-periphery relationship between these two sectors of the country. As the map suggests, such contrasts, less sharply defined, also mark other Southeast Asian countries, and the primate cities here (Bangkok, Manila, Yangon, Kuala Lumpur) are particularly dominant. Vietnam even contains two such anchors, which respectively represent its historic northern (Hanoi) and southern (Ho Chi Minh City) core areas.

As the table in Appendix B indicates and as the map confirms, Southeast Asia's states are not, by world standards, especially populous. Indonesia today is the world's fourth-ranking country in terms of population (just under 250 million), but no other Southeast Asian country contains even half that total. Three mainland countries contain between

50 and 100 million people. But take Laos, quite a large country territorially (about the size of the United Kingdom) and note that its population is less than 7 million; similarly, Cambodia, half the size of Germany, has only 15.5 million. In part, such modest numbers on the mainland reflect natural conditions less favorable to farming than those prevailing on volcanic soils or in fertile river basins, but more generally this realm did not grow as explosively during the past century as did neighboring realms. Indeed, Appendix B indicates that several countries in Southeast Asia today are growing at or below the global average of 1.2 percent annually.

The Ethnic Mosaic

Southeast Asia's peoples come from a common stock just as (Caucasian) Europeans do, but this has not prevented the emergence of regionally or locally discrete ethnic or cultural groups. Figure 10A-4 displays the broad distribution

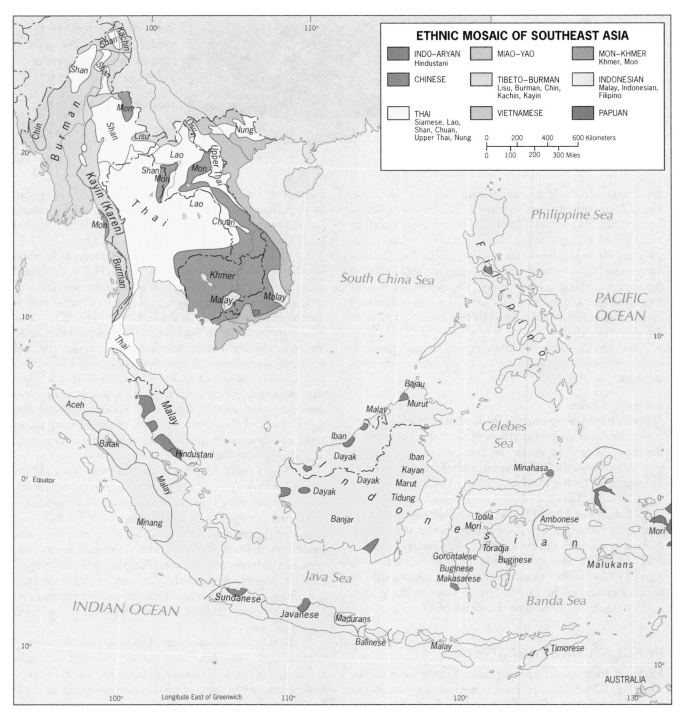

FIGURE 10A-4

© H. J. de Blij, P. O. Muller, and John Wiley & Sons, Inc.

of ethnolinguistic groups in the realm, but be aware that this is a generalization. At the scale of this map, myriad smaller groups cannot be represented.

Figure 10A-4 shows the rough spatial coincidence, on the mainland, between major ethnic group and contemporary political state. The Burman dominate in the country formerly called Burma (now Myanmar); the Thai occupy the state once known as Siam (now Thailand); the Khmer form the nation of Cambodia and extend northward into Laos; and the Vietnamese inhabit the long strip of territory facing the South China Sea.

Territorially, by far the largest population shown in Figure 10A-4 is classified as Indonesian, the inhabitants of the great island chain that extends from Sumatera west of the Malay Peninsula to the Malukus (Moluccas) in the east and from the Lesser Sunda Islands in the south to the Philippines in the north. Collectively, all these peoples shown on the map—the Filipinos, Malays, and Indonesians—are known as Indonesians, but they have been divided by history and politics. And note as well that the Indonesians in Indonesia itself include Javanese, Madurese, Sundanese, Balinese, and other major groups; again, hundreds of smaller ones cannot be mapped at this scale. In the Philippines, too, island isolation and contrasting ways of life are reflected in the cultural mosaic. Also part of this Indonesian ethnic-cultural complex are the Malays, whose heartland lies on the Malay Peninsula but who form minorities in other areas as well. Like most

Indonesians, the Malays are Muslims, although Islam is a more powerful force within Malay society than it generally is in Indonesian culture.

In the northern part of the mainland region, numerous minorities inhabit remote corners of the countries in which the Burman (Burmese), Thai, and Vietnamese dominate. Those minorities tend to occupy areas on the peripheries of their countries, where the terrain is mountainous and the forest is dense, and where the governments of their national states do not exert complete control. This remoteness and sense of detachment give rise to aspirations of secession, or at least resistance to government efforts to establish full authority, often resulting in bitter ethnic conflict.

Immigrants

Figure 10A-4 further reminds us that, again like eastern Europe, Southeast Asia is home to major ethnic minorities from outside the realm. On the Malay Peninsula, note the South Asian (Hindustani) cluster. Such Hindu communities with Indian ancestries exist in many parts of the peninsula, but in the southwest they form the majority in a small area. In Singapore, too, South Asians form a significant minority. These communities emerged during the European colonial period, but South Asians had arrived in this realm many centuries earlier, propagating Buddhism and leaving their architectural and cultural imprints on places as far removed as Jawa and Bali.

From the Field Notes . . .

"Like most major Southeast Asian cities, Bangkok's urban area includes a large and prosperous Chinese sector. No less than 14 percent of Thailand's population of 71 million is of Chinese ancestry, and the great majority of Chinese live in the cities. In Thailand, this large non-Thai population is well integrated into local society, and intermarriage is common. Still, Bangkok's 'Chinatown' is a distinct and discrete part of the great city. There is no mistaking Chinatown's limits: Thai commercial signs change to Chinese, goods offered for sale also change (Chinatown contains a large cluster of shops selling gold, for example), and the urban atmosphere, from street markets to bookshops, is dominantly Chinese. This is a boisterous, noisy, energetic part of multicultural Bangkok, a vivid reminder of the Chinese commercial success in Southeast Asia."

© H.J. de Blij   **www.conceptcaching.com**

The Chinese

By far the largest immigrant minority in Southeast Asia, however, is Chinese. The Chinese began arriving here during the Ming and early Qing (Manchu) dynasties, and the largest exodus occurred during the late colonial period (1870–1940), when as many as 20 million immigrated. The European powers at first encouraged this influx, using the Chinese in administration and trade. But soon these Overseas Chinese [5] began to congregate in the major cities, where they established Chinatowns and gained control over much of the commerce. By the time the Europeans tried to limit Chinese immigration, World War II was about to break out and the colonial era would end soon thereafter.

Figure 10A-5 shows the migration routes and current concentrations of Chinese in Southeast Asia. Most migrants originated in southern China's Fujian and Guangdong provinces, and a large number invested much of their wealth back in China when it opened up to foreign businesses three decades ago. Clearly, the Overseas Chinese of Southeast Asia have played a significant role in shaping the economic miracle in this sector of the Pacific Rim.

Southeast Asia is now home to about 33 million Overseas Chinese, more than two-thirds of the world total. Their lives have often been difficult. The Japanese relentlessly persecuted Chinese living in Malaya during World War II. Later, during the 1960s, Chinese in Indonesia were accused of communist sympathies, and hundreds of thousands were killed. In the late 1990s, Indonesian mobs again attacked Chinese and their property because of their relative wealth and because many Chinese had become Christians during the colonial era and were now targeted by Islamic throngs. Resentment still continues, expressed by episodic flare-ups against Chinese in various parts of Southeast Asia.

During this decade, Singapore is experiencing its own unique challenges with the latest wave of Overseas Chinese. Unique, because the overwhelming majority of native Singaporeans are themselves of Chinese descent—even though they are third-, fourth-, or fifth-generation and have, to varying degrees, blended in with surrounding Malay culture (Singapore and Malaya were part of the same British colonial entity for more than 130 years before independence in

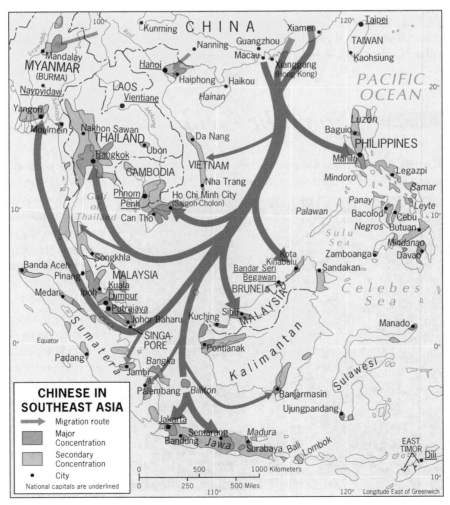

FIGURE 10A-5   © H. J. de Blij, P. O. Muller, and John Wiley & Sons, Inc.

Regional ISSUE   The Chinese Presence in Southeast Asia

THE CHINESE ARE TOO INFLUENTIAL!

"It's hard to imagine that there was a time when we didn't have Chinese minorities in our midst. I think I understand how Latin Americans [sic] feel about their 'giant to the north.' We've got one too, but the difference is that there are a lot more Chinese in Southeast Asia than there are Americans in Latin America. The Chinese even run one country because they are the majority there, Singapore. And if you want to go to a place where you can see what the Chinese would have in mind for this whole region, go there. They're knocking down all the old Malay and Hindu quarters, and they've got more rules and laws than we here in Indonesia could even think of. I'm a doctor here in Bandung and I admire their modernity, but I don't like their philosophy.

"We've had our problems with the Chinese here. The Dutch colonists brought them in to work for them, they got privileges that made them rich, they joined the Christian churches the Europeans built. I'm not sure that a single one of them ever joined a mosque. And then shortly after Sukarno led us to independence they even tried to collaborate with Mao's communists to take over the country. They failed and many of them were killed, but look at our towns and villages today. The richest merchants and the money lenders tend to be Chinese. And they stay aloof from the rest of us.

"We're not the only ones who had trouble with the Chinese. Ask them about it in Malaysia. There the Chinese started a full-scale revolution in the 1950s that took the combined efforts of the British and the Malays to put down. Or Vietnam, where the Chinese weren't any help against the enemy when the war happened there. Meanwhile they get richer and richer, but you'll see that they never forget where they came from. The Chinese in China boast about their coastal economy, but it's coastal because that's where our Chinese came from and where they sent their money when the opportunity arose.

"As a matter of fact, I don't think that China itself cares much for or about Southeast Asia. Have you heard what's happening in Yunnan Province? They're building a series of dams on the Mekong River, our major river, just across the border from Laos and Burma. They talk about the benefits and they offer to destroy the gorges downstream to facilitate navigation, but they won't join the Mekong River Commission. When the annual floods cease, what will happen to Tonlé Sap, to fish migration, to seasonal mudflat farming? The Chinese do what they want—they're the ones with the power and the money."

THE CHINESE ARE INDISPENSABLE!

"Minorities, especially successful minorities, have a hard time these days. The media portray them as exploiters who take advantage of the less fortunate in society, and blame them when things go wrong, even when it's clear that the government representing the majority is at fault. We Chinese arrived here long before the Europeans did and well before some other 'indigenous' groups showed up. True, our ancestors seized the opportunity when the European colonizers introduced their commercial economy, but we weren't the only ones to whom that opportunity was available. We banded together, helped each other, saved and shared our money, and established stable and productive communities. Which, by the way, employed millions of locals. I know: my family has owned this shop in Bangkok for five generations. It started as a shed. Now it's a six-floor department store. My family came from Fujian, and if you added it all up we've probably sent more than a million U.S. dollars back home. We're still in touch with our extended family and we've invested in the Xiamen SEZ.

"Here in Thailand we Chinese have done very well. It is sometimes said that we Chinese remain aloof from local society, but that depends on the nature of that society. Thailand has a distinguished history and a rich culture, and we see the Thais as equals. Forgive me, but you can't expect the same relationship in East Malaysia. Or, for that matter, in Indonesia, where we are resented because the 3 percent Chinese run about 60 percent of commerce and trade. But we're always prepared to accommodate and adjust. Look at Malaysia, where some of our misguided ancestors started a rebellion but where we're now appreciated as developers of high-tech industries, professionals, and ordinary workers. This in a Muslim country where Chinese are Christians or followers of their traditional religions, and where Chinese regularly vote for the Malay-dominated majority party. So when it comes to aloofness, it's not us.

"The truth is that the Chinese have made great contributions here, and that without the Chinese this place would resemble parts of South or Southwest Asia. Certainly there would be no Singapore, the richest and most stable of all Southeast Asian countries, where minorities live in peace and security and where incomes are higher than anywhere else. In fact, mainland Chinese officials come to Singapore to learn how so much was achieved there. Imagine a Southeast Asia without Singapore! It's no coincidence that the most Chinese country in Southeast Asia also has the highest standard of living."

Vote your opinion at www.wiley.com/go/deblijpolling

the 1960s). That shared ethnicity has not stopped many Singaporeans from becoming ever more critical of the rapid recent influx of 'newly rich' mainland Chinese, who tend to come with a sense of entitlement coupled with a lack of interest in the regional culture. Tensions peaked in 2012 when an intoxicated Chinese immigrant ran a red light, crashed his Ferrari (!) into a taxicab, and killed two natives. More generally, resentment focuses on the role of arrogant wealthy immigrants in driving up real-estate prices, taking the best jobs, and showing disrespect for the city-state's strict codes of public conduct. Overall, this increasingly erodes social relations because 'old' Chinese and 'new' Chinese now refer to distinctly different identities within Singapore's multicultural mosaic.

RELIGIONS OF SOUTHEAST ASIA

Southeast Asia, more than any other realm, is a historic crossroads of religions. With the migrants from the Indian subcontinent came their faiths: first Hinduism and Buddhism, later Islam. The Muslim religion, promoted by the growing number of Arab traders who appeared on the scene, became the predominant religion in Indonesia (where nearly 90 percent of the population adheres to Islam today). But in Myanmar, Thailand, and Cambodia, Buddhism remained supreme, and in all three countries today more than 90 percent of the people are adherents. In culturally diverse Malaysia, the Malays are Muslims (to be a Malay *is* to be a Muslim), and almost all Chinese are Buddhists; but most Malaysians of Indian ancestry remain Hindus.

Although Southeast Asia has generated its own local cultural expressions, most of what remains in tangible form has resulted from the infusion of foreign elements.

Take, for instance, Angkor Wat, the enormous complex of religious structures built in Cambodia during the twelfth century AD and today one of the world's most famous monuments (see photos). It was originally constructed as a Hindu temple, dedicated to the god Vishnu. The carvings on the walls of Angkor Wat tell the stories of the Hindu epics, and the temple's designs are closely associated with Hindu cosmology. But during the fourteenth century Buddhism took over this area and the temple complex became a place of worship for Buddhists.

Vietnam is perhaps the ultimate religious crossroads of the realm, where for many centuries there has been an almost casual blending of early Hinduism with Buddhism, Daoism, and Confucianism—all mixing comfortably with age-old traditions of ancestor worship.

COLONIALISM'S HERITAGE: HOW THE POLITICAL MAP EVOLVED

When the European colonizers arrived in Southeast Asia, they encountered a patchwork of kingdoms, principalities, sultanates, and other traditional political entities whose leaders they tried to co-opt, overpower, or otherwise fold into their imperial schemes. There was no single powerful center of indigenous culture as had developed in Han-dominated China. In the river basins and on the plains of the mainland, as well as on the islands offshore, a flowering of cultures had produced a diversity of societies whose languages, religions, arts, music, foods, and other achievements formed an almost infinitely varied mosaic—but none of those cultures had risen to imperial power when the Europeans arrived. Those European colonizers forged empires here, often by playing one state off against another; the Europeans divided and ruled. Out of this foreign intervention came the modern map of Southeast Asia, and only Thailand (formerly Siam) survived the colonial era as an independent entity. Thailand was useful to two competing powers, the French to the east and the British to the west: it served as a convenient buffer, and although the colonists carved pieces off Thailand's domain, the kingdom endured.

Indeed, the Europeans accomplished what local powers could not: the formation of comparatively large, multicultural states that encompassed diverse peoples and societies and welded them together. Were it not for the colonial intervention, it is unlikely that the 17,000 islands of far-flung Indonesia would today constitute the world's fourth-largest country in terms of population. Nor would the nine sultanates of Malaysia have been united, let

Cambodia's renowned Angkor Wat offers a blend of Hindu and Buddhist iconographies: a statue of Vishnu (left) and a nearby one of the Buddha (right).

© Jan Nijman

© Jan Nijman

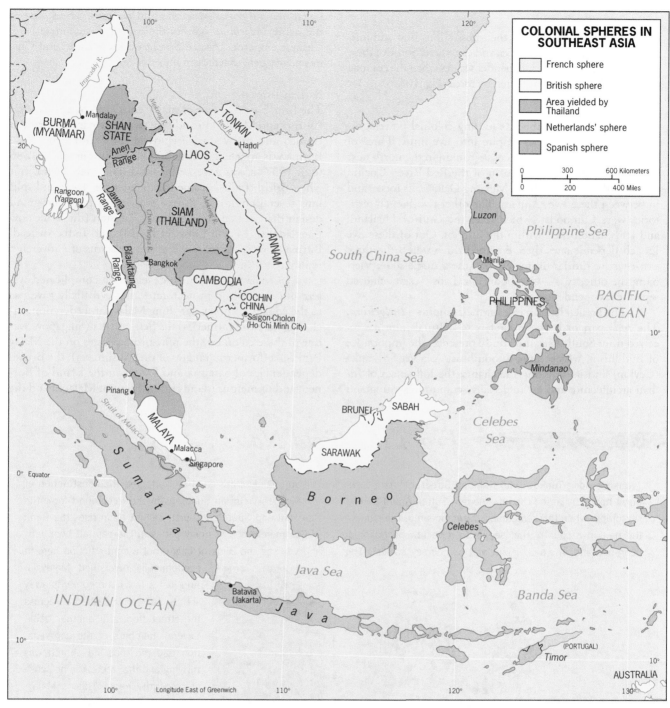

FIGURE 10A-6

© H. J. de Blij, P. O. Muller, and John Wiley & Sons, Inc.

alone with the peoples of northern Borneo across the South China Sea. For good or ill, the colonial intrusion consolidated a realm of few culture cores and numerous ministates into less than a dozen countries. The leading colonial competitors here in Southeast Asia were the Dutch, British, French, and Spanish (with the Spanish later replaced by the Americans in their stronghold, the Philippines). The Japanese had colonial objectives here as well, but those aspirations came and went during the course of World War II.

Figure 10A-6 shows the colonial framework in the late nineteenth century, before the United States assumed control over the Philippines in 1898. Note again that only Thailand survived as an independent state, but it was compelled to yield territory to the British in Malaya and Burma and to the French in Cambodia and Laos.

The Colonial Imprint

The colonial powers divided their possessions into administrative units as they did in Africa and elsewhere. Some of these political entities became independent states when the colonial powers withdrew or were ousted by force (Fig. 10A-6).

French Indochina

France, one of the mainland's leading colonial powers, divided its Southeast Asian empire into five units. Three of these units lay along the east coast: Tonkin in the north next to China, centered on the basin of the Red River; Cochin China in the south, with the Mekong Delta as its focus; and in between these two, Annam. The other two French territories were Cambodia, which faces the Gulf of Thailand; and Laos, landlocked within the interior. Out of these five French dependencies there emerged three states: the three east-coast territories ultimately became a single state, Vietnam; the other two—Cambodia and Laos—each achieved separate independence.

The French had a name for their empire—*Indochina*. The *Indo* part of Indochina refers to cultural imprints received from South Asia: the Hindu presence; the importance of Buddhism, which came to Southeast Asia via Sri Lanka (Ceylon) and its seafaring merchants; the influences of Indian architecture and art (especially sculpture), writing and literature, and social structures and patterns. The *China* in the name *Indochina* signifies the role of the Chinese here. Chinese emperors coveted Southeast Asian lands, and China's power penetrated deep into this realm.

British Imperialism

The British ruled a pair of major entities in Southeast Asia (Burma and Malaya) in addition to a large part of northern Borneo and many small islands in the South China Sea. Burma was attached to Britain's Indian Empire; from 1886 until 1937, it was governed from distant New Delhi. But when British India became independent in 1947 and split into several countries, Burma was not part of the grand design that created West and East Pakistan (the latter now Bangladesh), Ceylon (now Sri Lanka), and India. Instead, Burma (now Myanmar) was given the status of a sovereign republic in 1948.

In Malaya, the British developed a complicated system of colonies and protectorates that eventually gave rise to the equally complex, far-flung Malaysian Federation. Included were the former Straits Settlements (Singapore was one of these colonies), the nine protectorates on the Malay Peninsula (former sultanates of the Muslim era), the British dependencies of Sarawak and Sabah on the island of Borneo, and numerous islands in the Strait of Malacca and the

From the Field Notes . . .

"Walking along Tunku Abdul Rahman Street in Kuala Lumpur, I had just passed the ultramodern Sultan Abdul Samad skyscraper when this remarkable view appeared: the old and the new in a country that seems to have few postcolonial hang-ups and in which Islam and democracy coexist. The British colonists designed and effected the construction of the Moorish-Victorian buildings in the foreground (now the City Hall and Supreme Court); behind them rises the Bank of Commerce, one of many banks in the capital. Look left, and you see the Bank of Islam, not a contradiction here in economically diversified Malaysia. And just a few hundred yards away stands St. Mary's Cathedral, across the street from still another bank. Several members of the congregation told me that the church was thriving and that there was no sense of insecurity here. 'This is Malaysia, sir,' I was told. 'We're Muslims, Buddhists, Christians. We're Malays, Chinese, Indians. We have to live together. By the way, don't miss the action at the Hard Rock Café on Sultan Ismail Street.' Now there, I thought, was a contradiction as remarkable as this scene."

www.conceptcaching.com

© H.J. deBlij

South China Sea. The original Federation of Malaysia was created in 1963 by the political unification of recently independent mainland Malaya, Singapore, and the former British dependencies on the largely Indonesian island of Borneo. Singapore, however, left the Federation in 1965 to become a sovereign city-state, and the remaining units were later restructured into peninsular Malaysia and, on Borneo, Sarawak and Sabah. Thus the term *Malaya* properly refers to the geographic territory of the Malay Peninsula, including Singapore and other nearby islands; the term *Malaysia* identifies the politico-geographical entity of which Kuala Lumpur is the capital city.

Netherlands "East Indies"

Following in the wake of the Portuguese, the first European colonizers in this realm, the Dutch, came in search of what Southeast Asia had to offer and now one aspect of this realm's biodiversity had fateful consequences. Among the plants domesticated by the local people on the islands of present-day Indonesia was a group collectively known as the *spices*. We know them today as black pepper, cloves, cinnamon, nutmeg, ginger, turmeric, and other condiments essential to flavorful meals. In Figure 10A-1 you can detect, in eastern Indonesia between Sulawesi and New Guinea, a group of small islands called the Maluku Islands (formerly Moluccas). The Dutch colonizers called these the **Spice Islands** because of the lucrative commerce in spices long carried on by Arab, Indian, and Chinese traders. What the Europeans wanted was control over this trade, and they were willing to go to war for it.

It may seem odd in today's world that spices could be important enough to be fought over, but at that time, in the prerefrigeration era, spices not only conserved food but also added flavor to otherwise bland diets. Spices commanded sky-high prices on European markets. The Dutch East India Company, the commercial arm of the Dutch government, managed to take control of the Spice Islands, bringing untold wealth to the Netherlands and ushering in an era of enrichment through colonial exploitation known as the country's Golden Age.

Java (Jawa), the most populous and productive island, became the focus of Dutch administration; from its capital at Batavia (now Jakarta), the Dutch East India Company extended its sphere of influence into Sumatra (Sumatera), Celebes (Sulawesi), and much of Borneo (Kalimantan) as well as the smaller islands of the East Indies. This was not accomplished overnight, and the struggle for territorial control was carried on long after the Company had yielded its administration to the Netherlands government in 1800. Dutch colonialism therefore threw a girdle around Indonesia's more than 17,000 islands, paving the way for the creation of the realm's largest and most populous state that is now home to a quarter-billion people.

From Spain to the United States

In the colonial tutelage of Southeast Asia, the Philippines, long under Spanish domination, had a unique experience.

As early as 1571, the islands north of Indonesia were under Spain's control (they were named for Spain's King Philip II). There was much profit to be made, but the indigenous peoples shared little in it. Great landholdings were awarded to loyal Spanish civil servants and to men of the church. Oppression eventually yielded revolution, and Spain was confronted with a major uprising in the Philippines just as the Spanish-American War broke out elsewhere in 1898.

As part of the settlement of that brief war, the United States replaced Spain in Manila as colonial proprietor. That was not the end of the revolution, however. The Filipinos now took up arms against their new foreign ruler, and not until 1905, after terrible losses of life, did American forces manage to pacify their new dominion. Subsequently, U.S. administration in the Philippines was more progressive than Spain's had been and eventually (after a temporary occupation by Japan during World War II) led the Philippines to independence in 1946.

Today all of Southeast Asia's states are independent, but centuries of imperial rule have left strong cultural imprints. In their urban landscapes, their education systems, and countless other ways, this realm still carries the legacy of its colonial past.

SOUTHEAST ASIA'S EMERGING MARKETS

If Japan and the Asian Tigers set the early example in the 1960s and 1970s, with post-Mao China following suit since the mid-1980s, it now seems to be the turn of several Southeast Asian countries to join the ranks of the world's rapidly emerging markets [6]. Vietnam, Indonesia, and Malaysia, in particular, have in recent years attracted substantial foreign investment and exhibited decidedly robust economic growth rates.

In the table in Appendix B, look at the column that shows per-capita income and note the very considerable disparities that mark this realm. The tiny oil state of Brunei has an income higher than that of the United States (although this figure is not indicative of the earnings of its relatively large foreign workforce). However, it is comprehensively developed Singapore that records Southeast Asia's highest income—at a level halfway between those of wealthy Luxembourg and Switzerland (and 18 percent higher than that of the U.S.). Malaysia comes in a distant third and is followed by Thailand. Populous Indonesia and the Philippines exhibit per-capita incomes less than one-twelfth of Singapore's. Finally, Vietnam, Laos, Cambodia, and Myanmar, in that order, rank at the bottom of the list. This table, however, only provides a 2010 snapshot and does not reflect the newest economic trends. According to many current observers, Vietnam has been growing the fastest in this decade. Of course, it remains a very poor country (whose per-capita income is only 5.6 percent of Singapore's) in urgent need of high growth rates to lift its masses to a better standard of living. Vietnam also remains a communist state, and in certain ways its government is more conservative than China's. But a stock exchange did open in Ho Chi Minh City (formerly Saigon) in 2000, and seven years later the country joined the World Trade Organization. If Vietnam takes further steps to liberalize its economy, observers say, it could become Asia's next economic miracle.

Singapore's Leadership

With its soaring per-capita income, there can be no doubt that Singapore is the economic heart of Southeast Asia. With a mere 5.4 million citizens and only 619 square kilometers (240 sq mi) of territory, we are obviously not referring to size—this is all about the connections and centrality that enable Singapore to function as the leading **node [7]** in a realmwide economic network. At the same time, geographers also rank Singapore as a top-tier world-city because it has major international linkages and exerts global influence. Singapore's container port is not only the largest in the realm but in the entire world, underscoring its key role within and far beyond Southeast Asia (see photo). Moreover, ultramodern Changi Airport Singapore is rated among the world's best international airports.

Singapore's exceptional regional position is based on its superb relative location. In the seventeenth century, it was Malacca farther up the Malay Peninsula that was the leading hub for trade and shipping in Southeast Asia. The Strait of Malacca (Fig. 10A-6), named after that town, was already the most important sea route providing access to the realm's waters for ships coming from the west. When the British sought to displace Dutch dominance in the region during the eighteenth century, they discovered an even better local base of operations: Singapore Island. Because it possessed a larger and deeper natural harbor than Malacca to accommodate the larger steamships of the time, Singapore swiftly rose to prominence as the British consolidated their power over this key corner of the world.

Most importantly, Singapore today is a symbol of modernity, a model for Southeast Asia's future. Throughout the realm, those who can afford it go there to shop, to connect to international flights, to transact business, to invest in real estate, or to send their children to one of the city-state's highly ranked universities. Imagine major parts of Southeast Asia following in Singapore's footsteps over the next two decades and how that would affect the realm and the world!

Prospects of Realmwide Integration: ASEAN

The overall development of Southeast Asia still has a long way to go. Political stability and increased regional integration will facilitate the process, and that is the long-term goal of **ASEAN [8]**, the Association of Southeast Asian Nations. Founded in the late 1960s, this supranational organization has primarily been concerned with security. But that has been a constantly challenging effort because a wide range of conditions mark its ten member-states. With the lone exception of minuscule East Timor, ASEAN encompasses all of the realm's countries. These include one influential city-state; an Islamic oil state (Brunei); two impoverished communist regimes (Vietnam and Laos); and a reforming military dictatorship whose population is rising from the ranks of the most deprived on Earth (Myanmar).

One conflict in which ASEAN has been conspicuously absent is a long-running border dispute between Cambodia and Thailand, directly north of the Cambodian city of Siem Reap (Fig. 10A-1). At issue is the location of the ancient Preah Vihear Temple, which according to a 1962 ruling by the International Court of Justice belongs to Cambodia but continues to be aggressively claimed by Thailand. The temple was declared a UNESCO World Heritage Site in 2008, and that only exacerbated matters. Gunfire across the border in 2010 and 2011 killed a dozen soldiers before a bilateral agreement was reached to withdraw troops from the area. In the spring of 2013, the Thai and Cambodian defense ministers met to strengthen peace and cooperation in the border area (ASEAN could have played a significant role in this dispute, but did not).

Another problem that ASEAN has failed to resolve, one that literally affects health across much of this realm, is the recurrent air pollution caused by Indonesia's massive, human-ignited forest fires. Depending on weather conditions and prevailing winds, thick plumes of smoke emanating from Indonesia's Sumatera (where most of the burning occurs, often to enlarge oil palm plantations) stream out toward Jawa, Singapore, Malaysia, and countries farther afield. Repeatedly, Singapore's government has had to advise residents to stay indoors (a new record high pollution level was set in June 2013). Indonesia, the realm's most powerful country, has been painfully slow to address this environmental crisis and

Singapore, Southeast Asia's unmatched world-city, has the biggest container port on Earth. This burgeoning city-state simultaneously functions as the heart of the realm's spatial economic system and a vitally important gateway to the global economy.

© Justin Guariglia/Corbis Images

even refused to ratify the 2002 ASEAN Agreement on Transboundary Haze Pollution.

In 1992, 25 years after its founding, ASEAN was able to expand into the economic domain through **AFTA** [9], the ASEAN Free Trade Agreement, and here the payoff has been more substantial. AFTA has both triggered the lowering of tariffs and encouraged an upsurge in trade within Southeast Asia. With lower wages than China, certain foreign investments (e.g., in the garment industry) have shifted to Southeast Asia. Moreover, intra-realm trade has surged in recent years—an important development to avoid being completely overshadowed by China.

CHINA IN SOUTHEAST ASIA TODAY

This is hardly the first time that Southeast Asia finds itself entangled in the spheres of influence of external powers. Over the past century alone, this realm was first dominated by European powers; next it was absorbed into Japan's short-lived empire; following postwar independence, it was later integrated within the Japanese-led *Yen bloc*; and since 2000, it is increasingly drawn into the economic (and political) orbit of China. In 2010, ASEAN and China concluded a free-trade agreement, with the Chinese especially interested in acquiring raw materials from mainland Southeast Asia as well as accessing the region's growing export markets.

Boosting Economic Development

The results of this agreement have been significant. China now provides the biggest share of imports flowing into Cam-

bodia, Indonesia, Malaysia, Myanmar, the Philippines, Singapore, and Vietnam; at the same time, China has become the leading export destination for Thailand, Vietnam, Singapore, and Malaysia (Fig. 10A-7). China's growing trade dominance in Southeast Asia has been achieved largely at the expense of Japan and the United States (the latter's trade with this realm now totals less than half of China's).

In addition to boosting trade, the Chinese are investing heavily across Southeast Asia in the exploitation of raw materials, construction, and massive infrastructure projects that facilitate the shipment of these commodities to China. They include a state-of-the-art rail connection from Kunming, capital of China's southern Yunnan Province, to Vientiane, Laos, fanning out from there in stages to Cambodia, Vietnam, Thailand, Malaysia, and Singapore; and if obstacles can be overcome, another key link will be a direct rail line from Kunming to Myanmar's Indian Ocean coast.

Although China is directly and indirectly contributing to the realm's economic development, its assertiveness and drive for dominance is also cause for growing unease. Some of this stems from China's formidable economic prowess, which produces rather asymmetrical relationships; for instance, many infrastructure projects are huge joint ventures that require comparatively larger investments from these much smaller Southeast Asian countries. And, more often than not, the benefits are clearly more favorable for China than for the host nation. Moreover, it is not all about economics: for countries such as Vietnam or Japan, historic sensitivities and/or longstanding rivalries come into play. Another issue is a perceived lack of Chinese

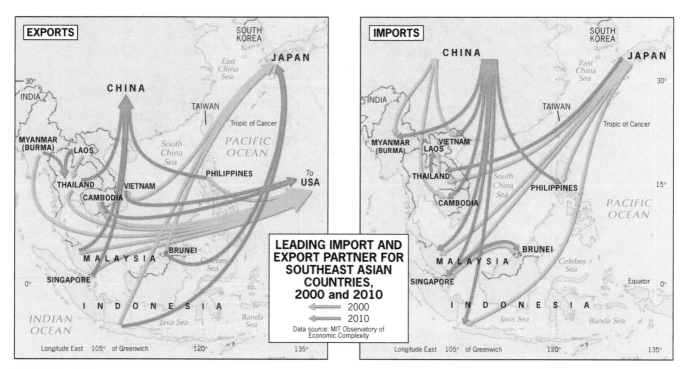

FIGURE 10A-7

© H. J. de Blij, P. O. Muller, J. Nijman, and John Wiley & Sons, Inc.

diplomacy and consideration for regional and national interests. Consider this 2010 remark by the Chinese foreign minister that "China is a big country and other countries are small countries, and that is just a fact." In response, the increasingly prevalent view in Southeast Asia is that, in order to avoid excessive dependence on China, its emerging markets must develop rapidly, diversify their trade partners, and strengthen intra-realm economic connections. And, as we are about to discover, this mindset also has a consequential geopolitical dimension, with a growing number of countries (most notably Vietnam, the Philippines,

and Indonesia) wanting the United States to play a more prominent regional role.

Geopolitics in the South China Sea

If China's economic role in Southeast Asia is often viewed with mixed feelings, its recent geopolitical and military forays are increasingly met with indignation and opposition. Much of this revolves around China's maritime ambitions and its claims in the South China Sea. Since 2009, the Chinese government has circulated the so-called *nine-dash*

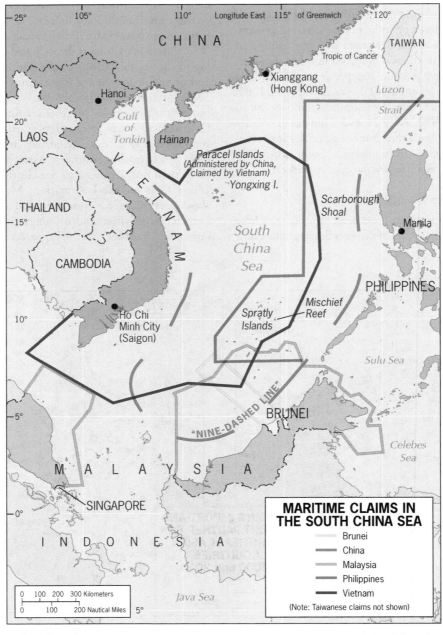

FIGURE 10A-8   © H. J. de Blij, P. O. Muller, J. Nijman, and John Wiley & Sons, Inc.

map showing Chinese claims in these waters—a map said to date back to 1949, the year the PRC was founded. The 'nine dashes' refer to the delimitation of Chinese claims that effectively cover most of the Sea (Fig. 10A-8). In the words of one high-ranking Chinese official in 2012, "China does not want all of the South China Sea, it just wants 80 percent." That 80 percent includes some 40 islands that China says are illegally occupied by other countries as well as seafloor zones believed to be rich in deposits of oil and natural gas.

The South China Sea, according to official government communications, "is crucial to the future of China as a growing maritime nation." Indeed, the PRC already controls many islands in this body of water, and in 2012 it expanded its military facilities on Yongxing (largest of the Paracel Islands), more than 200 miles southeast of Hainan Island, with the declared purpose of 'exercising sovereignty' across the South China Sea. The Sea contains about 250 islands, most of them lifeless rocks inundated at high tide, as well as numerous shoals that are permanently submerged. Even though the Chinese-controlled islands are inhabited by only a few hundred people, the PRC's assertion is mainly about sovereignty over surface waters and automatic ownership of oil and gas reserves that may be buried in the seabed below them.

The disputes and conflicts concerning territorial waters are numerous and complicated, but the most important concern: (1) the Paracel Islands, claimed by China, Taiwan, and Vietnam; (2) the Spratly Islands, claimed by China, Vietnam, Malaysia, and Brunei; and (3) the Scarborough Shoal, claimed by China, Taiwan, and the Philippines (Fig. 10A-8). Not surprisingly, ASEAN has been hopelessly divided on these geopolitical controversies, with Vietnam, Malaysia, and the Philippines as well as Malaysia strongly countering Chinese claims; Cambodia and Laos (tacitly) supporting China; and Singapore and Indonesia trying to steer a more neutral, diplomatic course. Recent ASEAN summit meetings have ended in open disagreement. Interestingly, Vietnam and the Philippines have sought a closer relationship with the United States, clearly in search of a counterweight to Chinese leverage.

Whereas the United States has declared its neutrality on the matter of who owns the islands and shoals, it has emphasized the paramount importance of free and open international access to the waters of the South China Sea. Why? Because this is one of the most essential oceanic trade corridors in the world. Think not only of the major shipping routes within the Southeast Asian realm that interconnect its chief ports of Manila, Singapore, Saigon, Bangkok, and Jakarta, but also of all the intercontinental trade coming from the west—from Europe and Africa as well as South and Southwest Asia—that passes through the Malacca and Singapore straits and then across the South China Sea on the way to China, Taiwan, South Korea, and Japan (not to mention all the seaborne cargoes that are transported along this route in the opposite direction).

In a recent joint military exercise, Filipino and American troops enacted the recapture of a small Philippine island from 'hostile forces.' The United States already had a mutual defense agreement with the Philippines; in 2012, it initiated joint military training with Vietnamese forces as well as signing a new military pact with Thailand. China is never mentioned by name as the hypothetical enemy in these exercises, but nobody is under any delusions as to where the threat to free access to these waters comes from. The South China Sea has quickly become a global geopolitical hotspot in this decade, and is certain to be closely monitored for the foreseeable future.

STATES AND BOUNDARIES

Although we tend to think of boundaries as lines on the map or fences on the ground, the legal definition of a boundary goes much farther than that. In fact, boundaries are actually invisible vertical planes extending above the ground into the air and below the ground into soil and rock (or water). Where these planes intersect with the ground, they form lines—the lines on the map.

A useful way to think about boundaries is to regard them as contracts between states. Such contracts take the form of treaties that contain the **definition** of every segment of the boundaries between them. These written definitions refer to actual landforms of the terrain through which the boundary lies—streams, larger water bodies, hills, ridges. Next, surveyors translate these descriptions into lines on large-scale maps that show every detail in the landscape. This process of **delimitation** creates the official boundary agreed to by the parties, and we see the results in generalized form on atlas maps. Sometimes neighboring states start arguing over the treaty language or the outcome of delimitation, which can result in armed conflict (as occurred between Sudan and South Sudan in 2012). To avoid such problems, states mark certain stretches of their borders with fences, walls, or other barriers on the cultural landscape, a process referred to as **demarcation.** Even though this clearly expresses a state's claims, it does not always resolve the dispute.

Classifying Boundaries

Boundaries have many functions, and to understand this (and to learn why some boundaries tend to produce more trouble than others) it is helpful to view them in a categorical perspective. Some boundaries conform to elongated features in the natural landscape (mountain ranges, rivers) and have **physiographic** origins. Others coincide with historic breaks or transitions in the cultural landscape and are sometimes referred to as *anthropogeographic,* or more recently as **ethnocultural** boundaries. And as any world political map shows, many boundaries are simply straight lines, defined by endpoint coordinates with no reference to physical or human landscape features; these **geometric**

From the Field Notes . . .

"I stood on the Laotian side of the great Mekong River which, during the dry season, did not look so great! On the opposite side was Thailand, and it was rather easy for people to cross here at this time of the year. But, the locals told me, it is quite another story in the wet season. Then the river inundates the rocks and banks you see here, it rushes past, and makes crossing difficult and even dangerous. The buildings where the canoes are docked are built on floats, and rise and fall with the seasons. The physiographic-political boundary between Thailand and Laos lies in the middle of the valley we see here."

© Barbara A. Weightman   **www.conceptcaching.com**

boundaries often lead to problems when valuable natural resources are found to lie across or beneath them.

In general, the colonial powers and their successor governments defined the boundaries of Southeast Asia more judiciously than was the case in several other now-postcolonial parts of the world that lay in remote and/or sparsely peopled areas (for instance, across interior Borneo). Nonetheless, a number of Southeast Asian boundaries have triggered disputes, among them the geometric boundary between Papua, the portion of New Guinea ruled by Indonesia, and the country of Papua New Guinea, which occupies the eastern part of that island. In fact, the artificiality of this boundary continues to intensify secessionist feelings among the population of Indonesian Papua.

Even on a small-scale map of the kind we use in this chapter, we can categorize the boundaries in this realm. A comparison between Figures 10A-1 and 10A-4 demonstrates that the boundary between Thailand and Myanmar over long stretches is ethnocultural, most notably where the name **Kayin (Karen)**, the Myanmar minority, appears in Figure 10A-4. And Figure 10A-1 shows that a lengthy segment of the Vietnam–Laos boundary is physiographic-political, in that it coincides with the crest of the Annamite Cordillera (Highlands).

Boundaries in Changing Times

A number of the world's boundaries are centuries old, whereas others are of more recent origin. Hence, another way of interpreting their functions is to examine their evolution as part of the cultural landscape they partition. We distinguish four types of these **genetic** (evolutionary) boundaries; as it happens, examples of all four can be found in Southeast Asia.

Certain boundaries were defined and delimited before the present-day human landscape materialized. In Figure 10A-9 (upper-left map), the border between Malaysia and Indonesia across the island of Borneo is an example of the first boundary type, an antecedent boundary [10]. Most of this border passes through very sparsely inhabited tropical rainforest, and the break in the settlement pattern can even be detected in the realm's population map (Fig. 10A-3).

A second category of boundaries evolved as the cultural landscape of an area took shape and became part of the ongoing process of accommodation between neighboring states. These subsequent boundaries [11] are represented in Southeast Asia by the map in the upper right of Figure 10A-9, which shows in some detail the border between Vietnam and China. This border is the result of a long process of adjustment and modification, the end of which may not yet have occurred.

The third category involves boundaries drawn forcibly across a unified or at least homogeneous cultural landscape. The colonial powers did this when they divided the island of New Guinea by delimiting a boundary in a nearly straight line (curved in only one place to allow for a bend in the Fly River), as shown in the lower-left map of Figure 10A-9. The superimposed boundary [12] they delimited gave the Netherlands the western half of New Guinea. When Indonesia became independent in 1949, the Dutch did not yield their part of New Guinea, which is peopled

GENETIC POLITICAL BOUNDARY TYPES

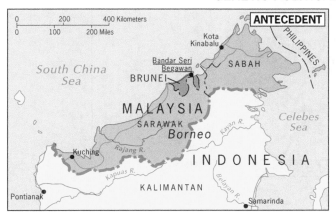

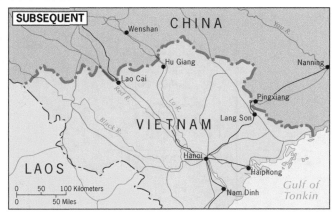

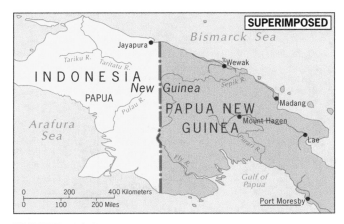

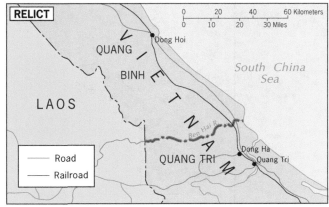

FIGURE 10A-9

© H. J. de Blij, P. O. Muller, and John Wiley & Sons, Inc.

mostly by ethnic Papuans, not Indonesians. In 1962, the Indonesians invaded the territory by force of arms, and in 1969 the United Nations recognized its authority there. This made the colonial, superimposed boundary the eastern border of Indonesia and had the effect of projecting Indonesia from the Southeast Asian realm into the adjoining Pacific Realm. Geographically, all of New Guinea lies within the Pacific Realm.

The fourth genetic boundary type is the so-called **relict boundary [13]** a border that has ceased to function but whose imprints (and sometimes influence) are still evident in the cultural landscape. The boundary between former North and South Vietnam (Fig. 10A-9, lower-right map) is a classic example: once demarcated militarily, it has held relict status since 1976 following the reunification of Vietnam in the aftermath of the Indochina War (1964–1975).

Southeast Asia's boundaries have colonial origins, but they have continued to influence the course of events in postcolonial times. Take one instance: the physiographic boundary that separates the main island of Singapore from the rest of the Malay Peninsula, the Johor Strait (see Fig. 10B-6). That physiographic-political boundary facilitated, perhaps crucially, Singapore's secession from the state of Malaysia in 1965. Without it, Malaysia might have been

persuaded to halt the separation process; at the very least, territorial issues would have arisen to slow the sequence of events. As it was, no land boundary needed to be defined: the Johor Strait demarcated Singapore and left no question as to its limits.*

State Territorial Morphology

Boundaries define and delimit states; they also create the mosaic of often interlocking territories that give individual countries their shape. This shape or ***territorial morphology*** can affect a state's condition, even its survival. Vietnam's extreme elongation has influenced its existence since time immemorial. And, as is noted in Chapter 10B, Indonesia has tried to redress its fragmented nature (thousands of islands) by promoting unity through the "transmigration" of residents of Jawa from the most populous island to many of the others.

---

*Except one: a tiny island at the eastern entrance to the Strait named Pedra Blanca (as Singapore calls it) or Pulau Batu Putih (the Malaysian version), which is still disputed today.

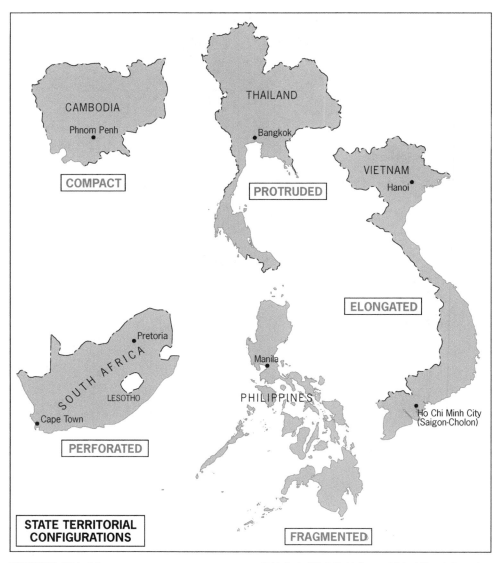

FIGURE 10A-10

© H. J. de Blij, P. O. Muller, and John Wiley & Sons, Inc.

Political geographers identify five dominant state territorial configurations, all of which we have encountered in our world regional survey but which we have not categorized until now. All but one of these shapes is represented in Southeast Asia, and Figure 10A-10 provides the terminology and examples:

- Compact states [14] have territories shaped somewhere between round and rectangular, without major indentations. This encloses a maximum amount of territory within a minimum length of boundary. Southeast Asian example: Cambodia.

- Protruded states [15] (sometimes called *extended*) have a substantial, usually compact territory from which extends a peninsular or other corridor that may be landlocked or coastal. Southeast Asian examples: Thailand and Myanmar.

- Elongated states [16] (also known as *attenuated*) have territorial dimensions in which the length is at least six times the average width, creating a state that lies astride environmental or cultural transitions. Southeast Asian example: Vietnam.

- Fragmented states [17] consist of two or more territorial units separated by foreign territory or a substantial body of water. Subtypes include mainland-mainland, mainland-island, and island-island. Southeast Asian examples: Malaysia, Indonesia, the Philippines, and East Timor.

- Perforated states [18] completely surround the territory of other states, so that they have a "hole" in them. No Southeast Asian example; the most illustrative case on the world political map is South Africa, perforated by Maryland-sized Lesotho.

In Chapter 10B, we will have frequent occasion to refer to the shapes of Southeast Asia's states. For so comparatively small a realm with so few countries, Southeast Asia displays a considerable variety of state morphologies. But one point of caution: states' territorial morphologies do not determine their viability, cohesion, unity, or lack thereof; they can, however, influence these qualities. Cambodia's compactness has not ameliorated its divisive political geography, for instance. But as we will find in our survey of the realm's regional geography, shape does play a key role in the still-evolving political and economic geography of Southeast Asia.

REALM BETWEEN THE GIANTS

Southeast Asia's 11 states create a geographic panorama of diverse cultures, economic contrasts, and political options, but this realm's looming reality today is the rise of China on land and rea. Take another look at Figure 10A-1: it is somehow symbolic that the realm's mainland and offshore regions encircle a large body of water named the South China Sea even though, by the time you sail the water between Vietnam and Malaysia, you are well over 1500 kilometers (930 mi) from the nearest coast of China. The Chinese colossus is everywhere in Southeast Asia today—from the bustling Chinatowns in the cities to the commercially productive minorities on remote islands, from the dams and pipelines being laid for local governments to the farmlands the Chinese are leasing for the future. Diversity is Southeast Asia's hallmark, and certainly the realm's governments are reacting differently to China's growing influence. On the mainland, the government of Cambodia has become a strong ally of China while neighboring Vietnam takes a very different view. Offshore, the Philippines two decades ago sought to distance itself from greater American involvement, but today the Philippine government sees the United States as a counterweight to China's potential dominance.

If all eyes are on China in Southeast Asia these days, it is useful to remember that another colossus adjoins this realm to the west: India. Southeast Asia is where the Indian Ocean meets the Pacific, and although India is no China in terms of its economic strength or political power, India's geopolitical view of the Indian Ocean is not totally unlike China's perspective on the western Pacific: India, too, takes a proprietary view of "its" maritime region. India, like China but with fewer resources, is expanding and modernizing its navy and proclaiming its presence among Asia's naval forces. India eyed warily China's long-term relationship with the generals who ran Myanmar, its neighbor, until Myanmar's current transition began. Now India takes an active interest in the fate of its neighbor's reformist efforts, but with a different attitude. And let us not forget that while Chinese minorities are numerous and economically prominent within Southeast Asia, there also are substantial Indian minorities (and cultural legacies) in Malaysia, Singapore, Indonesia, and elsewhere. Might India someday become the counterweight to China in this realm? At present it appears unlikely, but political geography can take unexpected turns.

As we traverse the physical and cultural landscapes of the countries that make up this fascinating geographic realm, be prepared for some surprises. In one of the most modern, you cannot say uncomplimentary things about the king or risk going to jail (Thailand). In another, you would believe that you had arrived in an Arab petro-sheikdom (Brunei). In still another, you are at the center of globalization—the airport by itself will make you think you've come from the Third World (Singapore). But drive into some of the countrysides, and it will seem as though you are back in an earlier century, and time has stood still. This truly is an entire world in a single, diminutive realm.

> ### POINTS TO PONDER
>
> - Certain Southeast Asian states have achieved much in their efforts to accommodate diverse cultural traditions.
> - The two smallest countries of the realm are also by far the wealthiest.
> - China's influence in Southeast Asia is growing. Is the Mainland region becoming a Chinese periphery?
> - In your daily life, how many products do you use that contain palm oil? How can you find out? As a consumer, do you contribute to deforestation?

GLOSSARY*

Aboriginal land issue The legal campaign in which Australia's **indigenous peoples** have claimed title to traditional land in several parts of that country. The courts have upheld certain claims, fueling Aboriginal activism that has raised broader issues of indigenous rights.

Aboriginal population Native or *aboriginal* peoples; often used to designate the inhabitants of areas that were conquered and subsequently colonized by the **imperial** powers of Europe.

Absolute location The position or place of a certain item on the surface of the Earth as expressed in degrees, minutes, and seconds of **latitude** and **longitude**.

Accessibility The degree of ease with which it is possible to reach a certain location from other locations. *Inaccessibility* is the opposite of this concept.

Acculturation Cultural modification resulting from intercultural borrowing. In **cultural geography**, the term refers to the change that occurs in the **culture** of **indigenous peoples** when contact is made with a society that is technologically superior.

Advantage The most meaningful distinction that can now be made to classify a country's level of economic **development**. Takes into account geographic **location, natural resources**, government, political stability, productive skills, and much more.

AFTA The ASEAN Free Trade Agreement that since 1992, through lowered tariffs and other incentives, has fostered increased trade within Southeast Asia. This is the economic centerpiece of the **Association of Southeast Asian Nations (ASEAN)**, a **supranational** organization whose members include 10 of that realm's 11 states (only East Timor does not participate).

Agglomeration **Process** involving the clustering or concentrating of people or activities.

Agrarian Relating to the use of land in rural communities or to agricultural societies in general.

Agriculture The purposeful tending of crops and livestock in order to produce food and fiber.

Al-Qaeda The terrorist organization that evolved into an expanding global network under the directorship of Usama bin Laden between the mid-1990s and his elimination by the U.S. in 2011. It sought to coordinate the efforts of once loosely allied Muslim revolutionary movements, and unleash a *jihad* aimed at what it perceived to be Islam's enemies in the West.

Alluvial Referring to the mud, silt, and sand (collectively *alluvium*) deposited by rivers and streams. *Alluvial plains* adjoin many larger rivers; they consist of the renewable deposits that are laid down during floods, creating fertile and productive soils. Alluvial **deltas** mark the mouths of rivers such as the Nile (Egypt) and the Ganges (Bangladesh).

Altiplano High-elevation plateau, basin, or valley between even higher mountain ranges, especially in the Andes of South America.

Altitudinal zonation Vertical regions defined by physical-environmental zones at various elevations (see Fig. 4A-4), particularly in the highlands of South and Middle America.

American Manufacturing Belt North America's near-rectangular Core Region, whose corners are Boston, Milwaukee, St. Louis, and Baltimore.

Animistic religion The belief that inanimate objects, such as hills, trees, rocks, rivers, and other elements of the natural landscape, possess souls and can help or hinder human efforts on Earth.

Antarctic Treaty International cooperative agreement on the use of Antarctic territory.

Antecedent boundary A political boundary that existed before the **cultural landscape** emerged and stayed in place while people moved in to occupy the surrounding area.

Anthracite coal Hardest and highest carbon-content coal, and therefore of the highest quality.

Apartheid Literally, *apartness*. The Afrikaans term for South Africa's pre-1994 policies of racial separation, a system that produced highly segregated socio-geographical patterns.

Aquaculture The use of a river segment or an artificial pond for the raising and harvesting of food products, including fish, shellfish, and even seaweed. The Japanese pioneered the practice, which is now spreading globally, and is already the dominant source of seafood as the oceans become fished out.

Aquifer An underground reservoir of water contained within a porous, water-bearing rock layer.

Arable Land fit for cultivation by one farming method or another. See also **physiologic density**.

Archipelago A set of islands grouped closely together, usually elongated into a *chain*.

Area A term that refers to a part of the Earth's surface with less specificity than **region**. For example, *urban area* alludes generally to a place where urban development has occurred, whereas *urban region* requires certain specific criteria on which such a designation is based (e.g., the spatial extent of commuting or the built townscape).

Areal interdependence A term related to **functional specialization**. When one area produces certain goods or has certain raw materials and another area has a different set of raw materials and produces different goods, their needs may be *complementary*; by exchanging raw materials and products, they can satisfy each other's requirements.

Arithmetic density A country's population, expressed as an average per unit area, without regard for its **distribution** or the limits of **arable** land. See also **physiologic density**.

Aryan From the Sanskrit *Arya* (meaning "noble"), a name applied to an ancient people who spoke an **Indo-European language** and who moved into northern India from the northwest.

ASEAN The **Association of Southeast Asian Nations (ASEAN)**, a **supra-national** organization whose members include 10 of that realm's 11 states: Brunei, Cambodia, Indonesia, Laos, Malaysia, Myanmar (Burma), the Philippines, Singapore, Thailand, and Vietnam (only minuscule East Timor does not participate).

Asian Tiger See **economic tiger**.

Atmosphere The Earth's envelope of gases that rests on the oceans and land surface and penetrates open spaces within soils. This layer of nitrogen (78 percent), oxygen (21 percent), and traces of other gases is densest at the Earth's surface and thins with altitude.

Atoll A ring-like coral reef surrounding an empty lagoon that probably formed around the rim of a now-completely-eroded volcanic cone standing on the seafloor. They are common in certain tropical areas of the Pacific Ocean where they are classified among that realm's **low islands**.

Austral South.

Autocratic A government that holds absolute power, often ruled by one person or a small group of persons who control the country by despotic means.

Balkanization The fragmentation of a **region** into smaller, often hostile political units. Named after the historically contentious Balkan Peninsula of southeastern Europe.

Barrio Term meaning "neighborhood" in Spanish. Usually refers to an urban community in a Middle or South American city.

Biodiversity Shorthand for *biological diversity*; the total variety of plant and animal species that exists in a given area.

---

*Words in **boldface type** within an entry are defined elsewhere in this Glossary

Biodiversity hotspot A much higher than usual, world-class geographic concentration of natural plant and/or animal species. Tropical rainforest environments have dominated, but their recent ravaging by **deforestation** has had catastrophic results.

Biogeography The study of *flora* (plant life) and *fauna* (animal life) in spatial perspective.

Biome One of the broadest justifiable (geographic) subdivisions of the plant and animal world (less than a dozen exist overall). An assemblage and association of plants and animals that forms a regional ecological unit of subcontinental dimensions.

Birth rate The *crude birth rate* is expressed as the annual number of births per 1000 individuals within a given population.

Bituminous coal Softer coal of lesser quality than **anthracite**, but of higher grade than **lignite**. When heated and converted to coking coal or *coke*, it is used to make steel.

Boreal forest The subarctic, mostly **coniferous** snowforest that blankets Canada south of the **tundra** that lines the Arctic shore; known as the **taiga** in Russia.

Break-of-bulk point A location along a transport route where goods must be transferred from one carrier to another. In a port, the cargoes of oceangoing ships are unloaded and put on trains, trucks, or perhaps smaller river boats for inland distribution. An *entrepôt*.

BRIC Acronym for the four biggest emerging national markets in the world today—**B**razil, **R**ussia, **I**ndia, and **C**hina.

British Commonwealth Now renamed *The Commonwealth of Nations* (and known simply as *The Commonwealth*), this nonpolitical inter-governmental organization is constituted by 54 member-states. All but two (Rwanda and Moçambique) formerly belonged to the British Empire, from which the organization originated. Its members cooperate in free association to promote, among other things, democracy, human rights, free trade, and world peace.

Buffer state or Buffer zone A country or set of countries separating ideological or political adversaries. In southern Asia, Afghanistan, Nepal, and Bhutan were parts of a buffer zone set up between British and Russian-Chinese imperial spheres. Thailand was a *buffer state* between British and French colonial domains in mainland Southeast Asia.

Caliente See *tierra caliente*.

Cartogram A specially transformed map not based on traditional representations of **scale** or area.

Cartography The art and science of making maps, including data compilation, layout, and design. Also concerned with the interpretation of mapped patterns.

Caste system The strict **social stratification** and segregation of people—specifically in India's Hindu society—on the basis of ancestry and occupation.

Cay A low-lying small island usually composed of coral and sand. Pronounced *kee* and often spelled "key."

Cellphone revolution Applied specifically to much of Subsaharan Africa and certain other parts of the developing world, the linking of farmers with centers of information for weather and market conditions via cellphone text messaging—allowing them to negotiate higher prices for their products.

Central business district (CBD) The downtown heart of a central city; marked by high land values, a concentration of business and commerce, and the clustering of the tallest buildings.

Centrality The strength of an urban center in its capacity to attract producers and consumers to its facilities; a city's "reach" into the surrounding region.

Centrifugal forces A term employed to designate forces that tend to divide a country—such as internal religious, linguistic, ethnic, or ideological differences.

Centripetal forces Forces that unite and bind a country together—such as a strong national culture, shared ideological objectives, and a common faith.

Cerrado Regional term referring to the fertile savannas of Brazil's interior Central-West that make it one of the world's most promising agricultural frontiers. Soybeans are the leading crop, and other grains and cotton are expanding. Inadequate transport links to the outside world remain a problem.

Choke point A narrowing of an international waterway causing marine-traffic congestion, requiring reduced speeds and/or sharp turns, and increasing the risk of collision as well as vulnerability to attack. When the waterway narrows to a distance of less than 38 kilometers (24 mi), this necessitates the drawing of a **median line (maritime) boundary**.

City-state An independent political entity consisting of a single city with (and sometimes without) an immediate **hinterland**.

Climate The long-term conditions (over at least 30 years) of aggregate **weather** over a region, summarized by averages and measures of variability; a synthesis of the succession of weather events we have learned to expect at any given location.

Climate change theory An alternative to the **hydraulic civilization theory**; holds that changing **climate** (rather than a monopoly over **irrigation** methods) could have provided certain cities within the ancient Fertile Crescent with advantages over other cities.

Climate region A **formal region** characterized by the uniformity of the **climate** type within it. Figure G-7 maps the global distribution of such regions.

Climatology The geographic study of **climates**. Includes not only the classification of climates and the analysis of their regional distribution, but also broader environmental questions that concern climate change, interrelationships with soil and vegetation, and human–climate interaction.

Coal See **anthracite coal, bituminous coal, fossil fuels,** and **lignite**.

Collectivization The reorganization of a country's **agriculture** under communism that involves the expropriation of private holdings and their incorporation into relatively large-scale units, which are farmed and administered cooperatively by those who live there.

Colonialism Rule by an autonomous power over a subordinate and an alien people and place. Though often established and maintained through political structures, colonialism also creates unequal cultural and economic relations. Because of the magnitude and impact of the European colonial thrust of the last few centuries, the term is generally understood to refer to that particular colonial endeavor.

Command economy The tightly controlled economic system of the former Soviet Union, whereby central planners in Moscow assigned the production of particular goods to particular places, often guided more by socialist ideology than the principles of **economic geography**.

Commercial agriculture For-profit **agriculture**.

Common market A **free-trade area** that not only has created a **customs union** (a set of common tariffs on all imports from outside the area) but also has eliminated restrictions on the movement of capital, labor, and enterprise among its member countries.

Communal tension Persistent stress among a country's sociocultural groups that can often erupt into communal violence.

Compact state A politico-geographical term to describe a state that possesses a roughly circular, oval, or rectangular territory in which the distance from the geometric center to any point on the boundary exhibits little variance.

Complementarity Exists when two regions, through an exchange of raw materials and/or finished products, can specifically satisfy each other's demands.

Confucianism A philosophy of ethics, education, and public service based on the writings of Confucius (*Kongfuzi*); traditionally regarded as one of the cornerstones of Chinese **culture**.

Congo Two countries in Africa have the same short-form name, *Congo*. In this book, we use *DRCongo* for the larger Democratic Republic of the Congo, and *Congo* for the smaller Republic of Congo.

Coniferous forest A forest of cone-bearing, needleleaf evergreen trees with straight trunks and short branches, including spruce, fir, and pine. See also **taiga** and **boreal forest**.

Connectivity The degree of direct linkage between a particular location and other locations within a regional, national, or global transportation **network**.

Contagious diffusion The distance-controlled spreading of an idea, innovation, or some other item through a local population by contact from person to person—analogous to the communication of a contagious illness.

Conterminous United States The 48 **contiguous** or adjacent States that occupy the southern half of the North American realm. Alaska is not contiguous to these States because western Canada lies in between; neither is Hawai'i, separated from the mainland by over 3000 kilometers (2000 mi) of ocean.

Contiguous Adjoining; adjacent.

Continental drift The slow movement of continents controlled by the processes associated with **plate tectonics**.

Continental shelf Beyond the coastlines of many landmasses, the ocean floor declines very gently until the depth of about 660 feet (200 m). Beyond the 660-foot line the sea bottom usually drops off sharply, along the *continental slope*, toward the much deeper mid-oceanic basin. The submerged continental margin is called the continental shelf, and it extends from the shoreline to the upper edge of the continental slope.

Continentality The variation of the continental effect on air temperatures in the interior portions of the world's landmasses. The greater the distance from the moderating influence of an ocean, the greater the extreme in summer and winter temperatures. Continental interiors also tend to be dry when the distance from oceanic moisture sources becomes considerable.

Conurbation General term used to identify a large multimetropolitan complex formed by the coalescence of two or more major **urban areas**.

Copra The dried-out, fleshy interior of a coconut that is used to produce coconut oil.

Cordillera Mountain chain consisting of sets of parallel ranges, especially the Andes in northwestern South America.

Core See **core area**; **core-periphery relationships**.

Core area In geography, a term with several connotations. *Core* refers to the center, heart, or focus. The core area of a **nation-state** is constituted by the national heartland, the largest population cluster, the most productive region, and the part of the country with the greatest **centrality** and **accessibility**—probably containing the capital city as well.

Core-periphery relationships The contrasting spatial characteristics of, and linkages between, the *have* (core) and *have-not* (periphery) components of a national, regional, or the global **system**.

Corridor In general, refers to a spatial entity in which human activity is organized in a linear manner, as along a major transport route or in a valley confined by highlands. More specifically, the politico-geographical term for a land extension that connects an otherwise **landlocked state** to the sea.

Cross-border linkages The ties between two closely-connected localities or regions that face each other across an international boundary. These relationships are often longstanding, and intensify further as **supranationalism** proceeds (especially among the EU countries of western Europe).

Cultural diffusion The **process** of spreading and adopting a cultural element, from its place of origin across a wider area.

Cultural diversity A society marked by a variety of cultures, especially in its ancestral backgrounds.

Cultural ecology or cultural environment The myriad interactions and relationships between a **culture** and its **natural environment**.

Cultural geography The wide-ranging and comprehensive field of geography that studies spatial aspects of human **cultures**.

Cultural landscape The forms and artifacts sequentially placed on the **natural landscape** by the activities of various human occupants. By this progressive imprinting of the human presence, the physical (natural) landscape is modified into the cultural landscape, forming an interacting unity between the two.

Cultural pluralism A society in which two or more population groups, each practicing its own **culture**, live adjacent to one another without mixing inside a single **state**.

Cultural revival The regeneration of a long-dormant **culture** through internal renewal and external infusion.

Culture hearth (also called Cultural hearth) Heartland, source area, or innovation center; place of origin of a major **culture**.

Culture The sum total of the knowledge, attitudes, and habitual behavior patterns shared and transmitted by the members of a society. This is anthropologist Ralph Linton's definition; hundreds of others exist.

Culture hearth Heartland, source area, innovation center; place of origin of a major **culture**.

Culture region A distinct, culturally discrete spatial unit; a **region** within which certain cultural norms prevail.

Customs union A **free-trade area** in which member countries set common tariff rates on imports from outside the area.

Dalit The term now used for members of the lowest-ranking social layer in the **caste system** of Hindu India.

Death rate The *crude death rate* is expressed as the annual number of deaths per 1000 individuals within a given population.

Deciduous A deciduous tree loses its leaves at the beginning of winter or the onset of the dry season.

Definition In **political geography**, the written legal description (in a treaty-like document) of a boundary between two countries or territories. See also **delimitation**.

Deforestation The clearing and destruction of forests (especially tropical rainforests) to make way for expanding settlement frontiers and the exploitation of new economic opportunities.

Deglomeration Deconcentration.

Deindustrialization **Process** by which companies relocate manufacturing jobs to other regions or countries with cheaper labor, leaving the newly-deindustrialized region to convert to a service economy while struggling with the accompanying effects of increased unemployment and meeting the retraining needs of its workforce.

Delimitation In **political geography**, the translation of the written terms of a boundary treaty (the **definition**) into an official cartographic representation (map).

Delta **Alluvial** lowland at the mouth of a river, formed when the river deposits its alluvial load on reaching the sea. Often triangular in shape, hence the use of the Greek letter whose symbol is D.

Demarcation In **political geography**, the actual placing of a political boundary on the **cultural landscape** by means of barriers, fences, walls, or other markers.

Demographic burden The proportion of a national population that is either too old or too young to be productive and that must be cared for by the productive population.

Demographic transition Multi-stage **model**, based on western Europe's experience, of changes in population growth exhibited by countries undergoing industrialization. High **birth rates** and **death rates** are followed by plunging death rates, producing a huge net population gain; birth and death rates then converge at a low overall level.

Demography The interdisciplinary study of population—especially **birth rates** and **death rates**, growth patterns, longevity, **migration**, and related characteristics.

Dependencia theory Originating in South America during the 1960s, it was a new way of thinking about economic development and underdevelopment that explained the persistent poverty of certain countries in terms of their unequal relations with other (i.e., rich) countries.

Desert An arid expanse supporting sparse vegetation, receiving less than 25 centimeters (10 in) of precipitation per year. Usually exhibits extremes of heat and cold because the moderating influence of moisture is absent.

Desertification **Process** of **desert** expansion into neighboring **steppelands** as a result of human degradation of fragile semiarid environments.

Development The economic, social, and institutional growth of national **states**.

Devolution The **process** whereby regions within a **state** demand and gain political strength and growing autonomy at the expense of the central government.

Dhows Wooden boats with characteristic triangular sails, plying the seas between Arabian and East African coasts.

Dialect Regional or local variation in the use of a major language, such as the distinctive accents of many residents of the U.S. South.

Diffusion The spatial spreading or dissemination of a **culture** element (such as a technological innovation) or some other phenomenon (e.g., a disease outbreak). For the various channels of outward geographic spread from a source area, see **contagious, expansion, hierarchical,** and **relocation diffusion.**

Distance decay The various degenerative effects of distance on human spatial structures and interactions.

Diurnal Daily.

Divided capital In **political geography,** a country whose central administrative functions are carried on in more than one city is said to have divided capitals. The Netherlands and South Africa are examples.

Domestication The transformation of a wild animal or wild plant into a domesticated animal or a cultivated crop to gain control over food production. A necessary evolutionary step in the development of humankind: the invention of **agriculture.**

Domino effect or theory The belief that political destabilization in one **state** can result in the collapse of order in a neighboring state, triggering a chain of events that, in turn, can affect a series of **contiguous** states.

Double complementarity Complementarity exists when two regions, through an exchange of raw materials and/or finished products, can specifically satisfy each other's demands; *double complementarity* exists when that interaction occurs in both directions simultaneously.

Double cropping The planting, cultivation, and harvesting of two crops successively within a single year on the same plot of farmland.

Double Delta South Asia's combined **delta** formed by the Ganges and Brahmaputra rivers. All of Bangladesh lies on this enormous deltaic plain, which also encompasses surrounding parts of eastern India. Well over 200 million people live here, attracted by the fertility of its soils that are constantly replenished by the **alluvium** transported and deposited by these two of Asia's largest river systems. Natural hazards abound here as well, ranging from the flooding caused by excessive **monsoonal** rains to the intermittent storm surges of powerful cyclones (**hurricanes**) that come from the Bay of Bengal to the south.

Dravidian languages The language family, indigenous to the South Asian realm, that dominates southern India today; as opposed to the Indo-European languages, whose tongues dominate northern India.

Dry canal An overland rail and/or road **corridor** across an **isthmus** dedicated to performing the transit functions of a canalized waterway. Best adapted to the movement of containerized cargo, there must be a port at each end to handle the necessary **break-of-bulk** unloading and reloading.

Dynasty A succession of Chinese rulers that came from the same line of male descent, sometimes enduring for centuries. Dynastic rule in China lasted for thousands of years, only coming to an end just a bit more than a century ago in 1911.

Ecology The study of the many interrelationships between all forms of life and the natural environments in which they have evolved and continue to develop. The study of *ecosystems* focuses on the interactions between specific organisms and their environments. See also **cultural ecology, biome,** and **biodiversity.**

Economic geography The field of geography that focuses on the diverse ways in which people earn a living and on how the goods and services they produce are expressed and organized spatially.

Economic restructuring The transformation of China into a market-driven economy in the post-Mao era, beginning in the late 1970s.

Economic tiger One of the burgeoning beehive countries of the western **Pacific Rim.** Following Japan's route since 1945, these countries have experienced significant modernization, industrialization, and Western-style economic growth since 1980. Three leading economic tigers are South Korea, Taiwan, and Singapore. The term is increasingly used more generally to describe any fast-developing economy.

Economies of scale The savings that accrue from large-scale production wherein the unit cost of manufacturing decreases as the level of operation enlarges. Supermarkets operate on this principle and are able to charge lower prices than small grocery stores.

Ecosystem See **ecology.**

Ecumene The habitable portions of the Earth's surface where permanent human settlements have arisen.

Ejidos Mexican farmlands redistributed to peasant communities after the Revolution of 1910–1917. The government holds title to the land, but user rights are parceled out to village communities and then to individuals for cultivation.

Elite A small but influential upper-echelon social class whose power and privilege give it control over a country's political, economic, and cultural life.

El Niño-Southern Oscillation (ENSO) A periodic, large-scale, abnormal warming of the sea surface in the tropical latitudes of the eastern Pacific Ocean that has global implications, disturbing normal weather patterns in many parts of the world, especially South America.

Elongated state A **state** whose territory is decidedly long and narrow in that its length is at least six times greater than its average width.

Emerging market The world's fastest growing national market economies as measured by economic growth rates, attraction of **foreign direct investment,** and other key indicators. Led by the **BRICs** (Brazil, Russia, India, and China), but this club is now expanding to include many other countries.

Emigrant A person **migrating** away from a country or area; an out-migrant.

Empirical Relating to the real world, as opposed to theoretical abstraction.

Enclave A piece of territory that is surrounded by another political unit of which it is not a part.

Endemism Referring to a disease in a host population that affects many people in a kind of equilibrium without causing rapid and widespread deaths.

Entrepôt A place, usually a port city, where goods are imported, stored, and transshipped; a **break-of-bulk point.**

Environmental degradation The accumulated human abuse of a region's **natural landscape** that, among other things, can involve air and water pollution, threats to plant and animal **ecosystems,** misuse of **natural resources,** and generally upsetting the balance between people and their habitat.

Epidemic A local or regional outbreak of a disease.

Escarpment A cliff or very steep slope; often marks the edge of a plateau. The Great Escarpment that lines much of Africa's east coast is a classic example.

Estuary The widening mouth of a river as it reaches the sea; land subsidence or a rise in sea level has overcome the tendency to form a **delta.**

Ethanol The leading U.S. biofuel that is essentially alcohol distilled from corn mash. Much of it is produced in the historic Corn Belt centered on Iowa and Illinois. Many risks and problems accompany this energy source, which overall is not an efficient replacement for **fossil fuels.**

Ethnic cleansing The slaughter and/or forced removal of one **ethnic** group from its homes and lands by another, more powerful ethnic group bent on taking that territory.

Ethnicity The combination of a people's **culture** (traditions, customs, language, and religion) and racial ancestry.

European state model A **state** consisting of a legally defined territory inhabited by a population governed from a capital city by a representative government.

European Union (EU) **Supranational** organization constituted by 28 European countries to further their common economic interests. In alphabetical order, these countries are: Austria, Belgium, Bulgaria, Croatia, Cyprus, the Czech Republic, Denmark, Estonia, Finland, France, Germany, Greece, Hungary, Ireland, Italy, Latvia, Lithuania, Luxembourg, Malta, the Netherlands, Poland, Portugal, Romania, Slovakia, Slovenia, Spain, Sweden, and the United Kingdom.

Exclave A bounded (non-island) piece of territory that is part of a particular **state** but lies separated from it by the territory of another state.

Exclusive Economic Zone (EEZ) An oceanic zone extending up to 200 **nautical miles** (370 km) from a shoreline, within which the coastal **state** can control fishing, mineral exploitation, and additional activities by all other countries.

Expansion diffusion The spreading of an innovation or an idea through a fixed population in such a way that the number of those adopting it grows continuously larger, resulting in an expanding area of dissemination.

Extraterritoriality The politico-geographical concept suggesting that the property of one **state** lying within the boundaries of another actually forms an extension of the first state.

Failed state A country whose institutions have collapsed and in which anarchy prevails.

Fatwa Literally, a legal opinion or proclamation issued by an Islamic cleric, based on the holy texts of Islam, long applicable only in the *Umma*, the realm ruled by the laws of Islam. In 1989, the Iranian Ayatollah Khomeini extended the reach of the *fatwa* by condemning to death author Salman Rushdie, a British citizen living in the United Kingdom.

Favela Shantytown on the outskirts or even well within an urban area in Brazil.

Fazenda Coffee plantation in Brazil.

Federal state A political framework wherein a central government represents the various subnational entities within a **nation-state** where they have common interests—defense, foreign affairs, and the like—yet allows these various entities to retain their own identities and to have their own laws, policies, and customs in certain spheres.

Federal system A political framework wherein a central government represents the various subnational entities within a country where they have common interests—defense, foreign affairs, and the like—yet allows these various entities to retain their own identities and to have their own laws, policies, and customs in certain spheres.

Federation A country adhering to a political framework wherein a central government represents the various subnational entities within a **nation-state** where they have common interests—defense, foreign affairs, and the like—yet allows these various entities to retain their own identities and to have their own laws, policies, and customs in certain spheres.

Fertile Crescent Crescent-shaped zone of productive lands extending from near the southeastern Mediterranean coast through Lebanon and Syria to the **alluvial** lowlands of Mesopotamia (in Iraq). Once more fertile than today, this is one of the world's great source areas of **agricultural** and other innovations.

Fertility rate More technically the Total Fertility Rate, it is the average number of children born to women of childbearing age in a given population.

First Nations Name given Canada's **indigenous peoples** of American descent, whose U.S. counterparts are called Native Americans.

Fjord Narrow, steep-sided, elongated, and inundated coastal valley deepened by glacier ice that has since melted away, leaving the sea to penetrate.

Floating population China's huge mass of mobile workers who respond to shifting employment needs within the country. Most are temporary urban dwellers with restricted residency rights, whose movements are controlled by the *hukou* system.

Floodplain Low-lying area adjacent to a mature river, often covered by **alluvial** deposits and subject to the river's floods.

Forced migration Human **migration** flows in which the movers have no choice but to relocate.

Foreign direct investment (FDI) A key indicator of the success of an **emerging market** economy, whose growth is accelerated by the infusion of foreign funds to supplement domestic sources of investment capital.

Formal region A type of **region** marked by a certain degree of homogeneity in one or more phenomena; also called *uniform region* or *homogeneous region*.

Formal sector The total activities of a country's legal economy that is taxed and monitored by the government, whose **gross domestic product (GDP)** and **gross national product (GNP)** are based on it; as opposed to an **informal economy**.

Forward capital Capital city positioned in actually or potentially contested territory, usually near an international border; it confirms the **state's** determination to maintain its presence in the region in contention.

Fossil fuels The energy resources of **coal**, natural gas, and petroleum (oil), so named collectively because they were formed by the geologic compression and transformation of tiny plant and animal organisms.

Four Motors of Europe *Rhône-Alpes* (France), *Baden-Württemberg* (Germany), *Catalonia* (Spain), and *Lombardy* (Italy). Each is a high-technology-driven region marked by exceptional industrial vitality and economic success not only within Europe but on the global scene as well.

Fragmented modernization A checkerboard-like spatial pattern of **modernization** in an **emerging-market** economy wherein a few localized regions of a country experience most of the development while the rest are largely unaffected.

Fragmented state A **state** whose territory consists of several separated parts, not a **contiguous** whole. The individual parts may be isolated from each other by the land area of other states or by international waters.

Francophone French-speaking. Quebec constitutes the heart of Francophone Canada.

Free-trade area A form of economic integration, usually consisting of two or more **states**, in which members agree to remove tariffs on trade among themselves. Frequently accompanied by a **customs union** that establishes common tariffs on imports from outside the trade area, and sometimes by a **common market** that also removes internal restrictions on the movement of capital, labor, and enterprise.

Free Trade Area of the Americas (FTAA) The ultimate goal of **supranational** economic integration in North, Middle, and South America: the creation of a single-market trading bloc that would involve every country in the Western Hemisphere between the Arctic shore of Canada and Cape Horn at the southern tip of South America.

Fría See *tierra fría*.

Frontier Zone of advance penetration, usually of contention; an area not yet fully integrated into a national **state**.

Functional region A **region** marked less by its sameness than by its dynamic internal structure; because it usually focuses on a central **node**, also called *nodal region* or *focal region*.

Functional specialization The production of particular goods or services as a dominant activity in a particular location. See also **local functional specialization**.

Fundamentalism See **revivalism (religious)**.

Gentrification The upgrading of an older residential area through private reinvestment, usually in the downtown area of a central city. Frequently, this involves the displacement of established lower-income residents, who cannot afford the heightened costs of living, and conflicts are not uncommon as such neighborhood change takes place.

Geographic change Evolution of **spatial** patterns over time.

Geographic realm The basic spatial unit in our world regionalization scheme. Each realm is defined in terms of a synthesis of its total human geography—a composite of its leading cultural, economic, historical, political, and appropriate environmental features.

Geography of development The subfield of economic geography concerned with spatial aspects and regional expressions of **development**.

Geometric boundaries Political boundaries **defined** and **delimited** (and occasionally **demarcated**) as straight lines or arcs.

Geomorphology The geographic study of the configuration of the Earth's solid surface—the world's landscapes and their constituent landforms.

Ghetto An intraurban region marked by a particular **ethnic** character. Often an inner-city poverty zone, such as the black ghetto in U.S. central cities. Ghetto residents are involuntarily segregated from other income and racial groups.

Glaciation Period of global cooling during which continental ice sheets and mountain glaciers expand.

Globalization   The gradual reduction of regional differences at the world **scale**, resulting from increasing international cultural, economic, and political exchanges.

Global warming   A general term referring to the temperature increase of the Earth's atmosphere over the past century and a half, how humans may be contributing to this warming, and scenarios of future environmental change that could result if this trend continues.

Green Revolution   The successful recent development of higher-yield, fast-growing varieties of rice and other cereals in certain developing countries.

Gross domestic product (GDP)   The total value of all goods and services produced in a country by that state's economy during a given year.

Gross national product (GNP)   The total value of all goods and services produced in a country by that state's economy during a given year, plus all citizens' income from foreign investment and other external sources.

Growth pole   An urban center with a number of attributes that, if augmented by investment support, will stimulate regional economic **development** in its **hinterland**.

Growth triangle   An increasingly popular economic **development** concept along the western **Pacific Rim**, especially in Southeast Asia. It involves the linking of production in growth centers of three countries to achieve benefits for all.

Hacienda   Literally, a large estate in a Spanish-speaking country. Sometimes equated with the **plantation**, but there are important differences between these two types of agricultural enterprise.

Hanification   Imparting a cultural imprint by the ethnic Chinese (the "people of Han"). Within China often refers to the steadily increasing migration of Han Chinese into the country's **periphery**, especially Xinjiang and Xizang (Tibet). **Overseas Chinese** imprints, more generally referred to as **Sinicization**, have been significant as well, most importantly in the Southeast Asian realm.

Heartland theory   The hypothesis, proposed by British geographer Halford Mackinder during the early twentieth century, that any political power based in the heart of Eurasia could gain sufficient strength to eventually dominate the world. Furthermore, since Eastern Europe controlled access to the Eurasian interior, its ruler would command the vast "heartland" to the east.

Hegemony   The political dominance of a country (or even a region) by another country.

Helada   See *tierra helada*.

Hierarchical diffusion   A form of **diffusion** in which an idea or innovation spreads by trickling down from larger to smaller adoption units. An urban **hierarchy** is usually involved, encouraging the leapfrogging of innovations over wide areas, with geographic distance a less important influence.

Hierarchy   An order or gradation of phenomena, with each level or rank subordinate to the one above it and superior to the one below. The levels in a national urban hierarchy—or **urban** system—are constituted by hamlets, villages, towns, cities, and (frequently) the **primate city**.

High–island cultures   Cultures associated with volcanic islands of the Pacific Realm that are high enough in elevation to wrest substantial moisture from the tropical ocean air (see **orographic precipitation**). They tend to be well watered, their volcanic soils enable productive agriculture, and they support larger populations than **low islands.**

High seas   Areas of the oceans away from land, beyond national jurisdiction, open and free for all to use.

High value-added goods   Products of improved net worth.

Highveld   A term used in South Africa to identify the high, grass-covered plateau that dominates much of the country. The lowest-lying areas (mainly along the narrow coastlands) in South Africa are called *lowveld*; areas that lie at intermediate elevations form the *middleveld*.

Hindutva   "Hinduness" as expressed through Hindu nationalism, Hindu heritage, and/or Hindu patriotism. The cornerstone of a fundamentalist movement that has been gaining strength since the late twentieth century that seeks to remake India as a society dominated by Hindu principles prevail. It has been the guiding agenda of the Bharatiya Janata Party (BJP),

which has emerged a powerful force in national politics and in big States like Maharashtra, Gujarat, and Madhya Pradesh.

Hinterland   Literally, "country behind," a term that applies to a surrounding area served by an urban center. That center is the focus of goods and services produced for its hinterland and is its dominant urban influence as well.

Historical inertia   A term from manufacturing geography that refers to the need to continue using the factories, machinery, and equipment of heavy industries for their full, multiple-decade lifetimes to cover major initial investments—even though these facilities may be increasingly obsolete.

Holocene   The current *interglacial* epoch (the warm period of glacial contraction between the glacial expansions of an **ice age**); extends from 10,000 years ago to the present. Also known as the *Recent Epoch*.

Human evolution   Long-term biological maturation of the human species. Geographically, all evidence points toward East Africa as the source of humankind. Our species, *Homo sapiens*, emigrated from this hearth to eventually populate the rest of the **ecumene**.

Hukou **system**   A longstanding Chinese system whereby all inhabitants must obtain and carry with them residency permits that indicate where an individual is from and where they may exercise particular rights such as education, health care, housing, and the like.

Hurricane   A tightly-wound, tropical cyclonic storm capable of inflicting great wind and water damage in low-lying coastal zones. Originates at sea in the hot, moist atmosphere of the lower latitudes, and can reach Category-5 wind speeds in excess of 249 kph (155 mph). Minimal hurricane wind speed is 119 kph (74 mph); but even below that intensity, tropical storms (63-119 kph [39-74 mph]) can wreak significant damage. The name *hurricane* is confined to North and Middle America; in the western North Pacific Ocean, such storms are called *typhoons*; in the Indian Ocean Basin, they are known as (*tropical*) *cyclones*.

Hurricane Alley   The most frequent pathway followed by tropical storms and **hurricanes** over the past 150 years in their generally westward movement across the Caribbean Basin. Historically, hurricane tracks have bundled most tightly in the center of this route, most often affecting the Lesser Antilles between Antigua and the Virgin Islands, Puerto Rico, Hispaniola (Haiti/Dominican Republic), Jamaica, Cuba, southernmost Florida, Mexico's Yucatán, and the Gulf of Mexico.

Hydraulic civilization theory   The theory that cities which managed to control **irrigated** farming over large **hinterlands** held political power over other cities. Particularly applies to early Asian civilizations based in such river valleys as the Chang (Yangzi), the Indus, and those of Mesopotamia.

Hydrologic cycle   The **system** of exchange involving water in its various forms as it continually circulates between the **atmosphere**, the oceans, and above and below the land surface.

Ice age   A stretch of geologic time during which the Earth's average atmospheric temperature is lowered; causes the equatorward expansion of continental ice sheets in the higher latitudes and the growth of mountain glaciers in and around the highlands of the lower latitudes.

Immigrant   A person **migrating** into a particular country or area; an in-migrant.

Imperialism   The drive toward the creation and expansion of a **colonial** empire and, once established, its perpetuation.

Import-substitution industries   The industries local entrepreneurs establish to serve populations of remote areas when transport costs from distant sources make these goods too expensive to import.

Inaccessibility   See **accessibility**.

Indentured workers   Contract laborers who sell their services for a stipulated period of time.

Indigenous   Aboriginal or native; an example would be the pre-Columbian inhabitants of the Americas.

Indigenous peoples   Native or *aboriginal* peoples; often used to designate the inhabitants of areas that were conquered and subsequently colonized by the **imperial** powers of Europe.

Indo-European languages   The major world language family that dominates the European **geographic realm**. This language family is also the most widely dispersed globally (Fig. G-9), and about half of humankind speaks one of its languages.

Industrial Revolution The term applied to the social and economic changes in agriculture, commerce, and especially manufacturing and urbanization that resulted from technological innovations and greater specialization in late-eighteenth-century Europe.

Informal sector Dominated by unlicensed sellers of homemade goods and services, the primitive form of capitalism found in many developing countries that takes place beyond the control of government. The complement to a country's **formal sector**.

Infrastructure The foundations of a society: urban centers, transport networks, communications, energy distribution systems, farms, factories, mines, and such facilities as schools, hospitals, postal services, and police and armed forces.

Insular Having the qualities and properties of an island. Real islands are not alone in possessing such properties of **isolation**: an **oasis** in the middle of a **desert** also has qualities of insularity.

Insurgent state Territorial embodiment of a successful guerrilla movement. The establishment by antigovernment insurgents of a territorial base in which they exercise full control; thus a **state** within a state.

Intercropping The planting of several types of crops in the same field; commonly used by **shifting cultivators**.

Interglacial Period of warmer global temperatures between the end of the previous glaciation and the onset of the next one.

Intermontane Literally, between the mountains. Such a location can bestow certain qualities of natural protection or **isolation** to a community.

Internal migration **Migration** flow within a country, such as ongoing westward and southward movements toward the **Sunbelt** in the United States.

International migration **Migration** flow involving movement across an international boundary.

Intervening opportunity In trade or **migration** flows, the presence of a nearer opportunity that greatly diminishes the attractiveness of sites farther away.

Inuit **Indigenous** peoples of North America's Arctic zone, formerly known as Eskimos.

Irredentism A policy of cultural extension and potential political expansion by a **state** aimed at a community of its nationals living in a neighboring state.

Irrigation The artificial watering of croplands.

Islamic Front The southern border of the African Transition Zone that marks the religious **frontier** of the **Muslim** faith in its southward penetration of Subsaharan Africa (see Fig. 6B-9).

Islamization Introduction and establishment of the **Muslim** religion. A **process** still under way, most notably along the **Islamic Front**, that marks the southern border of the African Transition Zone.

Isohyet A line connecting points of equal rainfall total.

Isolation The condition of being geographically cut off or far removed from mainstreams of thought and action. It also denotes a lack of receptivity to outside influences, caused at least partially by poor **accessibility**.

Isoline A line connecting points of equal value; see **isohyet**, **isotherm**.

Isotherm A line connecting points of equal temperature.

Isthmus A **land bridge**; a comparatively narrow link between larger bodies of land. Central America forms such a link between Mexico and South America.

Jihad A doctrine within Islam. Commonly translated as *holy war*, it entails a personal or collective struggle on the part of **Muslims** to live up to the religious standards prescribed by the *Quran* (Koran).

Juxtaposition Contrasting places in close proximity to one another.

Karst The distinctive natural landscape associated with the chemical erosion of soluble limestone rock.

Land alienation One society or culture group taking land from another.

Land bridge A narrow **isthmian** link between two large landmasses. They are temporary features—at least when measured in geologic time—subject to appearance and disappearance as the land or sea level rises and falls.

Land hemisphere The half of the globe containing the greatest amount of land surface, centered on western Europe.

Land reform The spatial reorganization of **agriculture** through the allocation of farmland (often expropriated from landlords) to **peasants** and tenants who never owned land.

Land tenure The way people own, occupy, and use land.

Landlocked location/state An interior **state** surrounded by land. Without coasts, such a country is disadvantaged in terms of **accessibility** to international trade routes, and in the scramble for possession of areas of the **continental shelf** and control of the **exclusive economic zone** beyond.

Language family Group of languages with a shared but usually distant origin.

"Latin" American city model The Griffin-Ford model of intraurban spatial structure in the Middle American and South American realms.

Latitude Lines of latitude are **parallels** that are aligned east-west across the globe, from 0° latitude at the equator to 90° North and South latitude at the poles.

Leached soil Infertile, reddish-appearing, tropical soil whose surface consists of oxides of iron and aluminum; all other soil nutrients have been dissolved and transported downward into the subsoil by percolating water associated with the heavy rainfall of moist, low-latitude climates.

League of Nations The international organization that emerged after the First World War (1914–1918) whose purpose was to maintain international peace and promote cooperation in solving international economic, social, and humanitarian problems. It consisted of as many as 58 member-countries by the mid-1930s, but it failed to prevent World War II (1939–1945) and is best remembered as the flawed predecessor of the United Nations.

Leeward The protected or downwind side of a **topographic** barrier with respect to the winds that flow across it.

Liberation Theology A powerful religious movement that arose in South America during the 1950s, and subsequently gained followers all over the global **periphery**. At its heart is a belief system, based on a blend of Christian faith and socialist thinking, that interprets the teachings of Christ as a quest to liberate the impoverished masses from oppression.

Lignite Low-grade, brown-colored variety of **coal**.

Lingua franca A "common language" prevalent in a given area; a second language that can be spoken and understood by many people, although they speak other languages at home.

Littoral Coastal or coastland.

Llanos The interspersed **savanna** grasslands and scrub woodlands of the Orinoco River's wide basin that covers most of interior Venezuela and Colombia.

Local functional specialization A hallmark of Europe's **economic geography** that later spread to many other parts of the world, whereby particular people in particular places concentrate on the production of particular goods and services.

Location Position on the Earth's surface; see also **absolute location** and **relative location**.

Location theory A logical attempt to explain the locational pattern of an economic activity and the manner in which its producing areas are interrelated.

Loess Deposit of very fine silt or dust that is laid down after having been windborne for a considerable distance. Notable for its fertility under **irrigation** and its ability to stand in steep vertical walls.

Longitude Angular distance (0° to 180°) east or west as measured from the *prime meridian* (0°) that passes through the Greenwich Observatory in suburban London, England. For much of its length across the mid-Pacific Ocean, the 180th meridian functions as the *international date line*.

Low island cultures   Cultures associated with low-lying coral islands of the Pacific Realm that cannot wrest sufficient moisture from the tropical maritime air to avoid chronic drought. Thus productive agriculture is impossible, and their modest populations must rely on fishing and the coconut palm for survival.

Lusitanian   The Portuguese sphere, which by extension includes Brazil.

Madrassa   **Revivalist** (**fundamentalist**) religious school in which the curriculum focuses on Islamic religion and law and requires rote memorization of the *Quran* (Koran), Islam's holy book. Founded in former British India, these schools were most numerous in present-day Pakistan but have **diffused** as far as Turkey in the west and Indonesia in the east. Afghanistan's **Taliban** emerged from these institutions in Pakistan

Maghreb   The region occupying the northwestern corner of Africa, consisting of Morocco, Algeria, and Tunisia.

Main Street   Canada's dominant **conurbation** that is home to nearly two-thirds of the country's inhabitants; extends southwestward from Quebec City in the mid-St. Lawrence Valley to Windsor on the Detroit River.

Mainland-Rimland framework   The twofold regionalization of the Middle American realm based on its modern cultural history. The Euro-Indigenous *Mainland*, stretching from Mexico to Panama (minus the Caribbean coastal strip), was a self-sufficient zone dominated by **hacienda land tenure**. The Euro-African *Rimland*, consisting of that Caribbean coastal zone plus all of the Caribbean islands to the east, was the zone of the **plantation** that relied heavily on trade with Europe. See Figure 4A-7.

Maquiladora   The term given to modern industrial plants in Mexico's U.S. border zone. These foreign-owned factories assemble imported components and/or raw materials, and then export finished manufactures, mainly to the United States. Import duties are disappearing under **NAFTA**, bringing jobs to Mexico and the advantages of low wage rates to the foreign entrepreneurs.

Marchland   An area or **frontier** of uncertain boundaries that is subject to various national claims and an unstable political history. Refers specifically to the movement of various armies, refugees, and migrants across such zones.

Marine geography   The geographic study of oceans and seas. Its practitioners investigate both the physical (e.g., coral-reef **biogeography**, ocean–**atmosphere** interactions, coastal **geomorphology**) as well as human (e.g., **maritime boundary**-making, fisheries, beachside development) aspects of oceanic environments.

Maritime boundary   An international boundary that lies in the ocean. Like all boundaries, it is a vertical plane, extending from the seafloor to the upper limit of the air space in the atmosphere above the water.

Median-line boundary   An international **maritime boundary** drawn where the width of a sea is less than 400 **nautical miles**. Because the **states** on either side of that sea claim **exclusive economic zones** of 200 nautical miles, it is necessary to reduce those claims to a (median) distance equidistant from each shoreline. **Delimitation** on the map almost always appears as a set of straight-line segments that reflect the configurations of the coastlines involved.

Medical geography   The study of health and disease within a geographic context and from a spatial perspective. Among other things, this geographic field examines the sources, **diffusion** routes, and distributions of diseases.

Megacity   Informal term referring to the world's most heavily populated cities; in this book, the term refers to a **metropolis** containing a population of greater than 10 million.

Megalopolis   When spelled with a lower-case *m*, a synonym for **conurbation**, one of the large coalescing supercities forming in diverse parts of the world. When capitalized, refers specifically to the multimetropolitan (*Bosnywash*) corridor that extends along the northeastern U.S. seaboard from north of Boston to south of Washington, D.C.

Melting pot   Traditional characterization of American society as a blend of numerous **immigrant ethnic** groups that over time were assimilated into a single societal mainstream. This notion always had its challengers among social scientists, and is now increasingly difficult to sustain given the increasing complexity and sheer scale of the U.S. ethnic mosaic in the twenty-first century.

Mental maps   Maps that individuals carry around in their minds that reflect their constantly evolving perception of how geographic space (ranging from their everyday activity space to the entire world) is organized around them.

Mercantilism   Protectionist policy of European **states** during the sixteenth to the eighteenth centuries that promoted a **state**'s economic position in the contest with rival powers. Acquiring gold and silver and maintaining a favorable trade balance (more exports than imports) were central to the policy.

Meridian   Line of **longitude**, aligned north-south across the globe, that together with **parallels** of **latitude** forms the global grid system. All meridians converge at both poles and are at their maximum distances from each other at the equator.

Mestizo   Derived from the Latin word for *mixed*, refers to a person of mixed European (white) and Amerindian ancestry.

Métis   **Indigenous** Canadian people of mixed native (**First Nations**) and European ancestry.

Metropolis   Urban **agglomeration** consisting of a (central) city and its suburban ring. See also **urban** (**metropolitan**) **area**.

Metropolitan area   See **urban** (**metropolitan**) **area**.

Micro-credit   Small loans extended to poverty-stricken borrowers who would not otherwise qualify for them. The aim is to help combat poverty, encourage entrepreneurship, and to empower poor communities—especially their women.

Microstate   A sovereign **state** that contains a minuscule land area and population. They do not have the attributes of "complete" states, but are on the map as tiny yet independent entities nonetheless.

Migration   A change in residence intended to be permanent.

Migratory movement   Human relocation movement from a source to a destination without a return journey, as opposed to cyclical movement (see also **nomadism**).

Model   An idealized representation of reality built to demonstrate its most important properties. A **spatial** model focuses on a geographical dimension of the real world.

Modernization   In the eyes of the Western world, the **Westernization process** that involves the establishment of **urbanization**, a market (money) economy, improved circulation, formal schooling, the adoption of foreign innovations, and the breakdown of traditional society. Non-Westerners mostly see "modernization" as an outgrowth of **colonialism** and often argue that traditional societies can be modernized without being Westernized.

Monsoon   Refers to the seasonal reversal of wind and moisture flows in certain parts of the subtropics and lower-middle latitudes. The *dry monsoon* occurs during the cool season when dry offshore winds prevail. The *wet monsoon* occurs in the hot summer months, which produce onshore winds that bring large amounts of rainfall. The air-pressure differential over land and sea is the triggering mechanism, with windflows always moving from areas of relatively higher pressure toward areas of relatively lower pressure. Monsoons make their greatest regional impact in the coastal and near-coastal zones of South Asia, Southeast Asia, and East Asia.

Mosaic culture   Emerging cultural-geographic framework of the United States, dominated by the fragmentation of specialized social groups into homogeneous communities of interest marked not only by income, race, and **ethnicity** but also by age, occupational status, and lifestyle. The result is an increasingly heterogeneous sociospatial complex, which resembles an intricate mosaic composed of myriad uniform—but separate—tiles.

Mulatto   A person of mixed African (black) and European (white) ancestry.

Multilingualism   A society marked by a mosaic of local languages. Constitutes a **centrifugal force** because it impedes communication within the larger population. Often a *lingua franca* is used as a "common language," as in many countries of Subsaharan Africa.

Multinationals   Internationally active corporations capable of strongly influencing the economic and political affairs of many countries in which they operate.

Muslim   An adherent of the Islamic faith.

NAFTA (North American Free Trade Agreement) The **free-trade area** launched in 1994 involving the United States, Canada, and Mexico.

Nation Legally a term encompassing all the citizens of a **state**, it also has other connotations. Most definitions now tend to refer to a group of tightly knit people possessing bonds of language, **ethnicity**, religion, and other shared **cultural** attributes. Such homogeneity actually prevails within very few states.

Nation-state A country whose population possesses a substantial degree of **cultural** homogeneity and unity. The ideal form to which most **nations** and **states** aspire—a political unit wherein the territorial state coincides with the area settled by a certain national group or people.

NATO (North Atlantic Treaty Organization) Established in 1950 at the height of the Cold War as a U.S.-led **supranational** defense pact to shield postwar Europe against the Soviet military threat. NATO is now in transition, expanding its membership while modifying its objectives in the post-Soviet era. Its 28 member-states (as of mid-2013) are: Albania, Belgium, Bulgaria, Canada, Croatia, Czech Republic, Denmark, Estonia, France, Germany, Greece, Hungary, Iceland, Italy, Latvia, Lithuania, Luxembourg, the Netherlands, Norway, Poland, Portugal, Romania, Slovakia, Slovenia, Spain, Turkey, the United Kingdom, and the United States.

Natural hazard A natural event that endangers human life and/or the contents of a **cultural landscape**.

Natural increase rate Population growth measured as the excess of live births over deaths per 1000 individuals per year. Natural increase of a population does not reflect either **emigrant** or **immigrant** movements.

Natural landscape The array of landforms that constitutes the Earth's surface (mountains, hills, plains, and plateaus) and the physical features that mark them (such as water bodies, soils, and vegetation). Each **geographic realm** has its distinctive combination of natural landscapes.

Natural resource Any valued element of (or means to an end using) the environment; includes minerals, water, vegetation, and soil.

Nautical mile By international agreement, the nautical mile—the standard measure at sea—is 6076.12 feet in length, equivalent to approximately 1.15 statute miles (1.85 km).

Near Abroad The 14 former Soviet republics that, in combination with the dominant Russian Republic, constituted the USSR. Since the 1991 breakup of the Soviet Union, Russia has asserted a sphere of influence in these now-independent countries, based on its proclaimed right to protect the interests of ethnic Russians who were settled there in substantial numbers during Soviet times. These 14 countries include Armenia, Azerbaijan, Belarus, Estonia, Georgia, Kazakhstan, Kyrgyzstan, Latvia, Lithuania, Moldova, Tajikistan, Turkmenistan, Ukraine, and Uzbekistan.

Neocolonialism The term used by developing countries to underscore that the entrenched **colonial** system of international exchange and capital flow has not changed in the postcolonial era—thereby perpetuating the huge economic advantages of the developed world.

Neoliberalism A national or regional development strategy based on the privatization of state-run companies, lowering of international trade tariffs, reduction of government subsidies, cutting of corporate taxes, and overall deregulation to business activity.

Neolithic The "New Stone Age" (ca. 9500-4500 BC), which was the final stage of cultural evolution and technological development among prehistoric humans. Among the numerous accomplishments that took place, two of the most important for human geography were: (1) the rise of farming through the domestication of plants and animals, and (2) the first permanent village settlements that mark the origin of urbanization.

Network (transport) The entire regional **system** of transportation connections and **nodes** through which movement can occur.

Nevada See *tierra nevada*.

New World Order A description of the international system resulting from the 1991 collapse of the Soviet Union whereby the balance of nuclear power theoretically no longer determines the destinies of **states**.

Node A center that functions as a point of **connectivity** within a regional **network** or **system**. All urban settlements possess this function, and the

higher the position of a settlement in its **urban system** or **hierarchy**, the greater its nodality.

Nomadism Cyclical movement among a definite set of places. Nomadic peoples mostly are **pastoralists**.

Non-governmental organization (NGO) Legitimate organizations that operate independently from any form of government and do not function as for-profit businesses. They mostly seek to improve social conditions, but are not affiliated with political organizations.

North American Free Trade Agreement See **NAFTA**.

Northeast Passage The high-latitude sea route of the Arctic Ocean that follows the entire north coast of Eurasia from northern Norway in the west to the northeasternmost corner of Russia where it meets the Bering Strait. Increased seasonal melting of the Arctic ice cap in recent years has begun to open up this waterway as a summer route for shipping between Europe and East Asia.

Northwest Passage The high-latitude, Arctic Ocean sea route around North America extending from Alaska's Bering Strait in the west to the Davis Strait between Canada and Greenland in the east. Heightened summertime melting of the Arctic ice cap in recent years has increased the likelihood of opening up this waterway for shipping between Asia's Pacific Rim and the Atlantic seaboard of the Americas.

Nucleation Cluster; **agglomeration**.

Oasis An area, small or large, where the supply of water (from an **aquifer** or a major river such as the Nile) permits the transformation of the immediately surrounding **desert** into productive cropland.

Occidental Western. Also see *Oriental*.

Offshore banking Term referring to financial havens for foreign companies and individuals, who channel their earnings to accounts in such a country (usually an "offshore" island-state) to avoid paying taxes in their home countries.

Oligarchs Opportunists in post-Soviet Russia who used their ties to government to enrich themselves.

OPEC (Organization of Petroleum Exporting Countries) The international oil *cartel* or syndicate formed by a number of producing countries to promote their common economic interests through the formulation of joint pricing policies and the limitation of market options for consumers. The 12 member-states (as of mid-2013) are: Algeria, Angola, Ecuador, Iran, Iraq, Kuwait, Libya, Nigeria, Qatar, Saudi Arabia, United Arab Emirates (UAE), and Venezuela.

Oriental The root of the word "oriental" is from the Latin for *rise*. Thus it has to do with the direction in which one sees the sun "rise"—the east; *oriental* therefore means Eastern. *Occidental* originates from the Latin for fall, or the "setting" of the sun in the west; *occidental* therefore means Western.

Orographic precipitation Mountain-induced precipitation, especially when air masses are forced to cross **topographic** barriers. Downwind areas beyond such a mountain range experience the relative dryness known as the **rain shadow effect**.

Outback The name given by Australians to the vast, peripheral, sparsely settled interior of their country.

Outer city The non-central-city portion of the American **metropolis**; no longer "sub" to the "urb," this outer ring was transformed into a full-fledged city during the late twentieth century.

Outsourcing Turning over the partial or complete production of a good or service to another party. In **economic geography**, this usually refers to a company arranging to have its products manufactured in a foreign country where labor and other costs are significantly lower than in the home country (which experiences a commensurate loss in jobs).

Overseas Chinese The approximately 50 million ethnic Chinese who live outside China. About two-thirds live in Southeast Asia, and many have become quite successful. A large number maintain links to China and as investors played a major economic role in stimulating the growth of **SEZs** and Open Cities in China's **Pacific Rim**.

Pacific Rim A far-flung group of countries and components of countries (extending clockwise on the map from New Zealand to Chile) sharing the following criteria: they face the Pacific Ocean; they exhibit relatively high levels of economic development, industrialization, and urbanization; their imports and exports mainly move across Pacific waters.

Pacific Ring of Fire Zone of crustal instability along **tectonic plate** boundaries, marked by earthquakes and volcanic activity, that ring the Pacific Ocean Basin.

Paddies (paddyfields) Ricefields.

Pandemic An outbreak of a disease that spreads worldwide.

Pangaea A vast, singular landmass consisting of most of the areas of the present-day continents. This *supercontinent* began to break up more than 200 million years ago when still-ongoing **plate** divergence and **continental drift** became dominant **processes** (see Fig. 6A-3).

Parallel An east-west line of **latitude** that is intersected at right angles by **meridians** of **longitude**.

Partition The subdivision of the British Indian Empire into India and Pakistan at the end of colonial rule on August 15, 1947. Shortly before their departure from what is now the South Asian realm, the British were persuaded to create separate countries for South Asia's massive Hindu (India) and Muslim (West and East Pakistan) populations. Boundaries were drawn hurriedly and ineffectively through thousands of kilometers of highly complicated cultural terrain, triggering the biggest mass migration in human history as millions fled their homes to be sure they were not on the "wrong" side of the new border. Both India and Pakistan (the successor to West Pakistan; East Pakistan seceded in 1971 to become independent Bangladesh) continue to suffer the consequences of the Partition that occurred 65 years ago, including the scars of four subsequent armed conflicts, the dangerous unresolved impasse in Kashmir, and persistent tensions magnified by the nuclear capabilities of both.

Pastoralism A form of **agricultural** activity that involves the raising of livestock.

Peasants In a **stratified** society, peasants are the lowest class of people who depend on **agriculture** for a living. But they often own no land at all and must survive as tenants or day workers.

Peninsula A comparatively narrow, finger-like stretch of land extending from the main landmass into the sea. Florida and Korea are examples.

Peon (*peone*) Term used in Middle and South America to identify people who often live in serfdom to a wealthy landowner; landless **peasants** in continuous indebtedness.

Per capita Capita means *individual*. Income, production, or some other measure is often given per individual.

Perforated state A **state** whose territory completely surrounds that of another state.

Periodic market Village market that is open every third day or at some other regular interval. Part of a regional network of similar markets in a preindustrial, rural setting where goods are brought to market on foot and barter remains a leading mode of exchange.

Peripheral development Spatial pattern in which a country's or region's development (and population) is most heavily concentrated along its outer edges rather than in its interior.

Periphery Used in conjunction with core areas at many geographic scales. At the scale of the city-region, it is the outlying tributary area served by a city that produces food and raw materials for the urban core in exchange for receiving goods and services. At the world scale, it is all those less advantaged parts of the Earth's surface lying outside the affluent global core.

Permafrost Permanently frozen water in the near-surface soil and bedrock of cold environments, producing the effect of completely frozen ground. Surface can thaw during brief warm season.

Physical geography The study of the geography of the physical (natural) world. Its subfields encompass **climatology, geomorphology, biogeography, soil geography, marine geography**, and water **resources**.

Physical landscape Synonym for **natural landscape**.

Physiographic political boundaries Political boundaries that coincide with prominent physical features in the **natural landscape**—such as rivers or the crest ridges of mountain ranges.

Physiographic region (province) A **region** within which there prevails substantial **natural-landscape** homogeneity, expressed by a certain degree of uniformity in surface **relief, climate**, vegetation, and soils.

Physiography Literally means *landscape description*, but commonly refers to the total **physical geography** of a place; includes all of the natural features on the Earth's surface, including landforms, **climate**, soils, vegetation, and water bodies.

Physiologic density The number of people per unit area of **arable** land.

Pilgrimage A journey to a place of great religious significance by an individual or by a group of people (such as a pilgrimage [*hajj*] to Mecca for **Muslims**).

Plantation A large estate owned by an individual, family, or corporation and organized to produce a cash crop. Almost all plantations were established within the tropics; in recent decades, many have been divided into smaller holdings or reorganized as cooperatives.

Plate tectonics Plates are bonded portions of the Earth's mantle and crust, averaging 100 kilometers (60 mi) in thickness. More than a dozen such plates exist (see Fig. G-4), most of continental proportions, and they are in motion. Where they meet one slides under the other (**subduction**), crumpling the surface crust and producing significant volcanic and earthquake activity; a major mountain-building force.

Pleistocene Epoch Recent period of geologic time that spans the rise of humankind, beginning about 2 million years ago. Marked by *glaciations* (repeated advances of continental ice sheets) and more moderate *interglacials* (ice sheet contractions). Although the last 10,000 years are known as the **Holocene** Epoch, Pleistocene-like conditions seem to be continuing and we are most probably now living through another Pleistocene interglacial; thus the glaciers likely will return.

Polder Land reclaimed from the sea adjacent to the shore of the Netherlands by constructing dikes and then pumping out the water trapped behind them.

Police state A **state** in which the government (usually marked by dictatorial leadership) exercises totalitarian control over the political, social, and economic life of its citizens. Repression of the people includes rigid restrictions on their movements, freedom to communicate and express their views, and aggressive monitoring and enforcement by means of a secret-police force.

Political geography The study of the interaction of geographic space and political **process**; the spatial analysis of political phenomena and processes.

Political regime An assemblage of political structures that constitute a state; the form of government administered by those in power.

Pollution The release of a substance, through human activity, which chemically, physically, or biologically alters the air or water it is discharged into. Such a discharge negatively impacts the environment, with possible harmful effects on living organisms—including humans.

Population decline A decreasing national population. Russia, which now loses about half a million people per year, is the best example. Also see **population implosion**.

Population density The number of people per unit area. Also see **arithmetic density** and **physiologic density** measures.

Population distribution The way people have arranged themselves in geographic space. One of human geography's most essential expressions because it represents the sum total of the adjustments that a population has made to its natural, cultural, and economic environments. A population distribution map is included in every chapter in this book.

Population expansion (explosion) The rapid growth of the world's human population over the past century, attended by accelerating *rates* of increase.

Population geography The field of geography that focuses on the spatial aspects of **demography** and the influences of demographic change on particular countries and regions.

Population implosion The opposite of **population explosion**; refers to the declining populations of many European countries and Russia in which the **death rate** exceeds the **birth rate** and **immigration** rate.

Population movement See **migration** and **migratory movement**.

Population projection The future population total that demographers forecast for a particular country. For example, in the Data Table in Appendix B such projections are given for all the world's countries for 2025.

Population pyramid Graphic representation or *profile* of a national population according to age and gender. Such a diagram of age-sex structure typically displays the percentage of each age group (commonly in five-year increments) as a horizontal bar, whose length represents its relationship to the total population.

Primary sector/economic activity Activities engaged in the direct extraction of natural resources from the environment such as mining, fishing, lumbering, and especially agriculture.

Postindustrial economy Emerging economy, in the United States and a number of other highly advanced countries, as traditional industry is increasingly eclipsed by a higher-technology productive complex dominated by services, information-related, and managerial activities.

Primary economic activity Activities engaged in the direct extraction of **natural resources** from the environment such as mining, fishing, lumbering, and especially **agriculture**.

Primate city A country's largest city—ranking atop its urban **hierarchy**—most expressive of the national culture and usually (but not in every case) the capital city as well.

Process Causal force that shapes a spatial pattern as it unfolds over time.

Productive activities The major components of the spatial economy. For individual components see: **primary economic activity, secondary economic activity, tertiary economic activity, quaternary economic activity,** and **quinary economic activity**.

Protruded state Territorial shape of a **state** that exhibits a narrow, elongated land extension (or *protrusion*) leading away from the main body of territory.

Protrusion A pronounced extension of national territory that leads away from an otherwise compact state either as a long peninsula or land corridor.

Push-pull concept The idea that **migration** flows are simultaneously stimulated by conditions in the source area, which tend to drive people away, and by the perceived attractiveness of the destination.

Qanat In **desert** zones, particularly in Iran and western China, an underground tunnel built to carry **irrigation** water by gravity flow from surrounding mountains (where **orographic precipitation** occurs) to the arid flatlands below.

Quaternary economic activity Activities engaged in the collection, processing, and manipulation of *information*.

Quinary economic activity Managerial or control-function activity associated with decision-making in large organizations.

Racial profiling The use, by police and other security personnel, of an individual's race or ethnicity in the decision to engage in law enforcement.

Rain shadow effect The relative dryness in areas downwind of mountain ranges resulting from **orographic precipitation**, wherein moist air masses are forced to deposit most of their water content as they cross the highlands.

Rate of natural population increase See **natural increase rate**.

Realm See **geographic realm**.

Refugees People who have been dislocated involuntarily from their original place of settlement.

Region A commonly used term and a geographic concept of paramount importance. An **area** on the Earth's surface marked by specific criteria, which are discussed in the Introduction.

Regional boundary In theory, the line that circumscribes a **region**. But razor-sharp lines are seldom encountered, even in nature (e.g., a coastline constantly changes depending on the tide). In the **cultural landscape**, not only are regional boundaries rarely self-evident, but when they are ascertained by geographers they most often turn out to be **transitional** borderlands.

Regional complementarity Exists when two regions, through an exchange of raw materials and/or finished products, can specifically satisfy each other's demands.

Regional concept The geographic study of **regions** and regional distinctions.

Regional disparity The spatial unevenness in standard of living that occurs within a country, whose "average" overall income statistics invariably mask the differences that exist between the extremes of the affluent **core** and the poorer, disadvantaged **periphery**.

Regional geography Approach to geographic study based on the spatial unit of the **region**. Allows for an all-encompassing view of the world, because it utilizes and integrates information from geography's topical (**systematic**) fields, which are diagrammed in Figure G-14.

Regional state A "natural economic zone" that defies political boundaries and is shaped by the global economy of which it is a part; its leaders deal directly with foreign partners and negotiate the best terms they can with the national governments under which they operate.

Regionalism The consciousness of and loyalty to a **region** considered distinct and different from the **state** as a whole by those who occupy it.

Relative location The regional position or **situation** of a place relative to the position of other places. Distance, **accessibility**, and **connectivity** affect relative location.

Relict boundary A political boundary that has ceased to function, but the imprint of which can still be detected on the **cultural landscape**.

Relief Vertical difference between the highest and lowest elevations within a particular area.

Religious revivalism Religious movement whose objectives are to return to the foundations of that faith and to influence state policy. Often called *religious fundamentalism*; but in the case of Islam, **Muslims** prefer the term *revivalism*.

Relocation diffusion Sequential **diffusion process** in which the items being diffused are transmitted by their carrier agents as they relocate to new areas. The most common form of relocation diffusion involves the spreading of innovations by a **migrating** population.

Remittances Money earned by **emigrants** that is sent back to family and friends in their home country, mostly in cash; forms an important part of the economy in poorer countries.

Restrictive population policies Government policy designed to reduce the **rate of natural population increase**. China's one-child policy, instituted in 1979 after Mao's death, is a classic example.

Revivalism (religious) Religious movement whose objectives are to return to the foundations of that faith and to influence state policy. Often called *religious fundamentalism*; but in the case of Islam, **Muslims** prefer the term *revivalism*.

Rift valley The trough or trench that forms when a thinning strip of the Earth's crust sinks between two parallel faults (surface fractures).

Rural-to-urban migration The dominant **migration** flow from countryside to city that continues to transform the world's population, most notably in the less advantaged geographic realms.

Russification Demographic resettlement policies pursued by the central planners of the Soviet Empire (1924–1991), whereby ethnic Russians were encouraged to **emigrate** from the Russian Republic to the 14 non-Russian republics of the USSR.

Sahel Semiarid **steppeland** zone extending across most of Africa between the southern margins of the arid Sahara and the moister tropical **savanna** and forest zone to the south. Chronic drought, **desertification**, and overgrazing have contributed to severe famines in this area since 1970.

Satellite states The countries of eastern Europe under Soviet **hegemony** between 1945 and 1989. This tier of countries—the "satellites" captured in Moscow's "orbit" following World War II—was bordered on the west by the Iron Curtain and on the east by the USSR. Using the names then in force, they included Bulgaria, Czechoslovakia, East Germany, Hungary, Poland, and Romania.

Savanna Tropical grassland containing widely spaced trees; also the name given to the tropical wet-and-dry climate type (*Aw*).

Scale Representation of a real-world phenomenon at a certain level of reduction or generalization. In **cartography**, the ratio of map distance to ground distance; indicated on a map as a bar graph, representative fraction, and/or verbal statement. *Macroscale* refers to a large area of national proportions; *microscale* refers to a local area no bigger than a county.

Secession The act of withdrawing from a political entity, usually a **state,** as when the U.S. South tried unsuccessfully to secede from the United States in 1861 and sparked the Civil War.

Secondary economic activity Activities that process raw materials and transform them into finished industrial products; the *manufacturing* sector.

Sedentary Permanently attached to a particular area; a population fixed in its location; the opposite of **nomadic**.

Separate development The spatial expression of South Africa's "grand" **apartheid** scheme, whereby nonwhite groups were required to settle in segregated "homelands." The policy was dismantled when white-minority rule collapsed in the early 1990s.

Sex ratio A **demographic** indicator showing the ratio of males to females in a given population.

Shantytown Unplanned slum development on the margins of cities in disadvantaged countries, dominated by crude dwellings and shelters mostly made of scrap wood and iron, and even pieces of cardboard.

Sharecropping Relationship between a large landowner and farmers on the land wherein the farmers pay rent for the land they farm by giving the landlord a share of the annual harvest.

Sharia (law) The strict criminal code based in Islamic law that prescribes corporal punishment, amputations, stonings, and lashing for both major and minor offenses. Its occurrence today is associated with the spread of **religious revivalism** in **Muslim** societies.

Shatter belt **Region** caught between stronger, colliding external cultural-political forces, under persistent stress, and often fragmented by aggressive rivals.

Shifting agriculture Cultivation of crops in recently cut-down and burned tropical-forest clearings, soon to be abandoned in favor of newly cleared nearby forest land. Also known as *slash-and-burn agriculture*.

Sinicization Giving a Chinese cultural imprint; Chinese **acculturation**. See also **Hanification**.

Site The internal locational attributes of an urban center, including its local spatial organization and physical setting.

Situation The external locational attributes of an urban center; its **relative location** or regional position with reference to other non-local places.

Small-island developing economies The additional disadvantages faced by lower-income island-states because of their often small territorial size and populations as well as overland **inaccessibility**. Limited resources require expensive importing of many goods and services; the cost of government operations per capita are higher; and local production is unable to benefit from **economies of scale**.

Social stratification In a layered or stratified society, the population is divided into a **hierarchy** of social classes. In an industrialized society, the working class is at the lower end; **elites** that possess capital and control the means of production are at the upper level.

Southern Ocean The ocean that surrounds Antarctica (discussed in Chapter 11).

Sovereignty Controlling power and influence over a territory, especially by the government of an autonomous state over the people it rules.

Spatial Pertaining to space on the Earth's surface. Synonym for *geographic(al)*.

Spatial diffusion The spatial spreading or dissemination of a **culture** element (such as a technological innovation) or some other phenomenon (e.g., a disease outbreak).

Spatial perspective: Broadly, the geographic dimension or expression of any phenomenon; more specifically, anything related to the organization of space on the Earth' surface.

Spatial system The components and interactions of a **functional region**, which is defined by the areal extent of those interactions.

Special Administrative Region (SAR) Status accorded the former dependencies of Hong Kong and Macau that were taken over by China, respectively, from the United Kingdom in 1997 and Portugal in 1999. Both SARs received guarantees that their existing social and economic systems could continue unchanged for 50 years following their return to China.

Special Economic Zone (SEZ) Manufacturing and export center in China, created since 1980 to attract foreign investment and technology transfers. Seven SEZs—all located on China's Pacific coast—currently operate: Shenzhen, adjacent to Hong Kong; Zhuhai; Shantou; Xiamen; Hainan Island, in the far south; Pudong, across the river from Shanghai; and Binhai New Area, next to the port of Tianjin.

State A politically organized territory that is administered by a sovereign government and is recognized by a significant portion of the international community. A state must also contain a permanent resident population, an organized economy, and a functioning internal circulation system.

State boundaries The borders that surround **states** which, in effect, are derived through contracts with neighboring states negotiated by treaty.

State capitalism Government-controlled corporations competing under free-market conditions, usually in a tightly regimented society.

State formation The creation of a **state**, exemplifying traditions of human **territoriality** that go back thousands of years.

State planning Involves highly centralized control of the national planning process, a hallmark of communist economic systems. Soviet central planners mainly pursued a grand political design in assigning production to particular places; their frequent disregard of the principles of **economic geography** contributed to the eventual collapse of the USSR.

State territorial morphology A **state's** geographical shape, which can have a decisive impact on its spatial cohesion and political viability. A **compact** shape is most desirable; among the less efficient shapes are those exhibited by **elongated, fragmented, perforated**, and **protruded** states.

Stateless nation A national group that aspires to become a **nation-state** but lacks the territorial means to do so.

Steppe Semiarid grassland; short-grass prairie. Also the name given to the semiarid climate type (*BS*).

Stratification (social) In a layered or stratified society, the population is divided into a **hierarchy** of social classes. In an industrialized society, the working class is at the lower end; **elites** that possess capital and control the means of production are at the upper level. In the traditional **caste system** of Hindu India, the "untouchables" form the lowest class or caste, whereas the still-wealthy remnants of the princely class are at the top.

Subduction In **plate tectonics**, the **process** that occurs when an oceanic plate converges head-on with a plate carrying a continental landmass at its leading edge. The lighter continental plate overrides the denser oceanic plate and pushes it downward.

Subsequent boundary A political boundary that developed contemporaneously with the evolution of the major elements of the **cultural landscape** through which it passes.

Subsistence Existing on the minimum necessities to sustain life; spending most of one's time in pursuit of survival.

Subsistence agriculture Farmers who eke out a living on a small plot of land on which they are only able to grow enough food to support their families or at best a small community.

Subtropical Convergence A narrow marine **transition zone**, girdling the globe at approximately latitude 40°S, that marks the equatorward limit of the frigid **Southern Ocean** and the poleward limits of the warmer Atlantic, Pacific, and Indian oceans to the north.

Suburban downtown In the United States (and increasingly in other high-income countries), a significant concentration of major urban activities around a highly accessible suburban location, including retailing, light industry, and a variety of leading corporate and commercial operations. The largest are now coequal to the American central city's **central business district (CBD)**. A leading feature of the **outer city**.

Sunbelt The popular name given to the southern tier of the United States, which is anchored by the mega-States of California, Texas, and Florida. Its warmer climate, superior recreational opportunities, and other amenities have been attracting large numbers of relocating people and activities since the 1960s; broader definitions of the Sunbelt also include much of the western United States, even Colorado and the coastal Pacific Northwest.

Superimposed boundary A political boundary emplaced by powerful outsiders on a developed human landscape. Frequently ignores preexisting cultural-spatial patterns, such as the border that still divides North and South Korea.

Supranational A venture involving three or more **states**—political, economic, and/or cultural cooperation to promote shared objectives.

System Any group of objects or institutions and their mutual interactions. Geography treats systems that are expressed spatially, such as in **functional regions**.

Systematic geography Topical geography: **cultural, political, economic geography**, and the like.

Taiga The subarctic, mostly **coniferous** snowforest that blankets northern Russia and Canada south of the **tundra** that lines the Arctic shore. Known as the **boreal forest** in North America.

Takeoff Economic concept to identify a stage in a country's **development** when conditions are set for a domestic Industrial Revolution.

Taliban The term means "students" or "seekers of religion." Specifically, refers to the Islamist militia group that emerged from **madrassas** in Pakistan and ruled neighboring Afghanistan between 1996 and 2001; it has been trying to regain control of that country in its continuing conflict with U.S.-led NATO troops. Taliban rule, in adherence with an extremist interpretation of **Sharia** law, was marked by one of the most virulent forms of militant Islam ever seen.

Tar sands The main source of oil from non-liquid petroleum reserves. The oil is mixed with sand and requires massive open-pit mining as well as a costly, complicated process to extract it. The largest known deposits are located in the northeast of Canada's province of Alberta, and by most estimates these Athabasca Tar Sands constitute one of the largest oil reserves in the world. The high oil prices of recent years have led to greatly expanded production here, but the accompanying environmental degradation caused by strip-mining and waste disposal has triggered a widening protest movement that may limit the exploitation of this resource.

Technopole A planned techno-industrial complex (such as California's Silicon Valley) that innovates, promotes, and manufactures the products of the **postindustrial** informational economy.

Tectonic plates The slabs of heavier rock on which the lighter rocks of the continents rest. The plates are in motion, propelled by gigantic circulation cells in the red-hot, molten rock below. Most earthquakes and volcanic eruptions are associated with collisions of the mobile plates, as is the building of mountain chains.

Terms of trade In international economics refers to an agreement between trading partners that stipulates the quantity of imports that can be purchased by one country through the sale of a fixed quantity of exports to the other.

Terracing The transformation of a hillside or mountain slope into a step-like sequence of horizontal fields for intensive cultivation.

Territoriality A country's or more local community's sense of property and attachment toward its territory, as expressed by its determination to keep it inviolable and strongly defended.

Territorial sea Zone of seawater adjacent to a country's coast, held to be part of the national territory and treated as a component of the sovereign **state**.

Tertiary economic activity Activities that engage in *services*—such as transportation, banking, retailing, education, and routine office-based jobs.

Tierra caliente The lowest of the **altitudinal zones** into which the human settlement of Middle and South America is classified according to elevation. The *caliente* is the hot humid coastal plain and adjacent slopes up to 750 meters (2500 ft) above sea level. The natural vegetation is the dense and luxuriant tropical rainforest; the crops include sugar and bananas in the lower areas, and coffee, tobacco, and corn along the higher slopes.

Tierra fría Cold, high-lying **altitudinal zone** of settlement in Andean South America, extending from about 1800 meters (6000 ft) in elevation up to nearly 3600 meters (12,000 ft). **Coniferous** trees stand here; upward they change into scrub and grassland. There are also important pastures within the *fría*, and wheat can be cultivated.

Tierra helada In Andean South America, the highest-lying habitable **altitudinal zone**—ca. 3600 to 4500 meters (12,000 to 15,000 ft)—between the tree line (upper limit of the *tierra fría*) and the snow line (lower limit of the *tierra nevada*). Too cold and barren to support anything but the grazing of sheep and other hardy livestock.

Tierra nevada The highest and coldest **altitudinal zone** in Andean South America (lying above 4500 meters [15,000 ft]), an uninhabitable environment of permanent snow and ice that extends upward to the Andes' highest peaks of more than 6000 meters (20,000 ft).

Tierra templada The intermediate **altitudinal zone** of settlement in Middle and South America, lying between 750 meters (2500 ft) and 1800 meters (6000 ft) in elevation. This is the "temperate" zone, with moderate temperatures compared to the *tierra caliente* below. Crops include coffee, tobacco, corn, and some wheat.

Topography The surface configuration of any segment of **natural landscape**.

Toponym Place name.

Transculturation Cultural borrowing and two-way exchanges that occur when different **cultures** of approximately equal complexity and technological level come into close contact.

Transferability The capacity to move a good from one place to another at a bearable cost; the ease with which a commodity may be transported.

Transition zone An area of spatial change where the **peripheries** of two adjacent **realms** or **regions** join; marked by a gradual shift (rather than a sharp break) in the characteristics that distinguish these neighboring geographic entities from one another.

Transmigration The now-ended policy of the Indonesian government to induce residents of the overcrowded, **core-area** island of Jawa to move to the country's other islands.

Treaty ports **Extraterritorial enclaves** in China's coastal cities, established by European colonial invaders under unequal treaties enforced by gunboat diplomacy.

Triple Frontier The turbulent and chaotic area in southern South America that surrounds the convergence of Brazil, Argentina, and Paraguay. Lawlessness pervades this haven for criminal elements, which is notorious for money laundering, arms and other smuggling, drug trafficking, and links to terrorist organizations, including money flows to the Middle East.

Tropical deforestation The clearing and destruction of tropical rainforests in order to make way for expanding settlement frontiers and the exploitation of new economic opportunities.

Tsunami A seismic (earthquake-generated) sea wave that can attain gigantic proportions and cause coastal devastation. The tsunami of December 26, 2004, centered in the Indian Ocean near the Indonesian island of Sumatera (Sumatra), produced the first great natural disaster of the twenty-first century. Our new century's second major tsunami disaster occurred along the coast of Japan's northeastern Honshu Island on March 11, 2011.

Tundra The treeless plain that lies along the Arctic shore in northernmost Russia and Canada, whose vegetation consists of mosses, lichens, and certain hardy grasses.

Turkestan Northeasternmost region of the North Africa/Southwest Asia realm. Known as Soviet Central Asia before 1992, its five (dominantly Islamic) former Soviet Socialist Republics have become the independent countries of Kazakhstan, Uzbekistan, Turkmenistan, Kyrgyzstan, and Tajikistan. Today Turkestan has expanded to include a sixth state, Afghanistan.

Turkish model In the wake of the regime changes in the North Africa/Southwest Asia realm brought about by the "Arab Spring" of 2011, moderates have cited Turkey as the best model of democratic governance for this part of the world. Specifically, this involves a multi-party democracy that has a place for, but is not dominated by, Islamic political parties.

Uneven development The notion that economic development varies spatially, a central tenet of **core-periphery relationships** in realms, regions, and lesser geographic entities.

Unitary state A **nation-state** that has a centralized government and administration that exercises power equally over all parts of the **state**.

United Nations See discussion under **League of Nations**.

Unity of place The great German natural scientist Alexander von Humboldt's notion that in a particular locale or region intricate connections exist among climate, geology, biology, and human cultures. This laid the foundation for modern geography as an *integrative discipline* marked by a spatial perspective.

Urbanization A term with a variety of connotations. The proportion of a country's population living in urban places is its level of urbanization. The **process** of urbanization involves the movement to, and the clustering of, people in towns and cities—a major force in every geographic realm today. Another kind of urbanization occurs when an expanding city absorbs rural countryside and transforms it into suburbs; in the case of cities in disadvantaged countries, this also generates peripheral **shantytowns**.

Urban (metropolitan) area The entire built-up, non-rural area and its population, including the most recently constructed suburban appendages. Provides a better picture of the dimensions and population of such an area than the delimited municipality (central city) that forms its heart.

Urban realms model A spatial generalization of the contemporary large American city. It is shown to be a widely dispersed, multinodal **metropolis** consisting of increasingly independent zones or *urban realms*, each focused

on its own **suburban downtown**; the only exception is the shrunken central realm, which is focused on the central city's **central business district** (see Fig. 3A-11).

Urban system A **hierarchical** network or grouping of urban areas within a finite geographic area, such as a country.

Veld See **highveld**.

Voluntary migration Population movement in which people relocate in response to perceived opportunity, not because they are forced to **migrate**.

Wahhabism A particularly virulent form of (Sunni) **Muslim revivalism** that was made the official faith when the modern **state** of Saudi Arabia was founded in 1932. Adherents call themselves "Unitarians" to signify the strict fundamentalist nature of their beliefs.

Wallace's Line The zoogeographical boundary proposed by Alfred Russel Wallace that separates the marsupial fauna of Australia and New Guinea from the non-marsupial fauna of Indonesia (see Figure 11-4).

Weather The immediate and short-term conditions of the **atmosphere** that impinge on daily human activities.

West Wind Drift The clockwise movement of water as a current that circles around Antarctica in the **Southern Ocean**.

Westernization The Western view of the **process** of **modernization** that involves the establishment of **urbanization**, a market (money) economy, improved circulation, formal schooling, adoption of foreign innovations, and the breakdown of traditional society. Non-Westerners mostly see "modernization" as an outgrowth of **colonialism** and often argue that traditional societies can be modernized without being Westernized.

Windward The exposed, upwind side of a **topographic** barrier that faces the winds that flow across it.

World-city Either London, New York, or Tokyo. The highest-ranking urban centers of **globalization** with financial, high-technology, communications, engineering, and related industries reflecting the momentum of their long-term growth and **agglomeration**.

A page number followed by "f" indicates the entry is within a figure; a page number followed by "t" indicates the entry is within a table.